AN ATOMIC EMPIRE

A Technical History of the Rise and Fall of the British Atomic Energy Programme

AN ATOMIC EMPIRE

A Technical History of the Rise and Fall of the British Atomic Energy Programme

C N Hill

Formerly Charterhouse, UK

ICP

Imperial College Press

Published by

Imperial College Press
57 Shelton Street
Covent Garden
London WC2H 9HE

Distributed by

World Scientific Publishing Co. Pte. Ltd.
5 Toh Tuck Link, Singapore 596224
USA office: 27 Warren Street, Suite 401-402, Hackensack, NJ 07601
UK office: 57 Shelton Street, Covent Garden, London WC2H 9HE

British Library Cataloguing-in-Publication Data
A catalogue record for this book is available from the British Library.

Front cover: Cutaway drawing of Sizewell A power station (*Nuclear Engineering International*)
Back cover: The Queen formally opens Calder Hall, the world's first commercial nuclear power station

AN ATOMIC EMPIRE
A Technical History of the Rise and Fall of the British Atomic Energy Programme

ISBN 978-1-908977-41-0

Typeset by Stallion Press
Email: enquiries@stallionpress.com

Printed in Singapore by World Scientific Printers.

Contents

Acknowledgements

Many people have been a tremendous help in the writing of this book, and I am particularly grateful to:

Nick Hance MBE, formerly of AERE Harwell;

Dr Mike Forrest, formerly of AERE Harwell and Culham, and Nick Holloway, Media Manager, Culham Centre for Fusion Energy, for the help and assistance on the chapter concerning controlled thermonuclear research;

The staff of Harwell Archive, and in particular, Eric Jenkins;

Mrs M Olive for the use of the facilities of Charterhouse library;

Barry Marsden, Professor of Nuclear Graphite Technology at the University of Manchester, for his help on graphite technology;

Stephen Henry of EDF for organising a visit to Dungeness B power station, to Tim Collins for showing us round, and to Martin Pearson, the Station Manager, for giving up his time to talk to me;

William Dalrymple and Caroline Peachey of the journal *Nuclear Engineering International*. I am especially grateful for the access to their archive and for permission to reproduce images from past issues, in particular the cutaway drawing of Sizewell A power station on the front cover.

List of Acronyms

AEA	Atomic Energy Authority
AERE	Atomic Energy Research Established
AGR	Advanced Gas-Cooled Reactor
APC	Atomic Power Constructions
AWRE	Atomic Weapons Research Establishment
BEA	British Electrical Authority
BEPO	British Experimental Pile 0
BNDC	British Nuclear Design and Construction Ltd
BNFL	British Nuclear Fuels Ltd
BWR	Boiling Water Reactor
CANDU	Canada Deuterium Uranium Reactor
CEA	Central Electricity Authority
CEGB	Central Electricity Generating Board
CFR	Commercial Fast Reactor
CTR	Controlled Thermonuclear Research
DFR	Dounreay Fast Reactor
EDF	Électricité de France S.A.
GLEEP	Graphite Low Energy Experimental Pile
HECTOR	Heated Experimental Carbon Thermal Oscillator Reactor
HERALD	Highly Enriched Reactor Aldermaston
HERO	Heated Experimental Reactor (0) Zero Energy
HTGCR	High-Temperature Gas-Cooled Reactor
HTR	High-Temperature Reactor
ICI	Imperial Chemical Industries
JET	Joint European Torus
LEO	Low Enrichment Ordinary Water Reactor (or Light Water Reactor)
MAGNOX	MAGnesium Non-OXidising
MOX	Mixed OXide

NATO	North Atlantic Treaty Organisation
NDA	Nuclear Decommissioning Authority
NDC	Nuclear Design and Construction
NESTOR	Neutron Source Thermal Reactor
NNC	National Nuclear Corporation
NPPC	Nuclear Power Plant Company
NRPB	National Radiological Protection Board
OEEC	Organisation for European Economic Cooperation
PFR	Prototype Fast Reactor
PIPPA	Pressurised Pile Producing Industrial Power and Plutonium
PRO	Public Record Office
PWR	Pressurised Water Reactor
RAE	Royal Aircraft Establishment
RAF	Royal Air Force
SCHWR	Steam-Cooled Heavy Water Reactor
SGHWR	Steam Generating Heavy Water Reactor
SSEB	South of Scotland Electricity Board
TNA	The National Archives
TNPG	The Nuclear Power Group
UKAEA	United Kingdom Atomic Energy Authority
USAF	United States Air Force
ZEBRA	Zero-Energy Breeder Reactor Assembly
ZENITH	Zero-Energy High-Temperature Reactor
ZEST	Zero-Energy Support Reactor
ZETA	Zero-Energy Toroidal (or Thermonuclear) Assembly

Chapter 1

Introduction

At 12:16 on 17 October 1956, Her Majesty the Queen pulled the lever which would direct electricity from the Calder Hall nuclear power station into the National Grid for the first time. 'This new power, which has proved itself to be such a terrifying weapon of destruction,' she said, 'is harnessed for the first time for the common good of our community.'

Calder Hall was the world's first purpose built commercial nuclear power station and was the first of a series of gas-cooled nuclear reactors of entirely British design. The last of these, at Torness, was completed in 1988. Many other reactors were built in Britain during the same period — some for research and some as prototypes. In the 1950s, Harwell became an internationally renowned centre of research into atomic energy.

The atomic energy programme was, at first, entirely military. The decision to build an atomic weapon was taken by the Attlee government. Britain had been a partner with the United States in the construction of the first atom bombs. For Britain to build its own atomic weapons it needed plutonium and the timetable was dictated by the time it took to design and build the Windscale piles, which would produce the necessary plutonium in time for a test of the first British atomic device in 1952. Just as soon as Britain had successfully tested a fission device, the United States and Russia had produced fusion devices — popularly known as the hydrogen bomb. The scientists at Aldermaston then had to turn their attention to this new technology and, by the end of 1957, had produced and tested a successful British-designed fusion device. But the construction of the reactors needed to produce plutonium led to a design which would produce not only plutonium, but electrical power as well. This in turn led to the idea of a reactor whose sole purpose was to produce power, intended to supplement the coal burning stations then in use which were struggling to produce sufficient power for domestic and industrial use.

To give some idea of how enthusiastically the British government embraced nuclear power, Table 1.1 shows a breakdown of nuclear energy capacity country by country.[1] This was the situation as of March 1968:

Table 1.1. Nuclear energy capacity by country.

Country	Capacity/megawatts (MW)	Electricity generated/million kilowatt-hours (kWh)
UK	4,156	99,136
US	2,900	35,182
France	1,101	8,746
Italy	631	13,999
West Germany	317	2,323
Canada	245	334
Japan	178	1,277
Belgium	11	221
Sweden	10	137

Note: This data does not include the Soviet Union.

The total amount of electricity generated from nuclear power stations by countries other than the UK totalled $62{,}219 \times 10^6$ kWh compared with $99{,}136 \times 10^6$ kWh generated in the UK. In other words, the amount generated in the UK was more than half as much again as in all the other countries put together.

In 1995, the reactor at Sizewell B went critical and began commercial operation, but unlike all the other power reactors built in Britain, this was based on an American design. Since Sizewell B, no further reactors have been built in Britain. All the research and prototype reactors have been decommissioned and closed down. Most of the gas-cooled reactors built in the 1950s and 1960s have closed. The remaining power stations are now owned by a foreign company: EDF, or Électricité de France S.A., which is the second largest electric utility company in the world.

The UK no longer has companies capable of designing and building nuclear power stations. Any future nuclear stations will, by necessity, be built by foreign companies. This book will look first at how the British developed and exploited nuclear technology, not only for power stations, but also for military use.

Building a nuclear power station is a considerable engineering feat. Today there is an enormous heritage upon which engineers can draw. In the 1950s, the technology was entirely new and many of the problems were not fully understood. To put it another way, there were many 'unknown unknowns'. To solve these problems, research and prototype reactors had to be built. The story of these has not yet been told, and one of the objectives of this book is to tell those stories. All these research reactors in Britain have now been closed down and are being decommissioned. In some cases, they have been completely removed and the site returned to a green field. There are other sites which are still considerably contaminated with radioactivity and will therefore take longer to clear.

The cost of decommissioning the current generation of nuclear power stations is projected to run into billions of pounds. This is often used as an argument against nuclear power stations, but it is interesting to see how these sums relate to the electricity produced. To take an example, each of the reactors at the Wylfa Magnox power station generated over 10^{11} kWh of electricity in the course of its operational lifetime. If the decommissioning costs for the station are £1 billion, that adds 1p to the cost of each kWh generated.

Another purpose of this book is to describe the policy behind many of the decisions, both technical and political. It can be argued that much of the political policy was set by technical policy. This is seen most clearly in the unwavering support given by the Atomic Energy Authority (AEA) to gas-cooled reactors, even when other options looked more attractive both technically and commercially.

One of the more interesting features of the period is how little influence or input was provided by elected politicians. During the important part of this period, electricity generation was run by the Central Electricity Generating Board (CEGB). This was a nationalised industry with an appointed Chairman, who, whilst nominally responsible to the Minister of Power, had almost complete autonomy. The first Chairman was Sir Christopher Hinton, a man of very forceful personality, who would not have taken lightly to political interference. Similarly, the AEA was almost completely autonomous. During its history, it reported to a variety of different ministers, none of whom played any significant role in the work done by the Authority. The 1955 White Paper which set into motion the civil nuclear programme originated from a report written by an official in the Treasury. Almost all the nuclear power decisions were taken by officials rather than by politicians.

The AEA and CEGB were, in one sense, what would be described today as quangos, but with powers far exceeding the average present-day quango. They were also run by a generation of men who had made their mark as planners or directors during the war or in the immediate post-war period. Such men were part of what was described as 'the great and the good'. They were public servants in the best sense of that word. They were consummate administrators. They were good leaders of men, but it was a style of leadership that disappeared after the post-war period.

This book concentrates on the early period of atomic power, where, apart from the Windscale incident, Britain appeared to be taking great strides in this new and dynamic technology. Slowly, however, things began to unravel. The Authority went down too many blind alleys. The firms constructing the power stations were weak technically, and the fiasco of the first advanced gas-cooled reactor (AGR) at Dungeness was to prove a turning point. There were severe weaknesses in what might be called ‘project management’, as well as, in some cases, simple technical blunders.

In addition, the public mood, which had viewed atomic power in the 1950s as the heralding of a new age, began to swing against all matters nuclear. This was epitomised in the two public enquiries, the first concerning the Windscale reprocessing plant and the second concerning the building of the Sizewell B power station. The Windscale enquiry in 1977 lasted for 100 days; the Sizewell B enquiry from January 1983 to March 1985. Environmental groups began campaigning against nuclear power using arguments which were distinctly suspect from a technical point of view, but which resonated with the general public mood.

The nuclear power stations in Britain are now being brought out of service. Whether new power stations will be built in their place is an interesting question. One area which this book will not attempt to investigate is the economics of nuclear power — for a variety of reasons.

The early British programme was almost entirely military in origin, and the civil programme emerged from that. A good deal of money was then spent on researching and building prototypes for different types of reactor: the AGR with its prototype at Windscale, the fast reactor and its research and prototype reactors and the heavy water reactor at Winfrith. None of this expenditure was factored into the cost of the civil nuclear power programme. In all these examples, only the AGR would lead to commercial power stations. The magnox stations originated in a design intended to produce plutonium for military use. There was also the money spent investigating options which would never even reach the prototype stage, such as the sodium/graphite reactor. Again, none of this expenditure was set against the cost of the power stations.

The early power stations might have seemed commercially attractive against the coal-fired stations of their day, but the problem was that coal became cheaper and the conventional power stations became larger and more efficient and then gas-powered stations with a combined gas/steam cycle became more efficient still. To use the vernacular, the goalposts moved.

A further problem in attempting to evaluate the economics of the magnox stations is their sheer longevity. They were built in the late 1950s and early 1960s, and Oldbury ran for 42 years, from 1968 to 2012. Over that span of time, the value of the pound dropped about 50 fold, interest rates varied from 15% or more down to 0.5%. One of the features of atomic power stations is that they are very expensive to build — they have a very high capital cost. This has to be written down over their lifetime, but given the economic changes that took place, this becomes meaningless.

Thus, trying to make any form of valid economic assessment of their performance is impossible.

Figure 1.1. Oldbury power station. This was a magnox station which operated from 1968 to 2012.

The first magnox stations had been ordered by the Central Electricity Authority (the predecessor to the CEGB) very much at government behest. The economics of nuclear power became very much more exposed when electricity generation was privatised in 1989. One factor that had been completely ignored at the outset of the programme now became very much more significant — the cost of decommissioning. It was thought that with such an open-ended liability, it would be difficult to privatise the nuclear section of the industry, and it was initially held back before finally being privatised in 1995.

It is perhaps significant that the private companies have not sought to build nuclear stations since privatisation. EDF is proposing new stations, but it has the knowledge and expertise of the French part of its business.

At the start of this chapter, Calder Hall was proclaimed as the world's first nuclear power station. That claim has been disputed: the Russian reactor built at Obninsk in the USSR has a claim to being the first power station. This had a generating power of 5 MW(E) (Calder Hall had four reactors, each generating 60 MW, which were later downgraded to 49 MW after corrosion problems in the magnox reactors) and was connected to the local grid in June 1954. It used a graphite moderator and was water-cooled, being a forerunner of the RBMK reactors (which included Chernobyl RBMK stands for Reaktor Bolshoy Monshchnosti Kanalniy, Russian for 'high-power channel-type reactor'). On the other hand, the Russian station has been described as 'semi-experimental' — the Calder Hall reactors can probably still claim to be the world's first commercial nuclear power stations.

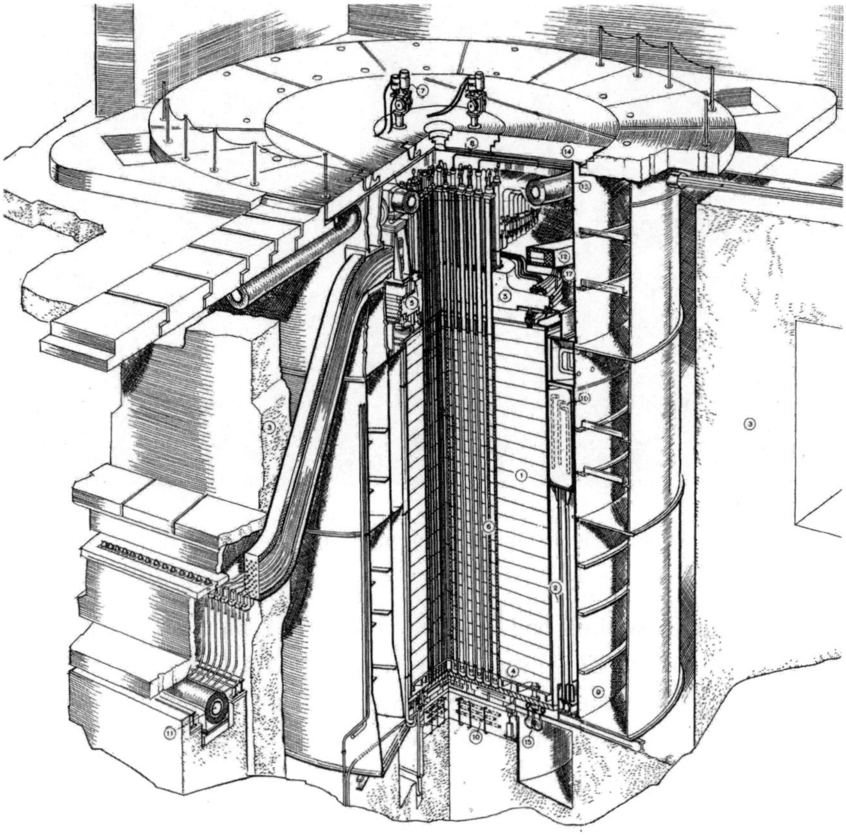

Figure 1.2. The Russian reactor at Obninsk.

[1] The National Archives (TNA): Public Record Office (PRO) AB 65/422. Advanced Thermal Reactors: National Policy etc. BE Eltham. 'British Nuclear Power Development.'

Chapter 2

Atomic Physics

Scientists began to understand the structure of the atom just before the start of the twentieth century. In 1897, JJ Thomson discovered the electron and found its mass to be a tiny fraction of the mass of an atom. He envisaged the atom to be a solid lump, rather like a plum pudding, with the electrons acting as the plums. This idea was overturned by Rutherford in 1911, when he realised the implications of experiments by Geiger and Marsden — that the atom consisted of a tiny positively charged nucleus surrounded by orbiting electrons, with most of it apparently being empty space.

Scientists also began to realise that the recently discovered phenomenon of radioactivity had its origins in the nucleus and by 1930, when Chadwick discovered the neutron, the modern idea of the atom had evolved.

In this model, the atom is made of three particles: the proton, the neutron and the electron. The proton and neutron have almost the same mass and are bound together in the nucleus while the much lighter electrons orbit at certain fixed distances from the nucleus — or, more exactly, in certain fixed energy levels. The proton carries a positive charge and the electron an equal negative charge. The neutron has no charge — i.e., it is neutral. This model is very much a simplification, but it will do for the moment.

It also meant scientists had to postulate a new force of nature. Up until then, the three basic forces of nature were gravitational, electrical and magnetic. Einstein had shown that the electrical and magnetic forces were different manifestations of the same phenomenon. But the protons in the nucleus all have the same electric charge, and should repel each other, so that the nucleus would be unstable and fly apart. There must be some other short range force holding the nucleus together, and this was called, not surprisingly, the nuclear force. Further experiments were to show that there are actually two nuclear forces: the strong nuclear force and the weak nuclear force. For present purposes, however, the idea that there is a nuclear force is sufficient.

This model could explain another problem. If atoms were made of only protons and neutrons, then the mass of an atom would be predictable. The proton and neutron have a very similar mass, and so the atomic mass should be a fixed multiple of the mass of a proton. But this was not always true — chlorine, for example, has an atomic mass of 35.5, not a whole number. Why was that?

The explanation put forward is that there are two types of chlorine atom, one with mass 35 and the other with mass 37. There are three atoms with mass 35 for every one with mass 37 — hence the average of 35.5. These two different types of atom are called *isotopes*, and have a different number of neutrons. Thus ^{35}Cl has 17 protons and 18 neutrons; ^{37}Cl has 17 proton and 20 neutrons. Atoms of the same element have the same number of protons and electrons, but may have a different number of neutrons.

The number of protons in a nucleus determines the position of the atom in the table of elements. Thus chlorine has 17 protons and is number 17 in the table of elements. The convention is that the mass number of an isotope is written as a superscript and the atomic number as a subscript thus: $^{35}{}_{17}Cl$. Often the atomic number is omitted.

Another point to be noted is that with many relatively light nuclei, the number of protons and neutrons are the same. Thus the most common isotope of oxygen has eight protons and eight neutrons. This ratio begins to change as the nucleus becomes larger, with more neutrons than protons. By the time we reach uranium, we have the two isotopes with 92 protons but 143 and 146 neutrons respectively.

Some isotopes are unstable, and will decay to a different, more stable, nucleus — that is, they are radioactive. For naturally occurring radioactivity, there are two ways in which the nucleus can decay, and when this happens, particles appear to be ejected from the nucleus. Rutherford named these alpha and beta particles respectively. Sometimes the particles are accompanied by high-energy electromagnetic waves — gamma rays.

An alpha particle was found to be made of two protons and two neutrons (a helium nucleus). Hence when a nucleus ejects an alpha particle, it becomes an atom of a different element — lighter by four units, and two places lower down in the list of elements.

A beta particle was found to be a high speed electron, which has a negative charge and negligible mass. Thus the new nucleus is effectively the same mass but has moved up one in the table of elements — the electron having a negative charge, the new nucleus has an extra positive charge to compensate.

For example:

$$^{235}{}_{92}U \rightarrow {}^{231}{}_{90}Pa + {}^{4}{}_{2}\text{alpha and } {}^{90}{}_{38}Sr \rightarrow {}^{90}{}_{39}Y + {}^{0}{}_{-1}\text{beta.}$$

The development of the mass spectrometer meant that the mass of atoms could be measured to a very high degree of precision — which revealed something rather odd. The mass of the nucleus was slightly less than the mass of the constituent protons and neutrons. This difference is known as the *mass defect.*

The explanation for this lies in Einstein's famous equation $E = mc^2$. A large amount of energy (relatively speaking) is released when a nucleus is formed. Part of the mass of the nucleus has been converted to energy. This is called the *binding energy* of the nucleus.

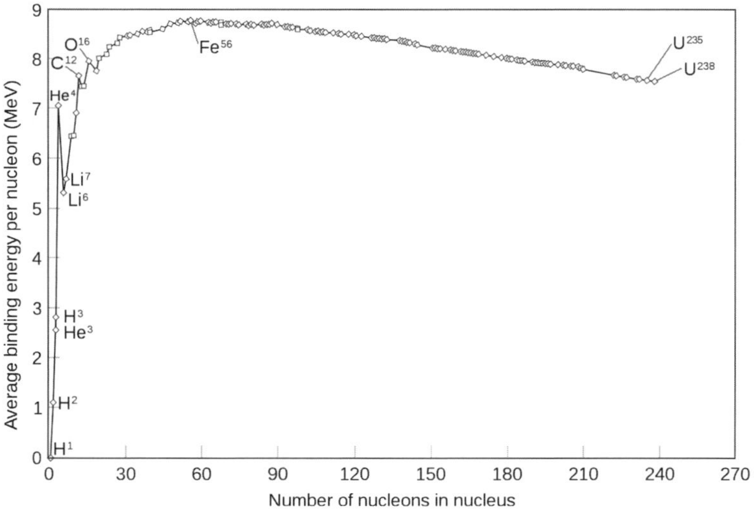

Figure 2.1. Curve of binding energy per nucleon against nucleon number.

Figure 2.1 is the graph of binding energy per nucleon. The data show that more energy is released per nucleon for ^{56}Fe than any other nucleus — that is, it is the most stable. Thus energy would be released if a heavy nucleus were split into two smaller fragments, or if two light nuclei were forced together to make a new, more massive nucleus. The first example is *nuclear fission*, the second is *nuclear fusion*.

But because a process is energetically favourable does not mean it will necessarily happen — or at least, not without a good deal of persuasion. The paper of this book is thermodynamically unstable in air, but it will not catch fire spontaneously — a lighted match is needed. Splitting a nucleus is difficult. Making nuclei fuse together is even more difficult. Controlled fusion has remained an El Dorado for scientists for well over half a century, and appears no closer to solution. Indeed, one of the earliest attempts at controlled nuclear fusion was the zero-energy toroidal (or thermonuclear) assembly (ZETA) experiment at Harwell in the 1950s, described in Chapter 9.

Like much work in the field of radioactivity, fission was inadvertently discovered as the result of an experiment that fell into a category which might be described as 'try it and see what happens'. When new particles were discovered, scientists would try firing them at various elements simply to see what happened. The neutron was discovered by Chadwick in 1932, and so Otto Hahn, Lise Meitner, and Fritz Strassmann tried bombarding uranium, the heaviest known atom at that time, with neutrons. The easiest way to find out whether new elements had been created was by chemical analysis, and to their surprise, barium, a much lighter nucleus was discovered. Meitner correctly interpreted this result as the uranium nucleus being split into two smaller fragments. This process was named *fission*.

There is still no one definitive model of the structure of the nucleus. To explain these results, the nucleus was pictured in the 'liquid drop' model, in which the nucleus is imagined as a drop of liquid. The force holding a drop together is surface tension, and like the nucleus, it can split apart if hit in certain ways. This model, although useful in other respects, does not say anything about the internal structure of the nucleus.

A nucleus that can be split by neutrons is called *fissionable*. Not all nuclei that are fissionable can be split by relatively slow moving neutrons. Ones that can are called *fissile*. To complicate matters, natural uranium consists of two isotopes, ^{235}U and ^{238}U. The ^{235}U isotope is fissile, but the ^{238}U is fissionable, since it can only be split by very energetic neutrons. Natural uranium contains only about 0.7% ^{235}U, the remainder being ^{238}U.

When the uranium is split, energy is released at the same time as the fission products. How much energy depends on exactly how the nucleus has been split. This energy may appear in various forms: as gamma radiation, as recoil kinetic energy of the two daughter nuclei and as kinetic energy of the neutrons released. Compared with most chemical or physical processes, the amount of energy released is very large. The energy released by the fission of 1 kg of ^{235}U is of the order of 10^{14} J, whereas the energy released from the combustion of 1 kg of methane (natural gas) is only around 5×10^7 J.

At the time, the results from the neutron bombardment experiments appeared to have no direct application, until it was discovered that during the fission process, extra neutrons are released — in other words, when the ^{235}U splits, two daughter nuclei are produced with some surplus neutrons as well. This led to the possibility of a chain reaction taking place, in which one fission would give rise to two or three extra neutrons, which could then go on to split two or three more uranium atoms, which would release even more neutrons, and so on. The reaction would increase exponentially. In practice, of course, matters are rather more complicated.

The neutrons may escape from the lump of uranium before hitting another ^{235}U nucleus, or they may be absorbed by a ^{238}U nucleus. If they escape faster than they are being produced then the reaction fizzles out. When as many neutrons are being produced as escaping (or being absorbed) then it is said that the lump has reached criticality. Obviously, this needs a certain minimum size lump, or else the neutrons will escape without hitting another nucleus on the way. This minimum size is referred to as the critical mass.

The critical mass will depend on the probability of a neutron hitting a nucleus and causing fusion as it passes through the atom. The nucleus is only a very small fraction of the size of the atom. To a first approximation, an atom is around 10^{-10} m in diameter; a nucleus is around 10^{-14} m. Hence the cross-sectional areas are 10^{-20} m^2 and 10^{-28} m^2. On this (extremely simplistic) basis, a neutron would pass through 10^8 atoms before hitting a nucleus — or a distance of $10^8 \times 10^{-10}$ m $= 10^{-2}$ m or 1 cm.

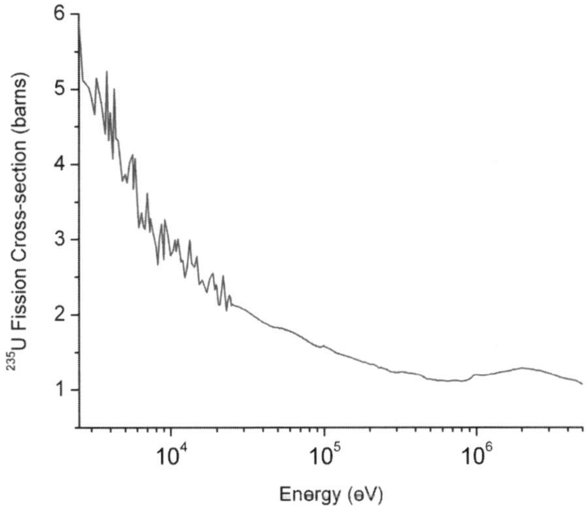

Figure 2.2. Apparent cross-sectional area of nucleus varies with neutron energy.

Unfortunately, matters are not that simple, as the graph in Figure 2.2 shows. The cross-sectional area of the uranium nucleus seems to change with the energy of the neutron. Slow neutrons have a much greater chance of colliding with a nucleus than fast neutrons — a matter that becomes of considerable importance when designing a reactor.

For bomb making, the trick is to convert a subcritical mass into a critical mass as rapidly as possible. In a power station, the neutron flux — that is, the number of neutrons — is governed by control rods, which are made of a neutron absorbing material. Insert the rods into the reactor and the reaction dies down due to lack of neutrons. The trick in the power station is to keep the rate of fission and thus the energy released constant.

If it is hit by fast neutrons, ^{238}U will fission, but cannot sustain a chain reaction. This is because the neutrons released lose energy in collisions and soon will not have enough left for further fission. The behaviour of ^{238}U with slow neutrons is very different. If the nucleus is hit by slow neutrons (the term is relative!) then the neutron is absorbed, converting the nucleus to ^{239}U. This decays fairly rapidly (half-life a little more than 23 minutes) to ^{239}Np, which decays (half-life 2.4 days) in turn to ^{239}Pu. ^{239}Pu is relatively stable, with a half-life of more than 24,000 years, and is also fissile. ^{239}Pu is preferable to ^{235}U in bombs, which is why much of the early British work on reactors was aimed at plutonium production.

As mentioned, only 0.7% of natural uranium is ^{235}U. This means that although reactors can be made with natural uranium, they tend to be large and cumbersome as a consequence. It is better to *enrich* the uranium — in other words, increase the proportion of ^{235}U. This is not an easy business.

Isotopes of a different element have identical chemical properties. The only way to separate them is to find some physical process that is affected by the mass of the molecule. One of these is diffusion — the rate at which gases diffuse through a membrane of extremely small holes depends on their speed, which in turn depends on their mass. At the same temperature, the mean speed of gas molecules is inversely dependant on the square root of its mass. Thus a molecule four times as heavy would diffuse at half the rate.

It is very rare to find compounds of metals that can be vaporised easily, but it happens that uranium hexafluoride, UF_6, sublimes (i.e., turns directly from solid to gas) at 56.5°C at atmospheric pressure. The ^{235}U hexafluoride has a molar mass of 349; the ^{238}U hexafluoride a molar mass of 352. The lighter one diffuses faster by a factor of $\surd(352/349) = 1.0043$.

This tiny separation factor means that the process has to be repeated again and again, gradually increasing the amount of ^{235}U each time. This is usually done with a cascading process, whereby the enriched fraction is fed to a further stage, and the depleted fraction fed back into the cascade lower down. Gaseous diffusion plants are large and highly energy intensive. Britain's gaseous diffusion plant was situated at Capenhurst in Cheshire, in what was then Europe's largest industrial building, 1,200 m long and 150 m wide. The plant consisted of a cascade of 4,800 stage units connected by 1,800 km of process gas pipe work of over half a metre in diameter, employing almost 4,000 personnel.

Diffusion is now an obsolete technology, with variations on the centrifuge technique being the most commonly used today.

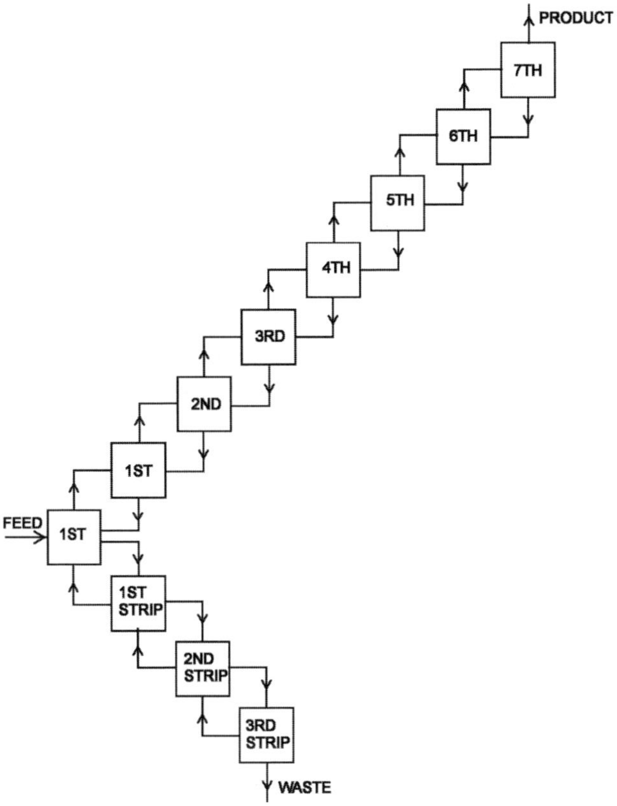

Figure 2.3. The cascade process used in gaseous diffusion.

Nuclear Reactors

In the early days, a nuclear reactor was often referred to as a 'pile', deriving from the name given to the very first reactor built in a squash court under the West Stands of Stagg Field Stadium in the middle of Chicago, which achieved criticality on 2 December 1942. The reactor was built by 'piling up' graphite and uranium until the combination became critical or divergent. Hence the reactor was described as a 'pile', and the name stuck, although it has become obsolete today.

In the pile, uranium atoms are being fissioned and producing more neutrons, which go on to split more uranium atoms and so on, but some of these neutrons will be lost in various ways: they may escape from the reactor or they may be absorbed by materials within the reactor, such as the control rods. If the rate of loss is greater than the rate of creation, the number of neutrons drops and the reaction will die away. The reactor is then convergent or subcritical. If the rate of creation and loss are the same, the reactor is critical. If the rate of creation is greater than the rate of loss, the number of neutrons will increase: the reactor has gone past critical and becomes supercritical and the reaction is now divergent. In such a situation, the activity will continue to increase exponentially, and the doubling time is a measure of the increasing activity; the doubling time being, not surprisingly, the time it takes for the activity to double.

One feature important to the control of a reactor is at which point the neutrons are produced. Most occur directly from the fission of the uranium or plutonium, and these are called prompt neutrons. Some neutrons are released a little time later from the decay products, perhaps a few seconds later, and these are called delayed neutrons. The delayed neutrons make the reactor easier to control, since without the delayed neutrons, a divergent reactor would increase in reactivity far too rapidly to control.

Apart from nuclear fuel, a reactor also needs control rods (or some other means) to regulate its activity, and some means of getting rid of the heat generated by the fission reactions. Most designs of reactors have a moderator.

A moderator is a material which will slow the energetic neutrons released from fission. As we have seen, slow neutrons have a better chance of splitting a ^{235}U nucleus. There are certain designs of reactors which will work without a moderator, but the great advantage of slowing down the neutrons is that it is then possible to use natural uranium as the reactor fuel. If the neutrons are faster, then the fuel has to be considerably enriched in ^{235}U — an expensive process.

The neutrons released by the fission of the ^{235}U collide with the nucleus of the atoms of the moderator, and will lose some kinetic energy in the collision. This is most effective with light nuclei. The fraction of the neutron's kinetic energy that will be lost to the other nucleus is given by $4\,M{\cdot}m/(M+m)^2$, where M is the mass of the nucleus and m the mass of the neutron. There is also a further requirement for the atoms of the moderator — that the neutron will bounce off the nucleus and not be absorbed by it. Very slow neutrons are sometimes referred to as 'thermal neutrons' — in other words, having the same energy as a particle at ambient temperature. This is $3\,kT/2$ (k being Boltzmann's constant, T being the absolute temperature), or around 0.03 eV at room temperature, whereas a fission neutron will typically have an energy in the region of 1 MeV.

Hydrogen in the form of water can be used as a moderator, but absorbs a significant number of neutrons, and so light water reactors need enriched uranium to work. 'Heavy water' can be used instead — this is water in which the hydrogen atoms have been replaced with the isotope deuterium, which has one proton and one neutron. Heavy water is a very effective moderator, but has the drawback that it is extremely expensive, since separating the deuterium present in natural hydrogen is highly energy intensive.

Beryllium would make an effective moderator, and was also suggested for the canning material for fuel elements, but it is likewise extremely expensive and very poisonous. The use of beryllium demands tremendous care. From the metallurgical point of view, beryllium turned out to be unsuitable as a canning material, and stainless steel was used in its stead. The next element in the periodic table is boron, but boron is a very good absorber of neutrons — so much so that it is used in control rods and safety devices in reactors.

The only other practical moderator is carbon in the form of graphite. One of the problems of using graphite as a moderator is making sure it has no boron impurities. The German wartime atomic programme used graphite with enough boron as impurity to render it useless, and as a consequence, had to use heavy water as a moderator — heavy water being much more scarce and expensive to produce. Norwegian hydroelectric power was used to produce the heavy water, leading to a long campaign of sabotage by the Norwegians and the Allies, delaying the programme further.

The next problem is how to get rid of the heat produced. As mentioned, the fission process releases a great deal of energy, which will appear in various forms, but mostly as heat. This is almost the only use for fission, either in a bomb or in a reactor. In a bomb, the heat is produced as quickly as possible, but not so in a reactor. One of the points of a reactor is that the rate of energy release can be controlled. This heat has to be removed from the core of the reactor — the core being the part of the reactor containing the fissile material. This can be done by circulating a fluid through the core. Here again, choices are limited. For example, the fluid must not be an absorber of neutrons, and it also needs good heat transfer characteristics if it is to remove the heat effectively.

As far as gases are concerned, helium would be ideal, and has been used in high temperature gas reactors. Hydrogen would be less useful, since it absorbs neutrons, as well as being explosive in air. The only other gas which has been used is carbon dioxide, particularly in the United Kingdom, although the idea of a steam-cooled reactor was also considered. This is not quite such a bizarre idea as it sounds, since steam is a gas like any other, but preventing corrosion might well have presented difficulties.

An obvious liquid coolant is water. Indeed there are many water-cooled reactors of various designs. There are two potential drawbacks. One is that water absorbs neutrons, the other is that heated water can easily vaporise into steam. The steam will not be nearly as effective a coolant and so the reactor will overheat. There are various other related problems and the design of water-cooled reactors has to allow for these difficulties.

The other possibility is a liquid metal. Mercury was used in an experimental reactor in America, but the use of mercury poses some obvious hazards. A lead bismuth alloy is a possibility, since it has a low melting point (having the coolant freeze in the reactor is not a good move) but bismuth absorbs neutrons and decays to become radioactive polonium. The only other feasible option is to use sodium or a sodium–potassium alloy. This too has some obvious disadvantages, given the reactivity of these two metals.

The problem becomes much more acute in a fast reactor, where there is no moderator to slow down the neutrons. This means the core is far smaller, and megawatts of heat may be generated in very small volumes. In these reactors, liquid metals are the only viable option — the Dounreay Fast Reactor used sodium–potassium alloy and the Prototype Fast Reactor used liquid sodium.

The heat produced is used to generate steam exactly as in a conventional power station (gas turbines were suggested for some high-temperature designs, but the idea has never been followed through). The amount of electricity generated depends on the thermodynamic efficiency of the design, which in turn is governed by the temperature of the steam produced. The advanced gas-cooled reactors (AGRs) were particularly efficient, producing steam at a temperature of 565°C. The magnox stations had a thermal efficiency of around 30%, the AGRs around 42%.

Thus the output of a reactor can be described in terms of the heat produced (thermal or Th) or of the electricity generated (E). The latter is the more useful figure.

Fuel Elements

Often what may appear to be the most mundane parts of a design turn out to be the most important. Fuel elements or fuel rods are such an example. The story of the evolution of the gas-cooled reactor is as much as anything the story of the development of the fuel element. The fuel in reactors is almost always uranium

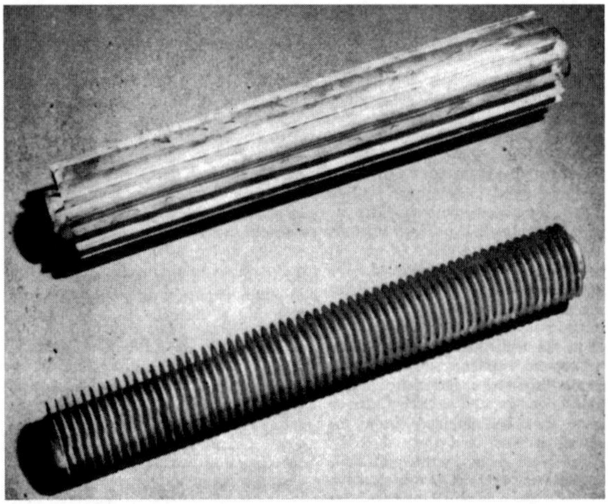

Figure 2.4. Examples of some early fuel rods. These would contain uranium metal in an aluminium casing. The fins were for cooling.

(which may or may not be enriched), sometimes in the form of the oxide but also as the metal. Plutonium is a possible fuel but has not been used very much except in some fast reactors.

One of the first jobs to be set into motion when the UK atomic programme began was the production of uranium metal from its ore, and an old wartime factory at Springfields near Preston, in Lancashire, was converted for the purpose. The steps in the production of fuel rods are shown in the graphic in Figure 2.5.

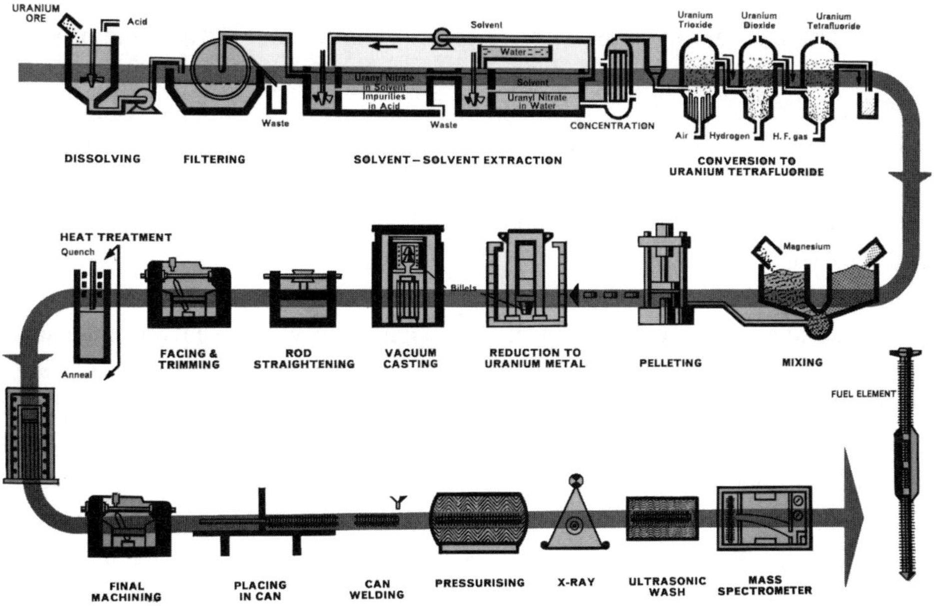

Figure 2.5. Fuel element production at Springfields, near Preston, Lancashire.

The fuel element has to perform a variety of jobs. First and foremost, the container or can must enclose the fuel so that no volatile fission products leak out to pollute the coolant. Some fission products are solid, so they are not a problem with a gas-cooled reactor, although they certainly would be with a water-cooled reactor. The most important gaseous fission products are ^{131}I and ^{135}Xe. Design of devices that will detect any leaking fission products is an important part of reactor design.

Secondly, and probably equally importantly, it must not be a neutron absorber, which limits the choice of material very considerably. Thirdly, and particularly in a gas-cooled reactor, it must be able to withstand very high temperatures. Fourthly, it should not be affected by intense neutron bombardment. Fifthly, there must be good heat transfer between the fuel, the container, and the coolant which flows through the reactor. Sixthly, it must be chemically compatible with the fuel and the coolant — in other words, not corrode in the coolant and not react or alloy with the fuel. There may well be other problems too — for example, the material and the uranium metal may expand at different rates as they are heated up, creating stresses in the fuel rod.

There was a further requirement in the case of the air-cooled reactors, which is that air should not be able to leak into the can, since the uranium would oxidise and particles of uranium oxide might well be released into the airflow and be carried away to the outside.

All this is reflected in the designs of the various British gas-cooled reactors. Graphite low energy experimental pile (GLEEP) was a low power, low temperature reactor, and the bars of uranium were given a thin coating of aluminium metal which was sufficient to contain the fission products. British experimental pile '0' (BEPO) and the Windscale piles ran at higher temperatures, and the uranium was put into aluminium cans. To prevent any chemical reaction between the two metals, the uranium was coated with graphite before canning. The can was also filled with helium gas, chosen in part for its good thermal conductivity, and the cans were also finned to help remove the heat.

Aluminium was not the best choice, since it did absorb neutrons to some extent. A better solution turned out to be an alloy of magnesium, which went under the name of magnox. Magnox (MAGnesium Non-OXidising) was an alloy of magnesium with aluminium (0.7–0.9%) and beryllium (0.002–0.3%). This has a melting point of around 647°C, and burns in damp carbon dioxide above about 600°C. The highest practicable temperature for magnox fuel elements is around 400°C. Despite an incident in the Chapelcross reactor in May 1967, magnox has had a very good safety record. The first cartridges were tested in the Windscale piles then used in the Calder Hall reactor in 1956; the last magnox power station is scheduled to close in 2014. Thus the system has been in successful use for more than half a century.

Zirconium has also proved to be suitable for canning highly enriched uranium in water-cooled reactors, being one of the few materials that does not absorb neutrons, has a high melting point and does not corrode in very hot water. One problem is that it is found in conjunction with hafnium, which is very similar chemically (they are in the same vertical group in the periodic table), but hafnium is a very good neutron absorber and has to be removed from the zirconium before it can be used. It melts at 1,855°C, so using it at high temperatures is not a problem.

Like aluminium, zirconium metal is coated with an oxide layer which is chemically very inert. To improve its corrosion properties, it is usually alloyed with other metals, and these are known generically as zircaloys. Zircaloy 2, for example, contains 1.2–1.7% tin.

There were problems with using metallic uranium as a fuel at high temperatures. The first is that uranium exists in various allotropic forms — that is, there are several possible physical forms of the metal, which are stable in various temperature

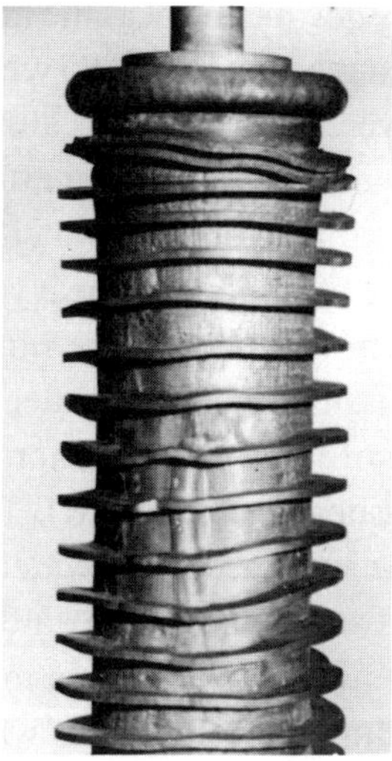

Figure 2.6. A fuel rod failure, probably caused by different expansions of the uranium and the can.

regions. The transition from the alpha phase to the beta occurs at 660°C, and there is a change of volume with the change in phase. The problem is that the fuel will be at a much higher temperature than the gas or coolant, and this fixes an upper limit to the fuel element temperature. The alternative is then to use uranium oxide, UO_2. This can be made into ceramic pellets, but has the drawback that the oxide is not a good conductor of heat, and is much less dense. This meant the fuel elements tended to be made from relatively long thin pins, and in the AGR, these pins were grouped together to make one complete unit.

The magnox reactors, which used natural uranium, produced plutonium as a by-product. The plutonium could be separated from the used fuel, and originally it was intended that it would be burned up in the fast reactors. The plutonium oxide would be mixed with uranium oxide to form a fuel described as MOX — mixed oxide. In the event, the commercial fast reactors were never built, although the steam generating heavy water reactor (SGHWR) at Winfrith was able to use the MOX fuel. As a consequence, there are large stockpiles of plutonium at the reprocessing plant at Sellafield. Plutonium in this form is not suitable for atomic weapons since it would have much too high a concentration of the 240 isotope.

The first British power reactors were the air-cooled Windscale piles which were intended to produce plutonium for the first British atom bombs. This led to what was described as PIPPA, an acronym with several possible origins, the most useful being plutonium and industrial power producing. The PIPPA design was built at Calder Hall, and improved versions for generating electricity were built as the magnox design. The next step up from magnox was the AGR. These were all cooled with carbon dioxide. The next step along the line was the high-temperature reactor (HTR) or high-temperature gas-cooled reactor (HTGCR) which used helium as the cooling gas. No commercial versions were built in Britain, although a small prototype known as DRAGON was built as part of an international effort.

The alternative to gas-cooled reactors was water-cooled reactors. A successful heavy water power reactor, the steam-cooled heavy water reactor (SCHWR) was built at Winfrith and the system was once in the running for a commercial power station. Harwell studied the possibility of light water reactors, but these were abandoned. The two main designs of light water reactors are the boiling water reactor (BWR) and the pressurised water reactor (PWR). These were the designs which originated in America and have since been sold widely throughout the world. There was considerable controversy from the 1960s onwards as to whether the UK should adopt these designs. The last power reactor built in the UK, Sizewell B, was a PWR to an American design. Any future power stations will almost certainly be variants on the PWR or BWR.

Chapter 3

People and Places

There were very many competent and dedicated people working as part of the UK atomic energy programme, and it is impossible to mention all of them. It may be invidious to concentrate on a few selected individuals, but there are those who need mention either for the roles they performed, or because they were genuinely men of outstanding calibre (and in this context 'men' is the correct word to use: very few women were involved in public life in the Britain of the 1950s and 60s, and even today engineering is very much a male-dominated profession).

The atomic energy programme originally began its life in 1945 as a department of the Ministry of Supply. This had been created in 1939 to coordinate the supply of military equipment to the Armed Forces, and since the early programme was in effect entirely military, this made sense, not least from the logistical point of view.

Lord Portal was appointed Controller of the new department with the directive to produce plutonium as soon as was possible. Portal had been made Commander in Chief of Bomber Command in April 1940, then Chief of the Air Staff in October 1940. Unfortunately, Portal was both exhausted from the war and had a poor technical grasp of the details of plutonium production. Although Portal was nominally in charge, in effect all the decisions were taken by the triumvirate of Hinton, Cockcroft and Penney. When Portal retired in 1951, he was replaced by General Morgan. Unfortunately, there were two General Morgans in the Army, and it is widely thought that the 'wrong Morgan' was chosen. Neither Portal nor Morgan made a great impact on the programme.[1]

When atomic energy was moved out of the Ministry of Supply to become an independent organisation, the AEA, it was headed by a Chairman. The first two were Edwin Plowden and Roger Makins, two of the class of administrators thrown up by the war. They were followed by William Penney.

Cockcroft, Hinton and Penney

The outstanding success of the early atomic programme can be put down to many factors, but certainly one was the leadership provided by three men: John Cockcroft,

Christopher Hinton and William Penney. Each had extremely able assistants, but there is no doubt the programme would have not achieved anything near as much as it did, in the time that it did, without these three. (General Morgan referred to them as the 'bold bad barons'.)

In some respects, their task was made both easier and more difficult by having to start completely from scratch. Easier, because they were able to stamp their own vision on the programme at the outset — it is much more difficult to make a name for yourself when taking over an organisation which is already running smoothly. More difficult, because there were no guidelines — all were breaking new ground, with absolutely no pre-existing infrastructure.

All three had come from what might have been described in that period as 'humble beginnings'. They were all educated at state secondary schools rather than public schools. Entrance to university was paid for by scholarships. They had all proved themselves as scientists and administrators during the war, which had been a forcing ground for many able scientific administrators who would go onto civilian work afterwards — Sir Bernard Lovell, creator of the Jodrell Bank radio telescope, being a typical example.

Figure 3.1. John Cockcroft.

John Cockcroft was born in Todmorden, Yorkshire, where his father had inherited a family business in dire financial straits. He was educated at a local church school then Todmorden Elementary School, moving on to Todmorden Secondary

School, before winning a County Scholarship to Manchester University.[2] Cockcroft moved from Manchester to Cambridge, where he worked with Rutherford at the Cavendish Laboratory, and collaborated with Walton on a high voltage apparatus for accelerating positive ions. In his words:

> At last we obtained a high energy proton beam ... we directed it onto a lithium target and at once observed, with a zinc sulphide screen, the bright scintillations which were obviously due to particle emission from the lithium.[3]

The reaction they had achieved was: ${}^{7}_{3}\mathrm{Li} + {}^{1}_{1}\mathrm{H} = {}^{4}_{2}\mathrm{He} + {}^{4}_{2}\mathrm{He}$

This was the first ever artificial nuclear transformation: Cockcroft and Walton would receive the Nobel Prize in Physics for this work in 1951.

Whilst at Cambridge, Cockcroft also began to show his talents as an administrator, both as Junior Bursar in St John's College and in the construction of the Mond Laboratory. At the outset of war, he moved into work on radar, as did so many other British scientists at the time, but was also a member of the military application of uranium detonation (MAUD) committee, which met to consider Peierls and Frisch's memorandum on atomic explosions. In 1944, he took over the atomic energy programme in Canada, and was responsible for the building of the NRX heavy water reactor at Chalk River, but came back to Britain in 1945 to head the new atomic establishment to be built in Britain.

He had been recommended by Sir James Chadwick, discoverer of the neutron, and leader of the British mission to Los Alamos. Chadwick said of Cockcroft:

> He has many virtues which would contribute to the smooth running of the establishment ... and he would keep his hand on all the strings. In common with most scientists he also has many faults and these we must recognise from the beginning so that we can supplement him by a suitable choice of assistants. For example his knowledge is wide but it is not at all profound; his views are of a rather dull every-day hue. On the other hand his temperament is so equable and his patience and persistence so inexhaustible that we can put in lively and relatively irresponsible men who have the real feeling for research without fear of upsetting the balance.[4]

Cockcroft was responsible for the choice of Harwell for the new research establishment, and was instrumental in building it up into a major centre for nuclear research.[5] When the AEA was created, he became one of the full-time technical members responsible for research.

It seems that at times he could be a somewhat remote figure: describing the progress on a high-temperature reactor, one writer said that he 'had a strong interest in the project, giving it far more attention than was usual in one so distant from his staff'.[6]

Basil Schonland replaced him as Director of Harwell in 1958, and he resigned as a full-time member of the Authority in 1959, becoming the first Master of Churchill College, Cambridge. He died in 1967.

Figure 3.2. Christopher Hinton.

Christopher Hinton was born on 12 May 1901 in the school house of the village of Tisbury, Wiltshire, where his father was headmaster of the boys' school. He attended the elementary school in Chippenham before moving on to the town secondary school in 1913. He left school in 1917, and unable to afford university, became an apprentice first in Kilmarnock, then the Great Western Railway Company in Swindon.

He attended night school at the local technical college, and won first the Great Western Chairman's Prize for the best apprentice of the year, then the WH Allen scholarship awarded by the Institute of Mechanical Engineers to Trinity College, Cambridge in 1923.[7] He took the Tripos in two years rather than three. He was one of the nine people awarded Firsts in his year, and spent his third year on research. Despite winning the Second Yates Prize and a Trinity Senior Scholarship in 1926, he left Cambridge for Brunner Mond in Northwich, Cheshire. He became Deputy Chief Engineer at 27 and Chief Engineer at 29.

After the outbreak of war he became Assistant Director of Ordnance Factory Construction, and in 1943 the Deputy Director General of the Explosives Filling Factories, which at its peak employed around 150,000 people. In mid-1945, Sir Wallace Akers, who had been in charge of tube alloys (the cover name given to the atomic energy programme during the war), invited him to take charge of the industrial organisation which would be built to produce plutonium. Hinton specified that he should be given full responsibility for the design, construction and operation of the factories, and also for the industrial applications of atomic energy.

As Assistant Controller of Atomic Energy his salary was £2,500 — a considerable drop from his wartime salary, although more than the salaries of Cockcroft and Penney. His first task was to find a site for the production piles, whose design had hardly even been started. In some frustration, he wrote a paper outlining how the site might be run, and Appendix Two of the report reads rather strangely to modern eyes:

> POLICY IN REGARD TO EMPLOYMENT OF WOMEN
>
> Men working on the factory will mainly reside in the Township, many of them will have wives and families. The houses there are likely to be of small modern types and will not provide full-time housewifery work for wives and certainly not for daughters. It is therefore highly desirable that work for as many women as possible should be found in the Factory.
>
> In the American plants women are employed in process buildings where there is a radiation hazard (e.g. on monitoring work in the pile building). This is considered inadvisable as an initial step and it is not proposed that women should be employed in process or other buildings where there are minor risks of exposure to mild radiation in the ordinary course of routine duties. This excludes them from Process buildings, laboratories, laundries etc in the Pile and Separation Groups.
>
> It is, however, proposed to employ them in other buildings (canteen, offices stores etc) on these groups. It is probable that, if there is a serious accident on process plant, many or all the operatives in the Group where the accident occurs will be seriously harmed and in the case of serious exposure it does not seem to be important whether the casualty is male or female . . .
>
> A rough analysis of the organisation charts suggests that out of a total payroll of about 1,050 approximately 200 jobs are suitable for women. Of these however about 40 are specialist jobs involving long periods of training (e.g. nurses). It is thought that the remaining 160 jobs provide enough female employment for the relatives of male employees. If this does not prove to be the case it will be necessary to make arrangements to employ women in light unskilled jobs (such as tradesmen's mates) or (by relaxation) on machine shop work in the Service Group.
>
> No marriage bar must operate against employment of women.[8]

It is not entirely clear from the context quite what 'by relaxation' implies. One can hardly imagine anything being written in that vein today: the social attitudes of the 1940s are now very alien, showing that the past is indeed 'another country'.

Opinions of Hinton's time heading the industrial group at Risley are mixed. There is no doubt he was given great autonomy and little or no oversight. He involved himself in almost every part of the project. The achievement of building the piles and producing plutonium in the limited time available, not to mention the many other tasks given to the Industrial Group, was extraordinary.

He was universally respected, but not always liked, and some felt his manner to be counterproductive. Gethin Davey, the General Manager at Windscale, writing to the historian Margaret Gowing, had this to say:

> Hinton alone had the complete fascinating picture and he had to supply the enthusiasm, inspiration, drive and sense of urgency, and I know of no other man who could have taken the programme to completion in the allotted time ... but I doubt if all the acrimony and bad feeling which he engendered were necessary ...
>
> On another occasion Hinton entered the Conference Room, sat down and said, "Having completed my inspection I see no point in holding a progress meeting because clearly there has been no progress during the last month".
>
> This will give some idea of the atmosphere which was created at these meetings. No time could be wasted with praise. Those portions of the work which were going reasonably well were not referred to and the whole of the meeting was devoted to discussing in considerable detail the reasons for unsatisfactory quality or failure to keep a programme date. Gradually the atmosphere both in these meetings and on the job became worse ... Undoubtedly the situation was anything but satisfactory but, what was worse, the morale of MOW [Ministry of Works] personnel had reached a very low ebb. The probability is that the vituperous comments and metaphorical beating about the head had reached the psychological point where they ceased to be effective.[9]

All of this may have been true, but building Windscale and producing plutonium in such a timely fashion was still an extremely impressive performance by Hinton and his team.

It is also true that there was considerable rivalry between the research establishment at Harwell and the production division at Risley. This began at the very top. Charles Rennie was the first Director of the DRAGON research programme, and a history of the programme says of him:

> During the early Fifties he had the delicate job of smoothing relations between Risley and Harwell at a time when Sir John Cockcroft's and Sir Christopher Hinton's mutual antagonism was at its height.[10]

Hinton left the Atomic Energy Authority just two months before the Windscale fire to become the first Chairman of the new CEGB. His time there was less successful. It is also curious to note that at that time the CEGB began expressing a preference not for the British gas-cooled reactor design, but American pressurised water reactors. This was to be a row that would linger on for many years after Hinton.

As will be seen in Chapter 11, his time as Chairman of the CEGB was not without controversy either: his apparent high-handedness concerning the allocation of a major contract caused the Minister for Science, Quintin Hogg, to write:

> What on earth is Hinton thinking about? ... He cannot just call off a contract for the construction of a nuclear power station at the present state of play without creating first-class political and economic chaos.[11]

It was also notable, and rather extraordinary, that, during his tenure at the CEGB, relations between the AEA and the CEGB were extremely poor, causing Hogg to write:

> This is very serious. It is damaging to the public service if two public bodies cannot cooperate .... You had better come and talk to me about this and what I ought to do ... You must tell me also what is really behind this.[12]

He retired from the CEGB in 1964 and in 1965 he was created a life peer as Baron Hinton of Bankside. He was active in retirement, being Chancellor of the University of Bath from 1966 to 1980, and died in 1983 at the age of 82.

By the mid-1970s, the British nuclear programme was in some disarray, and an article appeared in the *New Scientist* magazine in October 1976, written by Hinton, and entitled 'Two Decades of Nuclear Confusion.' At the conclusion of the article, he bemoans the cumbersome decision making process, and finishes by saying,

> Design by consensus of opinion between six different organisations is unlikely to lead to triumphant success. There must be one single competent engineer (it is an engineering job) who is ultimately responsible. He must stand or fall by his results; by whether his project is completed within the estimate and operate successfully on the programmed date.[13]

One wonders whether, like de Gaulle a little earlier, he hoped to be called back to lead the programme, running it not by committee, but as the autocrat he always was.

Figure 3.3. William Penney.

William Penney was born in Gibraltar, where his father was a sergeant major in the Army. He finished his schooling at Sheerness Junior Technical College, and after leaving took a job as a laboratory assistant, being paid 10 shillings (roughly 50p today) a week. When he was 18, he won a scholarship to study mathematics at the Royal College of Science, part of Imperial College London.[14]

Penney was engaged in scientific research at Cambridge and London in the 1930s. He was called up in 1940 and worked on the blast effects due to bombing, but was soon transferred to the British team who went to Los Alamos. Again he worked on blast effects, calculating the height at which the bomb should be detonated in order to achieve maximum destruction, and was also involved in the choice of targets. He was to have been an observer of the Hiroshima bomb, but was prevented by the American Air Force. Together with Group Captain Leonard Cheshire, he was in the aircraft which observed the Nagasaki bomb, and visited Nagasaki subsequently to investigate the blast effects. He also observed the 1946 atomic weapons trials at Bikini Atoll.

On his return to Britain, he would have preferred to have returned to academic life, but instead accepted the post of Chief Superintendent of Armament Research (CSAR) at Fort Halstead in Kent; part of the Ministry of Supply. He began the design of the first British atomic weapon in 1947, and it was apparent that Fort Halstead would not be adequate for the facilities that would be needed. The project moved to a new site: Aldermaston in Berkshire; again, another redundant RAF station.

During the 1950s, Penney would be involved not only in the fission device, but also in the testing of nuclear weapons in Australia, the design of new warheads, and the development and testing of the fusion weapon, as well as responsible for the report on the enquiry into the fire at Windscale. He was the Chairman of the AEA from 1964 until 1967, when he retired. He then became Rector of Imperial College London at a time when the student troubles of the late 1960s were at their height. This was not an easy time for Penney. He retired in 1973.

In 1985, the Australian government set up a Royal Commission on the British nuclear tests of the 1950s. Australian opinion had moved from full support in the 1950s to outright opposition in the 1980s, and Penney, as a witness, faced considerable hostile questioning.

Although Penney had been created a life peer in 1967, he played little part in the House of Lords. He died in 1991.

The most extraordinary aspect, from a modern point of view, of the jobs these men undertook was the salaries that were on offer. Hinton's salary was £2,500 a year, a good deal less than he had been receiving at Imperial Chemical Industries (ICI). Cockcroft had this to say about his appointment to Harwell:

> My salary was to be £2000 per annum — not overgenerous considering that my pre-war University emoluments have been about £1500 per annum and that there had been at least a twofold inflation since then . . . salaries were reviewed in 1946 and my salary was then increased to £2400.[15]

Penney's salary for his first four years was £1,900, and both Cockcroft and Penney could have returned to academic life on salaries at least equal to these, and would have lived in more congenial surroundings. Indeed, Penney was in great demand by the Americans, and could have demanded a salary far in excess of that which he was being paid in Britain.

For comparison, a permanent secretary in the Civil Service (the top post in a government ministry) would earn £3,500 a year, the Chief Scientist in the Ministry of Supply earned £3,000 a year, the Director of the National Physical Laboratory £2,250 a year, and the post of Chief Draughtsman £800–950 a year.[16]

These figures show that not only were they poorly paid; they also illustrate the inflation that has occurred since the 1940s. Sixty years later, salaries near the top of the Civil Service are of the order of £150,000 a year — roughly 50 fold greater.

But the talent in the atomic energy programme was not confined to these three men. A variety of different talents were needed. These were very large programmes, and needed capable administrators, scientists and engineers. Penney himself was a better scientist than administrator. It became apparent in the mid-1950s that someone needed to be drafted in to take on the role of administrator from Penney, who was desperately overworked. This was done by Sir William Cook, who became Penney's deputy, and directed a good deal of work on the British fusion weapon. After leaving Aldermaston he became the Authority member for engineering and production, replacing Hinton.

Atomic energy also attracted a large part of the scientific talent of 1950s Britain. Looking at the list of those who worked in high positions at Harwell and Risley, it is noticeable how many of them were elected Fellows of the Royal Society. Many of these also became involved in the work on controlled nuclear fusion, which moved to Culham in the late 1950s, and where much research is still being carried out.

Creation of the Atomic Energy Authority

Putting the atomic energy programme within the Ministry of Supply had advantages and disadvantages. One of the major advantages was that the department could call upon the services of the Ministry of Works and other parts of the Civil Service administration. One of the apparent disadvantages was that the pay scales would be fixed to Civil Service levels, and thus might not be attractive to people of calibre, who could earn much more in industry.

In 1952, the Conservatives won the general election and Winston Churchill formed the new government. He was not interested in the minutiae of administration. One of his principal advisers was Lord Cherwell, one-time professor at Oxford, who felt very strongly that the Civil Service was not the place for atomic energy, as the following passage from his speech in the House of Lords demonstrates:

> The manufacture of atomic weapons is quite unlike the manufacture of any other weapon. Research of the most recondite kind, such as measuring the cross-sections of nuclei under bombardment by neutrons of various velocities; development of methods to shoot together the sub-critical parts of the bomb and make them detonate; production of fissile material involving large-scale separation of isotopes or extraction of traces of new elements from mixtures so radioactive you dare not approach them — all these aspects interact upon one another and are so closely intermingled that it is an undertaking of quite a novel kind.
>
> The government quite rightly decided the project should be unified and welded together. The mistake was in handing it over to the civil service. If every decision and every plan, or change of plan, has to go through all the inter-departmental committees and obtain Treasury sanction, if every appointment approved by establishment officers, interminable delays are inevitable. What is needed is some much more flexible organisation, freed from the trammels and restrictions which are bound to hem in any sub-department of a Ministry. Naturally, it would be under government control. Indeed, in my view, considering the importance and urgency the project, it should be responsible to the head of the Government, for he alone could settle quickly any difficulties which might arise with any department, and he alone cut red tape. Only in this way can we get quick decisions and the right men. Rapid progress can only be expected if the people in charge are allowed a reasonably free hand. Only men used to tackling large industrial developments can successfully handle operations of this nature.
>
> But industrialists of this sort, accustomed to taking decisions and responsibility, cannot be fitted into the Civil Service machine. The Civil Service find them singularly indigestible; and they, for their part, except in wartime, would be very unwilling themselves to be swallowed by the Civil Service. If the project had been entrusted to some flexible organisation, freed from the inevitable restrictions of a Government Department, it would have been much easier to induce men experienced in large industrial undertakings to take a leading part in the work; and, given a reasonable freedom of action in making plans, in making contracts, engaging staff and so on, they would, I'm sure, have produced for us atomic bombs at least as fast as the Russians. This difficulty does not arise only in the top ranks; it extends all down the line, and rightly or wrongly, many good engineers and scientists do not like the idea of joining the Civil Service. They know they will be less independent than in industry, and that their work prescribed for them and regulated by the administrative civil servants who often know little about the subject and yet enjoy a much higher status. For this reason alone it is very hard to get and keep the right sort of man. In this country, unhappily, high-grade technologists all too scarce — there are more jobs than men.[17]

Cherwell got his way, and a new organisation was set up: the United Kingdom Atomic Energy Authority,[18] which came into being in January 1954, under the chairmanship of Sir Edwin Plowden. Plowden and his successor Roger Makins were representative of the administrators which emerged from the war. In the 1950s, men such as these ran large parts of Britain, not as government ministers or civil servants but as appointees. Although they nominally answered to ministers, the convention was that they should be left to run their organisations as they saw fit with little or no oversight.

Figure 3.4. Visit of Georgy Malenkov, Soviet politician, to Harwell in April 1956. Left to right: Georgy Malenkov, Sir John Cockcroft and Sir Edwin Plowden, Chairman of the AEA. (Image courtesy of NDA and copyright NDA.)

Prior to becoming Chairman of the new Authority, Plowden had been a senior Treasury civil servant. After leaving the AEA, Plowden remained in great demand by government and Whitehall. Part of his obituary in *The Telegraph* reads:

> Thus in 1959 he led a committee of inquiry into the Treasury's control of public expenditure. Its report laid emphasis on the importance of long-term planning rather than short-term expedience, and resulted in a wholesale reorganisation of the Treasury.
>
> Shortly afterwards it was the turn of the Foreign Office to come under Plowden's scrutiny. His committee's report, published in 1964, recommended the merger of the Foreign and Commonwealth offices. It also advocated that diplomats should be more closely concerned with commerce.
>
> In 1965 another Plowden committee investigated the future of the British aircraft industry. The committee advised that the government should acquire a majority shareholding in the British Aircraft Corporation and in the airframe elements of Hawker Siddeley.
>
> In 1975 Plowden headed an inquiry which proposed that the 13 electricity boards should be placed under direct control of the Electricity Council. And in 1982 a salaries review under his chairmanship embarrassed the Thatcher administration, which was trying to hold down costs in the public sector, by proposing large pay rises for civil servants, senior officers in the armed forces, and judges.[19]

Makins was also a senior Whitehall figure. He had been Ambassador to the USA and Joint Permanent Secretary at the Treasury before being appointed to the chair of the AEA. Makins was succeeded by William Penney.

It was not only the AEA that had such freedom of action: as part of the post-war nationalisation programme, organisations such as the National Coal Board, British Rail, the British Electrical Authority (later to become the CEGB) and the Gas Board were set up as independent authorities. In theory, they were answerable to particular ministers, so that the Chairman of the National Coal Board would be answerable to the Minister of Power, for example. In practice, they were virtually autonomous. It was unknown for the Chairman of such bodies to be sacked or to resign. In modern parlance, these organisations might be described as 'super quangos'.

The first annual report of the new AEA is addressed to the Marquess of Salisbury in his capacity as Lord President of the Council then, in the mid-1950s, reports are addressed to the Prime Minister himself. By 1960, the minister responsible had changed to the Minister of Science, who was Quintin Hogg, Lord Hailsham.[20] Subsequently the AEA reported to the Minister of Technology, a newly created post in the Wilson government, and after the abolition of the Ministry of Technology by the Heath government, to the Secretary of State for the Department for Trade and Industry (DTI).

The size of the AEA can be gauged by the number of staff employed: according to the seventh annual report for 1960–1961, the AEA employed 40,840 staff.[21] If sub-contractors and commercial firms were included, the number would be far more. The capital account for that year amounted to £481 million.

The atomic energy programme in all its different forms underwent many different organisational changes over the years, but structurally, it can be broken down, fairly approximately, into three basic areas.[22]

One was the weapons' side, which was initially based at Fort Halstead in Kent, before moving to Aldermaston. There were some outposts: the warhead manufacture took place at the Royal Ordnance Factory at Burghfield, and there was another Royal Ordnance Factory in Cardiff. Orford Ness on the Suffolk coast was used for environmental testing and explosives testing for nuclear weapons, although no fissile material was involved.

The second area was the major research and development centre, based at the Atomic Energy Research Establishment, Harwell.[23] This too expanded with various offshoots: the reactor division was moved to Winfrith in Dorset. As well as many research reactors, Winfrith would also be home to the high-temperature reactor DRAGON project and the steam generating heavy water reactor (SGHWR).

Controlled thermonuclear fusion work, including the ZETA experiment, was centred at Harwell until the late 1950s. Again, space restrictions at Harwell meant that the work had to be relocated, and after consideration of Winfrith, the nearby site of Culham was chosen.[24]

The third part of the organisation was the industrial and production work, centred at Risley in Cheshire, again with various outposts for different functions.[25] The factory at Springfields near Preston in Lancashire produced uranium hexafluoride for the diffusion plant, and manufactured uranium metal from the ore for use in fuel elements. It would also manufacture the fuel elements for all the commercial power stations, as well as the magnox stations built in Italy and Japan. The diffusion plant itself was sited at Capenhurst in Cheshire. There was also a Reactor Materials Laboratory at Culcheth, Warrington, in Cheshire.

The production plant at Windscale, designed for the production of plutonium fell under the aegis of the Industrial Group.[26] In addition to the two initial piles, the four reactors at Calder Hall were also designed to produce weapons grade plutonium, and a further power station similar to Calder Hall was built at Chapelcross in Scotland.

Finally, of course, there was the London office — never officially referred to as the headquarters, but which acted as such.

Harwell

Cockcroft was offered the post of the directorship of the new research establishment late in 1945. As with many post-war research establishments, a surplus airfield (of which there were many) was the obvious choice for the site, as it had a large open spaces, large hangars, accommodation and services. He and some of his colleagues visited a variety of RAF bases, looking for a site which would be not too far from London and the University towns of Oxford and Cambridge. The choice fell on Harwell, not far from Abingdon, then in Berkshire, but after the 1974 local government reorganisation, it was transferred to Oxfordshire.

It was handed over, slightly reluctantly, by the RAF in January 1946, whilst Cockroft was still in Canada. He described his first visit to the new establishment thus:[27]

> I visited the Harwell site on a stormy day, the rain coming down at a typical angle of 45°, at the end of January 1946, and inspected the existing buildings on the site. One of the aircraft hangars was suitable to house GLEEP and nuclear physics; a second BEPO and the engineering laboratory; a third could house the cyclotron and the fourth the main workshop. The blocks were suitable for conversion to house laboratories including a "warm" radioactive laboratory; and analytic chemistry laboratory; a radiochemical laboratory; a metallurgical laboratory. The officers and sergeants messes were to be converted to staff hostels; a hundred prefab houses were to be built on the site as rapidly as possible to be followed later by a further hundred; the Ministry of Works also agreed to build one hundred permanent houses in Abingdon and I looked at several alternative attractive sites.

Figure 3.5. Nikita Krushschev and Nikolai Bulganin visit Harwell in April 1956. Nikita Krushchev was the First Secretary of the Communist Party of the Soviet Union, Nikolai Bulganin (far right) the Soviet Premier. (Image courtesy of NDA and copyright NDA.)

Initial progress was slow, and Cockcroft relates how in May, Professor Peierls wrote from Birmingham to Chadwick, who was still in Washington, expressing his disquiet on the lack of progress. He spoke of 'the incredible inefficiency and red tape in the Ministry of Supply'.

Peierls (as quoted by Cockcroft) went on:

> Oliphant and I visited Harwell this week and there is practically nothing going on there. No construction work has progressed or even started. Skinner has an uphill job fighting petty officials over petty regulations. . . What I am particularly concerned about is that before the decision was taken to place the project under the Ministry of Supply it was our general impression that if the project were to come under an existing Ministry it would have a special organisation set up for it which would make use of the priority and financial arrangements of the Ministry but within the organisation it would have a completely independent structure.[28]

Conditions in post-war Britain were difficult, and matters were made worse by some of the exceptional bad weather, which in 1946–1947 brought much of Britain to a standstill, with frequent power cuts due to lack of fuel. Cockcroft goes on to say:

> The Ministry of Works were greatly handicapped by the severe winter of 1946/7 especially when snow came down through the open roof of the BEPO hangar. The construction workers were housed in a nearby housing estate at Kingston Bagpuize complained of low pay, which meant not enough overtime, poor food, poor accommodation. The small amount of overtime work was actually due to a trades union complaint that we had been infringing an agreement to limit overtime to "work of an urgent character". I was asked by the Ministry of Works to speak to the workers from a platform temporarily rigged up in the BEPO hangar. I told them about the importance and urgency of our programme and as a result of this plea agreement was reached to work 10 hours a day whereupon our labour troubles disappeared.

Living conditions at Harwell in the late 1940s were on the primitive side. Britain was rebuilding its infrastructure after the war, and both fuel and food were heavily rationed. To house the many staff needed, 200 'pre-fabs' were built. This was pre-fabricated housing put up as a temporary post-war measure to ease the housing situation, and around 160,000 were built nationally. They were very much intended as a temporary expedient, with a life expectancy of five to ten years, although some still survive today.

> One of our most difficult problems was to provide reasonable meals for our staff. Our first canteen was housed in a black painted Nissen hut appropriately named "the Black Beetle". Long queues used to form in the open during the winter months and I joined them from time to time to see how palatable or otherwise the food was so that I could provide personal experience to add to official urgings for improvements. We did not however achieve satisfactory meals until we were able to take over the original NAAFI building which was first used for technical work.[29]

Figure 3.6. Hugh Gaitskell, Labour Party leader, and Aneurin Bevan visiting Harwell in January 1959. (Image courtesy of NDA and copyright NDA.)

Cockcroft goes on to describe the construction of the first British reactors:

> The erection of GLEEP went on rapidly thanks to Watson Munroe's New Zealand drive and forceful language. Graphite was machined at Harwell and since we did not have sufficient uranium metal available a mixture of UO_2 and uranium metal fuel elements were loaded and the reactor diverged in October, 1947.
>
> In parallel with work on GLEEP, design and construction of the BEPO reactor went on rapidly. A good deal of preparatory work had been carried on by the "graphite group" in Canada. The production of high purity graphite had been established at Welland and over 800 tons of the BEPO graphite was shipped across the Atlantic in due course.
>
> As early as April, 1945, the graphite group had calculated the basic lattice, dimensions and overall dimensions and predicted that criticality would be achieved when 28 tons of uranium metal was loaded. The actual figure turned out to be 30 tons.[30]

Harwell was a research establishment, as opposed to Risley, which housed the Industrial Group. There was obviously some tension between the two establishments, which was partly a matter of rivalry and partly a difference of ethos and approach. In writing the history of the Dragon project, the author describes Harwell thus:

> At Harwell the spirit was one of adventure where systems were promoted as much for their scientific interest as for any convincing market reason. For example, the metallurgical division under Finniston was promoting the liquid metal fuelled reactor — the metallurgists' reactor; the Chemistry Division under Robert Spence was promoting the homogenous aqueous reactor — the chemists' system. Risley was making a determined bid to take over the fast reactor work . . .[31]

And then later:

> Nevertheless progress had been sufficiently encouraging for the Authority to form a High Temperature Gas-Cooled Reactor Research Committee to study the experiment, briefly called HUGO, which with Sir John Cockcroft in the chair brought together the top people from Harwell and Risley. Sir Leonard Owen, Director of Engineering and deputy to Hinton, led the Northern team looking more like an opposition than a collaboration.

Whilst the author might have been somewhat partial in his judgements, there does seem to have been considerable tension at times between the two establishments and their outlooks. As will be seen in the chapter on PIPPA, the first gas-cooled design, there was strong opposition to the project from Hinton, who preferred the fast reactor design and remained distinctly dismissive of the gas-cooled reactor. From the earlier sections of this chapter, it can be seen that Hinton was a man of strong views, and perhaps was inclined to ride roughshod over those who disagreed with him.

There is another interesting memo written by an official in the Department of Trade and Industry in 1971, when he was touring the Authority's establishments prior to producing a report on the reactor programme. He visited Risley and spoke to RV Moore.[32]

> Mr Moore spoke to me about the history of the AEA Reactor Group which needed to be understood before one could sensibly look at the present set-up. He went back to the era of rivalry between Hinton and Cockcroft which had led to immense duplication and proliferation of research and development facilities.[33]

Figure 3.7. Major UK AEA sites.

In the 1950s, there was a tremendous amount of fundamental research to be done into atomic energy, and both Harwell and Risley were at the forefront of this work. This can bring problems of its own — what to do with a large research organisation when the technology has become mature. A very prescient letter was written to Cockroft in September 1958 by Franz Mandl, who was leaving Harwell and moving to the Physics Department of Manchester University. The letter was originally written in the context of the proposed removal of the thermonuclear work at Harwell to Winfrith, which was strongly opposed by many of those working on fusion. Mandl comments:

> As far as Harwell is concerned, the removal of the reactor and CTR [Controlled Thermonuclear Research] projects to Winfrith leaves Harwell without any major projects such as are essential to a research establishment if it is to flourish. Apart from the Rutherford laboratory, which must not be counted as part of Harwell, there would be left at Harwell a small amount of pure research work but primarily Harwell will consist of "ancillary service divisions". As regards the pure research, the justification of Harwell never has and never could come from this. Rather, the small amount of pure research done here has been justified as being stimulating to the place generally, etc. . . . The general outlook for Harwell then is extremely black: one might say that the establishment has an 80% chance of stagnating utterly in the next few years. (An allied major problem, I believe, has never been faced up to, is the question of what to do with an establishment when the task which it was set up is completed, e.g. it has been solved or the project, for one reason or another, abandoned. I believe that an establishment should under these circumstances be dissolved. The general practice has been to let such a place decay slowly, doing less and less work of any significance, absorbing scientists, technicians, equipment and money. Examples of such places are easy to think of.) It has been suggested that this leaves Harwell free to tackle new projects arising out of brilliant ideas as yet not conceived. Frankly I consider this quite unrealistic. When the new brainwaves come along there is time enough to set up a new organisation of just the right type to deal with the new problems. To have a huge machinery ticking over, all the time getting bigger and rustier, in case a new development is around the corner, strikes me as a strange procedure.[34]

At the top of the letter, is a handwritten comment 'I could have written this myself some time ago. JDC'.

Mandl had a very good point. What was to become of Harwell when its time was up? One option, taken up in the mid-1960s, was to diversify into non-nuclear work. This might have kept Harwell busy, but the question arises: why should Harwell in particular do this work when there are many other establishments which could do it as well — as Mandl points out in his letter? Mandl also goes on to ask what should be done with an establishment when its task has been finished. Too many institutions have lingered on after their day is done.

It was not only insiders who noticed the decline in morale at Harwell. An editorial of 1959 in the journal *Nuclear Engineering International* had this to say:

> The flux of people from Harwell reflects not financial inadequacy but inadequacy of purpose in the establishment, a feeling of frustration with the somewhat over-bearing administration and a consciousness of being divorced from the mainstream of atomic energy development. This is a far cry from the days of the late forties when Harwell was the most glamorous research establishment in Europe and

> where the mere name conjured up the most dynamic development programme of the century.[35]

The editorial also made two further points. One was that salaries at Harwell were good by comparison with the outside world and certainly in comparison with the universities. The second was that much of the work had been moved away from Harwell with the creation of the establishment at Winfrith and with the removal of the work on controlled thermonuclear fusion going to Culham. It also went on to say:

> Whatever decision is taken by the Authority as to the future of Harwell this decision must be taken soon, or the standard of morale will be beyond recall.

By the 1980s, the relevance of Harwell and also of Winfrith was becoming smaller and smaller. There were no new reactor systems to be investigated. There was very little research and development left to be done. With the order for a pressurised water reactor at Sizewell B, the programme of gas-cooled reactors which for so long had been the backbone of development work at Harwell and elsewhere was effectively dead. The rationale for Harwell had finally disappeared. The last reactors closed in 1990. Since then, the facilities have been gradually decommissioned and the site is now being cleared. Harwell was a world-ranking establishment in the 1950s, and should be remembered in that context.

Dounreay

The experimental fast breeder reactor was considered to be something of a potential hazard, and a remote site was needed in case of accident. As mentioned above, the site chosen was Dounreay, on the northern coast of Caithness, in the Scottish Highlands. Two fast reactors would be built there: one which would be known as the Dounreay fast reactor (DFR), and the other being the prototype fast reactor (PFR). In a sense the DFR was the prototype; the second reactor was intended as a prototype for a commercial fast reactor which never materialised.

The fast breeder reactor had been in the government programme for some time before a firm decision was taken. A memorandum by the Marquess of Salisbury, who was at that time the Lord President of the Council, described the programme thus:

> Of the three elements of the civil programme approved in 1952, therefore, only the fast breeder reactor remains as a purely civil project. This reactor was planned in 1952 to operate at a gross rating of 200 MW with a useful power output of 50 MW. Since then a great deal of research work has been done on the project and difficulties have been encountered. Greater knowledge can only be obtained by building and operating a full scale fast reactor. It was thought, however, that it would be undesirable to make the reactor as large as was originally proposed, and it is now prepared that it should have a gross rating of 60 MW. In the first

> two or three years of its life it will be operating experimentally at low power and it is doubtful whether the addition of a plant for the generation of useful power could be justified on a strict economic basis; but valuable experience would be gained by the addition of this plant, which should produce 10 MW of useful power in favourable circumstances. If it were decided to omit this plant for power generation, there would be a saving in cost of £1 million. This reactor is the smallest and cheapest which can be built to provide information which is necessary for future development, whilst at the same time using medium enriched U235 which can be produced without interfering with the military requirements.
>
> In the long term, fast reactors would use plutonium as fuel, but sufficient quantities are not yet available and medium enriched U235 must be used instead in this first experimental reactor. A first charge of 850 kg [*sic*] of medium enriched U235 will be required, and this can be produced at Capenhurst without setting back the date when highly enriched uranium for weapons is first manufactured. Manufacture of replacement fuel can also be carried out during this period.
>
> It was at first thought that the fast breeder reactor would be built at Windscale. Further study showed that this would not be safe and the Calder site has now been used for the Pippa plants . . .
>
> All the possible sites have been examined, though of these by far the most suitable is the disused airfield at Dounreay, eight miles west of Thurso.
>
> Consultation with the local authorities will be necessary before a public statement is made. The Scottish Physical Planning Committee has given a clearance for the proposal subject to the acceptance by Ministers of the risk involved (see Appendix I). The Scottish office has suggested that there should be a public undertaking to pay compensation in the event of disturbance [and] loss of livelihood caused by an accident. A form of words which it is understood would be acceptable to them is given in Appendix II. The Treasury are (without prejudice to their views on the proposals in this paper as a whole) opposed to the giving of any such undertaking as it would be contrary to Crown practice. While, however, the undertaking would be given on behalf of the Crown by the Lord President, the fulfilment of the undertaking in the event of an accident would be the liability of the United Kingdom Atomic Energy Authority. So far as the Crown is concerned, therefore, no undesirable precedent would be created.[36]

The public undertaking referred to ran as follows:

> The Atomic Energy reactor which is to be built at Dounreay is a very advanced design and gives rise to scientific and engineering problems which lie far beyond the bounds of normal industrial practice. In any such pioneering work, they must inevitably be an element of risk; however careful the designers may be, however far they go to eliminate all of the risks which they can visualise, there must remain a very remote possibility that some risk which they have not been able to visualise may arise and cause an accident.
>
> If this happened with a reactor of the type which is being built there is a possibility that radioactive materials might be dispersed from the reactor and drift downwind away from it in a narrow band so that people living in this limited zone might be exposed to a certain amount of radioactivity.
>
> To guard against this very remote possibility, the reactor will be contained [in] a large spherical shell which would prevent the escape of these radioactive materials in the unlikely event of such an accident.

> There is, however, the even more remote possibility an accident might cause some slight damage to the spherical container and so permit a slight leakage of radioactive materials from it. If this happened, there will be no danger to life, but it might be necessary to evacuate a few people living in a narrow section of land down-wind from the reactor. The local authorities have been consulted and adequate arrangements will be made with their cooperation to ensure that everything necessary would be done; (and compensation will be paid to those affected to cover disturbance [and] loss of livelihood occasioned by such an accident.)

Figure 3.8. The iconic dome of the Dounreay Fast Reactor, designed to contain any radiation in the case of an accident with the reactor. (Image courtesy of NDA and copyright NDA.)

The brackets are as in the original, and, elsewhere in the document, the subject of compensation had been discussed: 'The Scottish office have suggested that there should be a public undertaking to pay compensation in the event of disturbance and loss of livelihood caused by an accident.' Needless to say, there were objections to this, and the source of the objection is not hard to guess:

> The Treasury are . . . opposed to the giving of any such undertaking as it would be contrary to Crown practice. While, however, the undertaking would be given on behalf of the Crown by the Lord President, the fulfilment of the undertaking in the event of an accident would be the liability of the United Kingdom Atomic Energy Authority. So far as the Crown is concerned, therefore, no undesirable precedent would be created.[37]

Appendix I of the report read as follows:

THE POSSIBILITIES OF AN ACCIDENT INVOLVING RADIOACTIVE HAZARDS

1. The thermal reactors at Windscale and those being built at Calder Hall are of an inherently safe design. With a fast reactor there is a conceivable cause of accident. This is one in which the coolant fails, the core melts and catches fire or in which the sodium (used for cooling) catches fire and subsequently fires uranium, volatilising and dispersing the fission products. For this reason, though we consider such an accident unlikely, the reactor is being housed in a metal sphere (as Americans are doing at Schenectady) and it is thought to be a reasonable assumption that this sphere would allow at most 1 per cent of the fission products to escape.
2. The estimation of the hazards (in the worst case and if our design is not further improved) which might arise are: —
   If the accident occurs in rainy conditions:
   (a) permanent evacuation (i.e. for several years) population up to 7 miles from the site might be necessary.
   (b) temporary evacuation (i.e. for a few days until monitoring and decontamination was complete) of population up to 14 miles from the site might be necessary.
   (c) control of milk production for a few days up to distances of 23 miles from the site might be necessary.

   If the accident occurs in dry conditions:
   (a) permanent evacuation up to 2 miles.
   (b) temporary evacuation up to 6 miles.
   (c) control of milk up to 20 miles.
3. It should be noted the contamination occurs only in the narrow fan of land down-land from the site over the given radius and not over the whole circle, as shown in the attached map. Estimated numbers of people affected in each segment are shown on the map but it should be noted that in an accident in the worst conditions and with a strong west wind temporary evacuation of Thurso might be necessary . . .

Although Dounreay was chosen for safety reasons, there were also political pressures to provide employment in the more remote areas such as Caithness, and to make the plant more viable, the fast reactor was not the only project to be built on the site.[38]

The fast reactor project also needed a considerable amount of ancillary work, particularly in respect to the new technology of liquid metal cooling. Research rigs were set up to study the behaviour of liquid sodium in bulk, and since one of the purposes of a fast reactor was to breed more fuel, a reprocessing plant was needed. But the first reactor to go critical at the site was not the fast reactor, but the Dounreay materials test reactor (DMTR), which was of the same design as the DIDO and PLUTO reactors at Harwell.

As well as the DMTR itself, a fuel fabrication plant was built to manufacture fuel elements for five similar reactors in Harwell, Australia, Denmark and West Germany, as well as LIDO, the MERLIN reactor at Aldermaston and Hawker Siddeley's JASON reactor. Later, the PFR was constructed there, although Dounreay was not the first choice for this site. It had been intended to build the PFR at Winfrith, which was the site of several other experimental reactors. This was overturned by the Minister of Technology, Anthony Wedgwood Benn, who announced to the Commons that 'after carefully considering all the relevant factors, the Government have decided that it should be built at Dounreay'.

When a minister makes a Commons statement, he is provided with a briefing sheet which supplies answers to a wide variety of questions which he might then be asked. One of the possible questions given on the briefing sheet[39] was 'Did the AEA recommend Dounreay?' His prepared response was 'As I said in my statement, the AEA put forward two sites as being technically suitable. HMG took into account the economic and social circumstances of Caithness, including considerable investment of public money in housing, schools etc. in Thurso.'

The AEA had put up several arguments against the choice of Dounreay as a site. One was a fairly obvious objection: the PFR was intended to produce power, and the power line connection from Dounreay was inadequate. As the AEA put it:

> Apart from the financial penalties discussed later, it is clear that it makes little sense technically to site a large source of power at the end of a long single line far from areas of major electrical demand.[40]

Other objections were those of staffing: 'Staffing at Dounreay is and will always be difficult, especially for Professional grades'. It would also be more expensive both in capital cost and running costs to build the reactor at Dounreay. Clearly, the AEA had been against the decision but were overruled by the minister.

It is probable that the government saw the PFR as an opportunity to bring investment and employment to a region that lacked both, and regional planning was a strong feature of governments of the 1950s and 1960s.

The DMTR was closed in 1969, the DFR in 1977, and the PFR in 1997. The site was heavily contaminated and is now being administered by the Nuclear Decommissioning Authority (NDA).

Winfrith

With all the various research and prototype reactors being constructed, Harwell was beginning to run out of space, and a decision was taken to move the Reactor Group to a new site. Dounreay had already been earmarked for the fast reactor project, but was too remote to act as an outpost for Harwell, and there was no more room at

Windscale. The choice fell on Winfrith in Dorset, which was a greenfield site.[41] The choice was again taken partly for political reasons, the motivation being to bring employment to the regions. Construction began in 1957, and the official opening ceremony took place in 1961.

Figure 3.9. The Winfrith site under construction in 1959. (Image courtesy of NDA and copyright NDA.)

The two major projects which were built at Winfrith were the DRAGON HTR and the SGHWR. Six low energy reactors were also built. These were:

ZENITH (zero-energy high-temperature reactor) was designed for research into high-temperature reactors;

NERO (later modified and renamed JUNO), a general-purpose research reactor;

HECTOR (heated experimental carbon thermal oscillator reactor) was used to measure the neutron absorbing properties of materials by moving them in and out of the reactor and the measuring the change in activity;

NESTOR was a modified JASON type reactor which acted as a source of neutrons;

DIMPLE (deuterium moderated pile of low energy) was a general-purpose experimental reactor;

ZEBRA (zero-energy breeder reactor assembly) provided data for the fast reactor at Dounreay.

Reorganisations

Having being set up as a single Authority in 1954, the AEA was to endure reorganisation after reorganisation. This was in part due to the rapidly changing role of the AEA, and partly due to other external circumstances.

The first major shakeup came about following the 1957 Windscale incident. Following the accident, Sir Alexander Fleck, who was then Chairman of ICI, was asked to draw up a series of reports[42] addressing this structure of the AEA and of the various safety issues which the accident had highlighted.

One of his recommendations was that the Industrial Group be split into two: one being the Production Group headed by Sir Leonard Owen (who had been Hinton's deputy) and the other being Development and Engineering, to be headed by Sir William Cook. In addition to the building of commercial power stations, the AEA was beginning to become involved in commercial transactions. It was the only supplier of fuel elements and, as part of its work, was spun off as British Nuclear Fuels Ltd (BNFL). This was, in theory, a purely commercial organisation, but it was wholly owned by the AEA and the Chairman of the AEA was also Chairman of BNFL.

Similarly, weapons development had less and less in common with the other work of the AEA, and in 1973, the Atomic Weapons Research Establishment (AWRE) at Aldermaston was transferred from the AEA to the Ministry of Defence.

Today the AEA has effectively ceased to exist, other than as part of the fusion work at Culham, and all its former sites (apart from Culham) have been taken over by the NDA, and are gradually being cleaned up.

The Electricity Industry

The customer for the electricity generated by nuclear power stations was the electrical industry, and it was the nationalised electricity industry which commissioned the stations. The history of the industry goes back as far as 1882, when the Electric Lighting Act was passed. Although the National Grid was established in 1926, power generation was still carried out by a mixture of private and municipal concerns until the industry was nationalised by the post-war Labour government and the British Electrical Authority (BEA) was created. In 1955, the BEA became the Central Electricity Authority (CEA) responsible for England and Wales, with the South of Scotland Electricity Board (SSEB) and the North of Scotland Hydro-Electric Board (NOSHEB) being responsible for Scotland. In 1957 the CEA was reorganised into the CEGB and the Electricity Council. In 1990, the privatisation of the electrical industry began.

The nuclear power stations were not included in the early privatisation programme but became a separate company known as Nuclear Electric. In 1996, the AGR and PWR assets of Nuclear Electric and Scottish Nuclear were combined and privatised as British Energy. The magnox assets of both companies were transferred to Magnox Electric, which became part of British Nuclear Fuels in 1998. Magnox is currently owned by Energy Solutions.

In theory, the BEA/CEGB and the SSEB would issue a requirement to the industrial firms which would then produce designs and submit them. The CEGB or the SSEB would then choose the bid which was the cheapest and most promising. In reality, matters were very different, as we shall see.

Figure 3.10. Examples of early protective clothing. These were classified as 'uncomfortable', 'slightly uncomfortable' and 'not uncomfortable'. Those wearing 'full PVC pressurized, frog or immersion suits' could claim 'Irksome Duty Allowances', payment at 1 shilling (5p) per hour, to a maximum of 7/6 (37.5p) a week.[43]

---

[1] Margaret Gowing (1974). *Independence and Deterrence: Britain and Atomic Energy, 1945–52. Volume 2: Policy Execution*, London: Palgrave Macmillan.

[2] Mark LE Oliphant and Lord Penney (1968). 'John Douglas Cockcroft. 1897–1967', *Biographical Memoirs of Fellows of the Royal Society* 14, 139–188.

[3] *Ibid.*

[4] As quoted in Gowing, 1974 (*op. cit.*).

[5] TNA: PRO AB 17/108. Harwell. The British Atomic Energy Research Establishment 1946–1951. (Re-issue of 1952 edition). Also TNA: PRO AB 17/190. Harwell Handbook.

[6] TNA: PRO AB 38/1206. Dragon Project history.

[7] Margaret Gowing (1990). 'Lord Hinton of Bankside, O. M., F. Eng. 12 May 1901–22 June 1983', *Biographical Memoirs of Fellows of the Royal Society* 36, 218–239.

[8] TNA: PRO AB 7/284. C Hinton. Factory planning for production pile.

[9] TNA: PRO AB 16/2701. HG Davey. History of Windscale: correspondence.

[10] EN Shaw (1983). *Europe's Nuclear Power Experiment: History of the O.E.C.D. Dragon Project*, London: Pergamon Press. The book may also be found in typescript form in the National Archives: TNA: PRO AB 32/1147. Official history of Dragon.

[11] TNA: PRO POWE 25/422. Lord Hailsham to Richard Wood, Minister of Power, 25 June 1963.

[12] TNA: PRO EG 1/355. UK nuclear power programme. 'The future of the Nuclear Power Programme'. MI Michaels, 22 January 1962.

[13] Christopher Hinton (1976). 'Two Decades of Nuclear Confusion', *New Scientist* 72(1024), 200–202.

[14] Lord Sherfield (1994). 'William George Penney, O.M., K.B.E. Baron Penney of East Hendred. 24 June 1909–3 March 1991', *Biographical Memoirs of Fellows of the Royal Society* 39, 282–302.

[15] TNA: PRO AB 27/64. JD Cockcroft: chapters, written in 1968, for book on atomic energy (autobiographical).

[16] Figures taken from Gowing, 1974.

[17] Atomic Energy, House of Lords Debate (Fifth series), 5 July 1951, Vol. 172, cc. 670–674.

[18] TNA: PRO AB 38/555. Discussions with the Minister of Technology.

[19] Lord Plowden. *The Telegraph*, 17 Feb 2001.

[20] Quintin Hogg had been a member of the Macmillan government as a hereditary peer, Viscount Hailsham. He renounced his peerage in an attempt to succeed Harold Macmillan as Prime Minister. He then fought a by-election and became a member for the constituency of St Marylebone. He was appointed Lord Chancellor by Edward Heath in 1970, taking a life peerage. He served as Lord Chancellor throughout the Heath government and in the Thatcher government from 1979 until 1987.

[21] TNA: PRO AB 22/12. Seventh Annual Report.

[22] TNA: PRO AB 17/298. The Nuclear Energy Industry of the United Kingdom. September 1958.

[23] TNA: PRO AB 17/293. The Atomic Energy Research Programme. Sir John Cockcroft, January 1960.

[24] TNA: PRO AB 17/58. Culham Laboratory. See also TNA: PRO AB 17/59. Culham Laboratory.

[25] TNA: PRO AB 17/351. The Reactor Group.

[26] TNA: PRO AB 17/291. Britain's Atomic Factories: The Story of Atomic Energy Production in Britain. London: HMSO. KEB Jay, January 1954.

[27] TNA: PRO AB 27/64. JD Cockcroft: chapters, written in 1968, for book on atomic energy (autobiographical).

[28] *Ibid.*

[29] *Ibid.*

[30] *Ibid.*

[31] TNA: PRO AB 38/1206. Dragon Project history.

[32] RV (Richard) Moore joined the atomic energy programme in its very early days and rose rapidly through the hierarchy. His obituary in *The Telegraph* says of him that 'With his fellow scientist Brian Goodlet at the Atomic Energy Authority site at Harwell in Berkshire, Moore started experimenting with harnessing atomic energy to provide electricity supplies, deemed a necessity as coal supplies ran short. His 1950 paper prompted the decision to go ahead with the Calder Hall project on the present Sellafield site in Cumbria, which became one of the world's first large-scale industrial power plants. Three years later the father of atomic energy in Britain, Sir John Cockcroft, hailed, with a touch of unscientific hyperbole, his two protégés. They were the "backroom boys" who were doing most to bring about Britain's second industrial revolution, he declared.' However, both this obituary and *The Guardian* obituary make much more of his wartime exploits when he was awarded the George Cross for his work defusing unexploded mines than his work in the nuclear field.

[33] TNA: PRO EG 12/67. Thermal Reactor Working Party Study Task 3: economics of High Temperature Reactors (HTRs) and Steam Generating Heavy Water Reactors (SGHWRs). JG Liverman to Vintner, 29 November 1971.

[34] TNA: PRO AB 6/2144. Siting of controlled thermonuclear work by UKAEA.

[35] Editorial (November 1959), *Nuclear Engineering International*, 4(42), 379–380.

[36] TNA: PRO CAB 134/745. Ministerial Committee on Atomic Energy: Meetings 1–5; Papers 1–7. Memorandum by the Lord President of the Council, 10 February 1954.

[37] *Ibid.*

[38] TNA: PRO AB 17/64. D.E.R.E. Information Booklet. May, 1961. See also TNA: PRO AB 17/68. Dounreay. TNA: PRO AB 17/70. Dounreay.

[39] TNA: PRO AB 38/348. Prototype Fast Reactor (PFR).

[40] *Ibid.*

[41] TNA: PRO AB 17/107. Winfrith. A Guide to the Establishment.

[42] Atomic Energy Office (1958). *Final Report of the Committee appointed by the Prime Minister to examine the Technical Evaluation of Information Relating to the Design and Operation of the Windscale Piles, and to Review the Factors Involved in the Controlled Release of Wigner Energy*, [White Paper] London: HMSO (Cmnd 471).

[43] TNA: PRO AB 16/340. Allowances: irksome duty. Minutes of Meeting at Harwell, May 1956.

Chapter 4

The British Production Piles

The two piles at Windscale were originally known as the 'British Production Piles' in official documents — 'Production' referring to the production of plutonium. Later, of course, they were simply referred to as the Windscale piles.

The idea of building atomic piles in Britain to produce plutonium had been in the minds of the scientific team working in America even before the war was over. In his memoir,[1] Cockcroft mentions the delay caused by the General Election of 1945 (Attlee had not been aware of the atomic programme) and goes on to say:

> It was decided that a technical committee should continue in being and it met on 11 September [1945]. Oliphant made an impassioned plea that a very strongly worded resolution should be sent to the advisory committee calling for an immediate decision to go ahead with . . . a 1,000 kilowatt pile and for immediate steps to be taken to set up production of U235 and PU239 . . .

The decision to build piles to produce plutonium was referred to indirectly in a statement which Attlee made in the House of Commons on 8 October 1946. The purpose of producing plutonium was referred to rather coyly as 'for other purposes'.

> As the House knows, the Government have already set up a large research establishment [Harwell], and we are arranging for the production of fissile material for that establishment, and for other purposes; and the responsibility has been placed with the Minister of Supply . . . I cannot tell the House exactly what will be the future cost. The programme of work already approved will cost something like £30 million, but the programme is being kept constantly under review, and it may well be that expenditure on a far greater scale may be necessary if we are to play our proper part.[2]

The Americans had built piles to produce plutonium on the Columbia River at Hanford, Washington in 1943. These were water-cooled, with around 110,000 litres of water being pumped through the pile each minute. A supply of water with very little in the way of impurities was essential to prevent the fuel cartridges from corroding. The problem with trying to build a similar plant in Britain was that there were very few places which had a sufficient supply of water of the required purity. One possibility was to build the plant overseas, and Canada was considered a strong possibility. There was even a suggestion from Ernest Bevin, the Foreign Secretary, of basing a plant near the Victoria Falls in Rhodesia.

> Mr Bevin no doubt had in mind the availability of large supplies of water for cooling purposes, but was also influenced by the idea that the plant would be within convenient reach of the uranium deposits in the Congo. He also considered that there would be a great advantage on security grounds in this location for the plant.[3]

The only site in the UK that seemed feasible was near Arisaig in the north of Scotland. The problem with Arisaig was that it was so remote that getting materials and labour to the site was thought to pose a very considerable problem. As a report to the Ministerial Committee put it:

> The difficulties in finding a suitable site for a water-cooled pile have been very great. A large supply of pure cooling water is required; the site should lie on the sea coast to enable effluent to be discharged into tidal water; it must be remote from large centres of population. This problem has been considered by a pile location panel who have decided that the only site in Great Britain which offers the facilities which are required lies between Arisaig and the mouth of the River Morar in Inverness-shire. This site is very remote: all construction labour would have to be imported and housed in construction camps and a new town to house 2,500 inhabitants would have to be built to house the staff required for the operation of the factory. Moreover the inducements necessary to obtain permanent staff in so remote an area may well prove expensive and embarrassing. The site is at present completely undeveloped and the factory with its buildings and accessories will have to be built on a green field. With present shortages of labour and materials, it is impossible accurately to assess the time required for the completion of such a scheme, but it is most improbable that a water-cooled pile could be working on this site before 1952.[4]

And with regard to the water supply:

> Although the water of Loch Morar is of quality equal to that from any other large source in the British Isles, its chlorine [*sic*: probably chloride] content is at least four times higher than the limit recommended by the U.S. project. It is believed to be difficult to carry out treatment to reduce the chlorine content and we are uncertain as corrosion difficulties which may be encountered.

Despite the design for the reactor not being finalised — indeed, it had hardly begun, although some sketches or outlines had been drawn up — Hinton began some preliminary planning for all the ancillary services that would be needed (including a police force of 3 sergeants and 150 constables), and published a report on 1 January 1947.[5] The report was written ‘To form a basis for the first detailed examination of the Arisaig site. This examination is intended to determine what is the most promising layout on that site’ and ‘To act as a basis on which detailed discussion on accommodation, layout and policy can be started.’

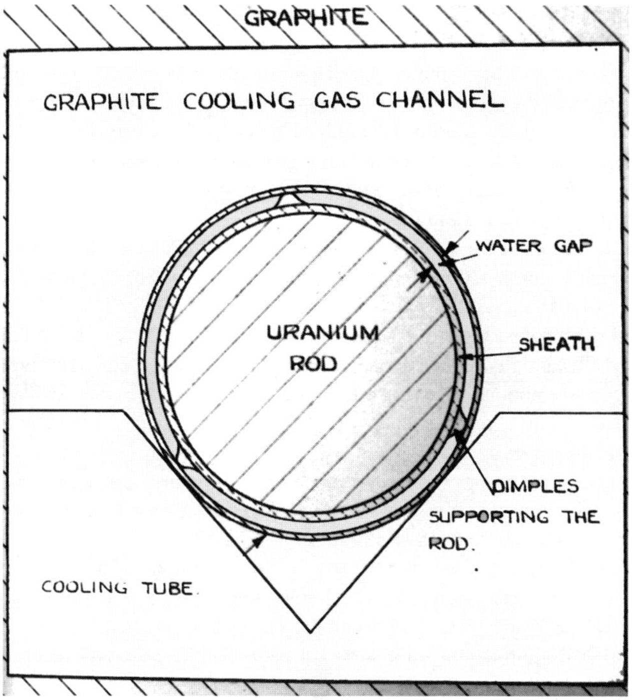

Figure 4.1. A sketch for a channel in a water-cooled pile. This shows a cutaway view of a pipe into which the uranium fuel rod has been inserted, and with a small gap for water to flow past.

Attempting to build the pile at Arisaig raised a host of logistical problems that could have delayed the programme for up to two years. Was there an alternative? Instead of water-cooling, air-cooling might be possible if the fins were added to the cartridges.[6] As Cockcroft put it:

> The alternative of building an air cooled pile . . . was therefore considered. Risley carried out a design study of an air cooled pile which had finned fuel element surfaces to increase the heat transfer. They concluded that this change to finned surface fuel elements would reduce the power required to drive the air through the pile by a factor of about 30 for a fixed total heat output. Harwell worked on the reactor physics of a pile containing about 100 tons of uranium and it was concluded that a reasonable plutonium output could be obtained. So at a technical committee meeting in April, 1947, I presented the case for changing from a water cooled pile to an air cooled pile. . . . The committee thereupon agreed to recommend . . . that air cooled piles should be built and an initial programme of two piles producing about 200 MW of heat was recommended.

A long report extolling the virtues of air-cooled piles was presented to the Ministerial Committee on Atomic Energy, which met to consider it on 18 July 1947, with the Prime Minister in the chair.

While the work of designing the water-cooled pile has been proceeding, some thought was devoted at Harwell and Risley to the possibility of designing gas-cooled piles to give the same output of plutonium as the water-cooled pile. The results are such that we think it necessary to review again the original decision in favour of building a water-cooled pile. The design . . . is broadly similar to the Harwell pile but the cartridges containing the uranium slugs are finned to increase the area available for removal of heat . . . The piles will together produce not less than 90 kilograms of plutonium a year.

The design will be a development of the Harwell pile [the BEPO pile, which was then under construction] and might be described as a 'Super-Harwell' pile . . .

The cost of the air-cooled piles scheme will be substantially less . . . The use of a prepared site having excellent rail access and a labour supply within short distance will very substantially reduce the man-hours of construction labour required. The very large and elaborate water treatment plant required for the water-cooled pile is not needed. For these reasons it is estimated that the overall cost would be reduced by at least 40 per cent.

The conversion of U235 to plutonium is more efficient . . . Elimination of the cooling water means less wastage of neutrons. In consequence we are likely to obtain 0.9 atoms of plutonium for each U235 atom destroyed in the air-cooled pile, as compared with 0.8 atoms of plutonium in the water-cooled pile. For a given power level we can therefore increase the rate of plutonium production by about 12 per cent.

Metal utilisation will be improved . . . Due to the lower wastage of neutrons in the air-cooled pile, it would probably be possible to use over again uranium once through the pile which has already become depleted in its U235 content . . . We may therefore obtain twice as much plutonium from a given quantity of uranium metal before having to resort to 'seeding' [i.e., using enriched uranium] in order to keep the pile working.[7]

A more interesting comment comes near the end:

The air-cooled pile is a step in the direction of future development.

It is desirable that power should be produced from atomic energy as soon as possible. It appears most likely that the first step in to power production will be by means of a gas-cooled pile [in] which gas is circulated under pressure to cool the cartridges. This gas would itself be cooled in boilers of more or less orthodox design in which steam would be raised and passed to condensing turbines. Many problems require solution before such a scheme could be developed. The construction of air-cooled 'Super-Harwell' piles which are proposed in this note will pave the way for the solution of some of these problems.

The minutes of the meeting included a comment by the Minister of Supply to the effect that:

When a decision had been taken, some public announcement would have to be made and the Advisory Committee had annexed to their report a draft announcement. He proposed that the last paragraph of this draft, which stated that the government were satisfied there would be no danger to health, should be omitted . . .

The paragraph in question ran thus:

> After taking the best scientific advice, the Government are satisfied that there will be no danger to the health of the population in the area where the plant is situated.
>
> Presumably the Minister felt that by drawing attention to the question of safety, fears would be increased rather than allayed. Why mention safety unless there were some degree of risk?

The Prime Minister summed up the discussion thus:

> It seemed clear that the right course was to establish the atomic energy plant at Sellafield. He did not think that it was necessary to make any announcement of the decision in Parliament, but it was important the Press announcement should be so drafted as to avoid misunderstanding and to emphasise the advantages from the point of view of amenity of not placing the rayon factory at Sellafield and of using the Sellafield site for the atomic energy plant [Courtaulds had been intending to build a factory on the site]. The United States Government and the Canadian Government should be informed of the decision in advance.

At which point the committee:

> (1) approved the proposal to build two or three air-cooled piles in substitution for a water-cooled pile;
> (2) agreed that the piles should be located at Sellafield.

Despite Attlee's comment, John Wilmot, the Minister of Supply did make an announcement in the Commons five days later:

> On 29th January, last year, the Prime Minister announced the setting up of an organisation to be responsible for the provision of fissile material. It has since been announced that the first stage of this process, the production of pure uranium from pitchblende concentrates, will be carried out at the Ministry of Supply factory at Springfields, near Preston. Consideration has been given to the location of the second stage of the process, the production in a chain-reacting pile of fissile material from the uranium produced, at Springfields. In addition to purely technical considerations, it was necessary, in order to save much time, to find a prepared site with services already developed, and, if possible, in reasonable proximity to Springfields.
>
> ...
>
> The atomic energy project will, therefore, be located at Sellafield. Building and engineering work will begin in the near future, and will employ a considerable number of men for some time to come.[8]

More interestingly, the conventional narrative of Britain and atomic weapons dates the decision to go ahead with the design and construction of a bomb to a meeting of a cabinet committee in January 1947. This committee had a relatively restricted membership: Clement Attlee, the Prime Minister; Ernest Bevin, the Foreign Secretary; Herbert Morrison, Deputy Prime Minister and Lord President; Viscount Addison, Secretary of State for Dominion Affairs; and John Wilmot, Minister of Supply.

But the decision, dating back almost before the war had ended, to build plants for the mass production of plutonium made no sense whatsoever except in the context of a weapons programme. There was no other use for plutonium at that time. If the initial intention had been merely atomic research, then a small scale programme would have been much more suitable. If the intention had been to develop atomic energy to produce electrical power, then again producing plutonium would be pointless. To devote money and resources on this scale to the production of plutonium in the difficulties of post-war Britain implies that the formal decision to go ahead with a bomb was just that: a formality.

There was also the question of how many piles should be built. Two were thought to be the minimum, but there was uncertainty as to whether a third was needed. The waters were muddied by the uneasy relationship with America regarding the development of atomic power in Britain: there were those in America who thought that atomic piles should not be built at all in Europe, and there was a further complication, also involving America: the supply of uranium.

Pre-war, the demand for uranium had been small. Most of the world's uranium had been mined in what was then the Belgian Congo, and the mine had closed down soon after the start of the war. When the atomic programme began, the mine was re-opened, but demand soon outstripped supply. America and Britain had come to an agreement as to how the ore should be divided between the two countries, but the question of uranium supplies was a perennial topic for discussion in the meetings of the cabinet committee in the early days of the atomic programme and a continual source of friction with the United States.

Even the two proposed piles were stretching supplies: 'on a 3-pile programme we would be out of ore by the end of 1952, and on a 2-pile programme a year later'.[9] The awkward relationship with America was the major problem:

> But if we remained at arms-length from the Americans, they might still further increase their production programme and their raw material usage. The conclusion to be drawn is, I think, that we must pursue the two-pile programme with undiminished urgency, but that we must, by hook or by crook, contrive a new raw materials arrangement with the U.S.A. by the end of 1951 at the latest.

Despite this, the Chiefs of Staff were demanding more plutonium for future atomic weapons and so a decision was later made to build a third production pile. But as the Minister of Supply wrote in a memo to his ministerial colleagues in October 1949:

> While the general outcome of the tripartite discussions [between Britain, America and Canada] in Washington is doubtful, it is already clear that the Americans would like us to forego the operation of our third pile, and that a satisfactory agreement is unlikely be reached unless we accept this request.[10]

Figure 4.2. An aerial view of the production piles. The building by the chimney houses the pile, and the blowers for the cooling air are in the buildings either side of the reactor building. Between the two piles is the fuel pond, where the fuel rods were stored after being taken out of the pile. They were then fed to the separation plant, seen centre right. The pipeline taking some of the less active effluent can be seen running from the separation plant to the sea. (Image courtesy of NDA and copyright NDA.)

What he was concerned about was the waste of resources if construction were to be abandoned at some point in the future:

> This raises the difficult question of timing. The present position is that the concrete raft for the third pile is largely complete, and the structural steel work has been fabricated. Site conditions are such that work could be stopped without undue inconvenience and without incurring more than a small proportion of the total expenditure, provided that the decision was taken within the next fortnight. If the question is left undecided beyond this time, action will have to be taken on the site which will (in the event of a later cancellation of the third pile) not only waste money, but will have undesirable reactions on the remainder of the Windscale programme.
>
> Moreover, 1500 tons of graphite for the third pile has been ordered from Canada at a cost of \$615,000. Manufacture of this graphite is programmed to begin in November, and if the contract is cancelled during the present month it may be possible to avoid all, or nearly all, of the liability. Once manufacture has begun, payment of a substantial proportion of the whole cost will be unavoidable . . .

The question was what course of action the government should take:

> The alternative possibilities are as follows:
>
> (i) to stop all work on the third pile at once, and cancel the graphite contract.
> (ii) to complete construction of the pile as a stand-by, up to but not including the laying of the graphite; i.e. the Canadian graphite contract would be cancelled.
> (iii) to complete construction of the pile as a stand-by, including laying of the graphite.
> (iv) to proceed with the programme of construction and operation of the third pile without regard to the tripartite discussions.
>
> The principal argument in favour of course (i) is that, if it is virtually certain that ... an agreement would be reached based on a two pile programme in the United Kingdom, the sooner we cut our losses and stop wasting effort on the third pile the better ...
>
> It is felt that the choice between these alternatives must be made by Ministers on the advice of the Chiefs of Staff, the issues being political and strategic rather than technical ...

And so the cabinet committee 'invited the Minister of Supply to stop work immediately on the third pile' on 1 November 1949. The decision was passed through to Hinton at Risley, who had to arrange for the cancellation of the contracts with builders and suppliers. The letter he sent out is a wonderful example of how to obscure the real reason in a cloud of verbiage:

> On a review of the programme in the light of possible developments in the near future it has been decided to suspend work on the third Atomic Energy Pile at the Windscale Works. This decision does not affect the overriding priority of atomic energy work and all other sections of the programme are to go forward if possible at increased speed.[11]

Although the third pile had been abandoned, Pile 1 became operational in October 1950 followed by Pile 2 in June 1951. Given that excavations for the foundations of the first of the two piles had begun in December 1947, this was a remarkable achievement.

The task of building the piles had been given to the Ministry of Works. When they took the site over, it was in a sorry state.

> Preliminary sighting has disclosed a really bad state of affairs; Courtaulds apparently employed some contractors (who are still on site) to demolish the majority of the buildings. The result is that the site is derelict and, I am told, even valuable cable has just been hauled out in foot lengths and strewn about the site.
>
> The canteen and other welfare accommodation is virtually 'non est' and it looks as if we shall not only have to start them from rock-bottom but even have to go below rock-bottom in order to destroy what destruction they have left![12]

Gethin Davey had been appointed as General Manager of the Windscale establishment, and he describes the Ministry of Works thus:

> . . . it is probably true to say that left to themselves they would not have constructed Windscale by the target date; in fact, they may have been many months late. The Ministry of Works tradition must be borne in mind. According to this tradition they did work of fairly high quality without any real sense of urgency. The salaries paid to staff were low compared with those obtained in private industry and it was not surprising that the organisation contained a large number of mediocre engineers, although it must be acknowledged that there were a few exceptionally competent people.[13]

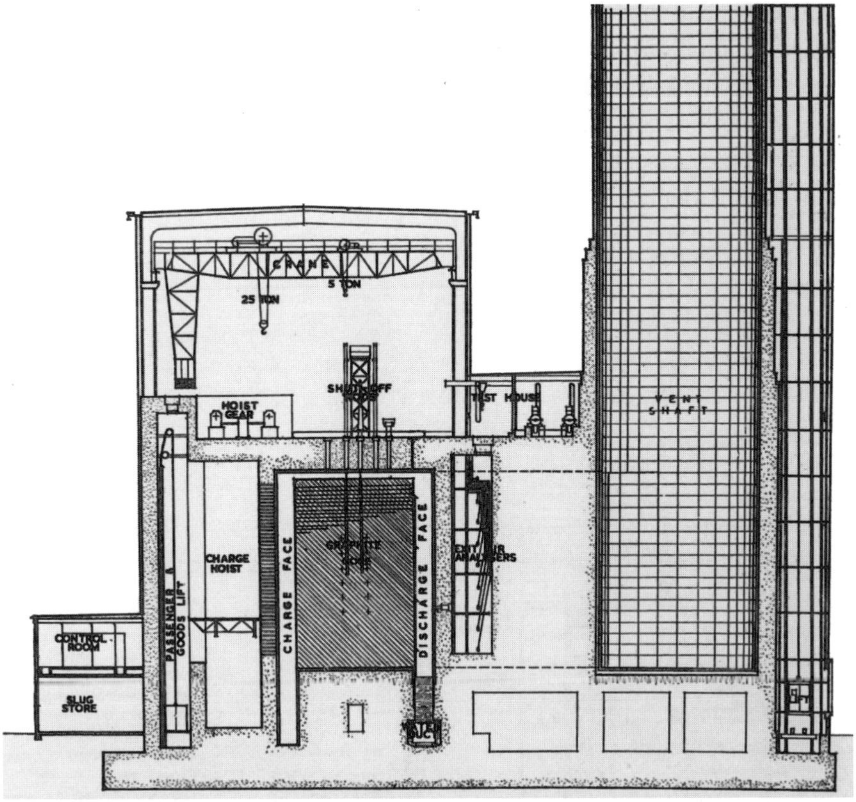

Figure 4.3. A cutaway view of the pile building. The reactor core is the section marked as 'graphite core'.

Davey was obviously a much more emollient personality than Hinton and, while acknowledging Hinton's capability for getting work done, obviously disapproved of the methods used.

Building the piles was a major constructional project.[14] Each pile, including its 400 feet high chimney, would weigh 57,000 tons and needed a concrete raft 10 feet deep, 200 feet long and 100 feet wide. At the height of the construction work, nearly 5,000 men were working on the site. There was plenty of scope for overtime, with some men working up to 80 hours per week. This was thought to affect the quality of their work, and the contractors agreed to limit the number of hours worked to only 65 a week.[15]

The Windscale facility consisted of much more than just the two atomic piles. Once the uranium cartridges had been irradiated and removed from the pile, facilities were needed for storing and processing the cartridges under water in ponds (this was to give some of the fission products time to decay, and the water would act as a shield for the radiation). There would be chemical plants where the cartridges would be dissolved in acid then the resulting solution would be processed to separate out plutonium, uranium and the various fission products. The plutonium, after suitable treatment, would be sent to Aldermaston to be made into warheads. The uranium, although slightly depleted in ^{235}U, could be treated and re-used. Some of the fission

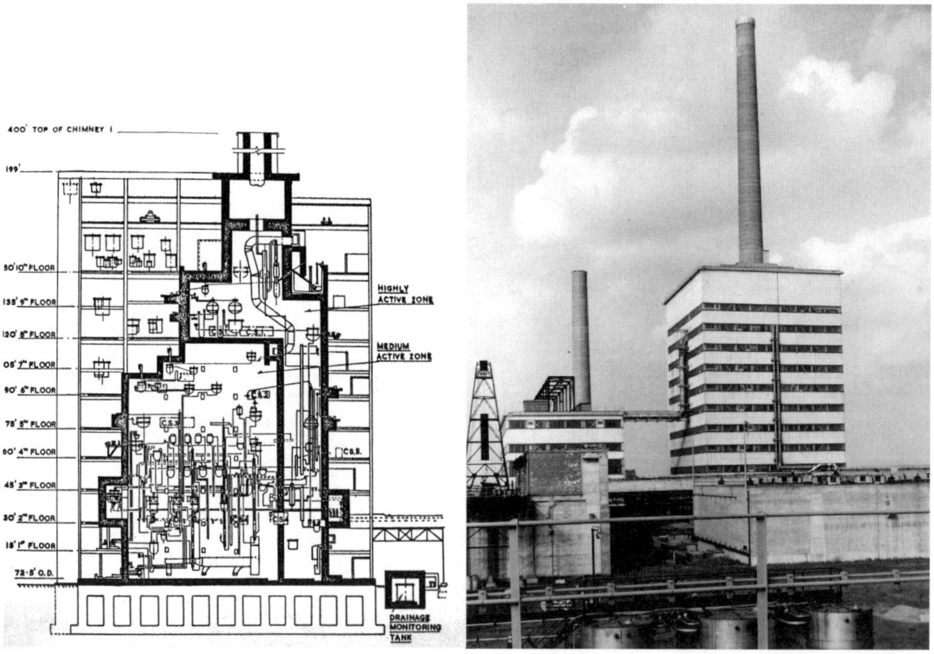

Figure 4.4. The separation plant. This would process the spent fuel cartridges to separate the plutonium, uranium and fission products from each other. Once the first set of fuel rods had been fed in, the plant would become highly radioactive and inaccessible for maintenance or modification.

products would be stored, although some of the radioactive effluent would be discharged to the Irish Sea through a long pipeline. Even the building of the pipeline was a constructional challenge.

It was also necessary to assume that all the process plants — both the piles and the chemical plants — might possibly become contaminated or cause contamination in their immediate vicinity. As a consequence the site was divided into four groups: a pile group, two chemical groups, and a general or main group. The pile group and chemical groups would be enclosed in separate internal fences, and entry and exit of both personnel and materials would be controlled, so that the main group, which contained all the general facilities and common services such as workshops, stores, surgery and administrative offices, would be kept free from contamination.

In conventional industry, there is usually a fairly clear line of demarcation between the ending of the construction phase and the taking over and commissioning of finished plant by the operating personnel, who would not appear on the scene until a few weeks before the completion date. The situation was very different at Windscale.

The engineers at Risley had to design atomic piles and chemical plants — largely from first principles and with no experience with radioactive materials — and produce working drawings not only for the entire plant but for all the individual items inside it. Contracts had to be placed with firms which were already heavily engaged in the post-war boom and not looking for additional work, particularly work outside their experience and which sometimes involved unusual materials, very exacting specifications, and target dates which were regarded as very difficult if not impossible to meet. In addition, constructional materials were scarce, and Risley had to ensure that supply kept pace with demand, not only in the Windscale site but also in manufacturers' shops and yards throughout the country.

As a consequence, it was decided to make the people who would eventually be running the plant responsible for a good deal of inspection and for the storage and issuing of special materials such as stainless steel plate and pipes, so that the people who one day would be operating and maintaining the plants would make sure that everything was built to the correct design and specification.

The second special task for the factory personnel was the machining of graphite. Graphite suitable for use as a moderator in nuclear reactors was a synthetic product which had been made by processing high purity petroleum coke. This material differed appreciably from natural graphite in physical properties, notably in its hardness and abrasive action.

In 1947, synthetic graphite was a relatively new material and there was little industrial experience in Britain in machining of it. A workshop had been set up at Harwell for the manufacture of the graphite moderators for GLEEP and BEPO, and

Figure 4.5. The workshop for the machining of graphite.

thus the expertise needed was located at Harwell. However, after taking over the new site, one of the first decisions was that the manufacture of the graphite lattices for the piles would be undertaken at Windscale and so construction of suitable facilities was a matter of urgency. By December 1947 preliminary drawings had been issued and construction work on the graphite facility had started.

In order to meet the overall programme for Pile 1, work on the machining of graphite had to start in April 1948. At that time, machines of all sorts were hard to come by, but, fortunately, Harwell's major graphite programme had ended with the completion of the lattice for BEPO and an agreement was reached to transfer most of the Harwell machines to Windscale.

The first line went into production with the preliminary aim of training personnel and, in doing so, producing featured blocks to accurate dimensions. By the end of June, two lines had been commissioned and a satisfactory rate of machining had been achieved, just as scientists at Harwell discovered a phenomenon known as the Wigner effect, where blocks of graphite expanded in size as they were subjected to more and more neutron bombardment. This had been already observed in American reactors, and the practical implication was that the Windscale lattices as currently designed would only have a limited life as a result of progressive expansion of the graphite. This meant an entire redesign of the graphite lattice, and in the new design, the graphite blocks would be stood on end so that the vertical expansion would be minimised and room could be made for expansion in the horizontal planes.

The new lattice design would consist of 50,000 main type blocks, 50,000 slats, 50,000 tiles, and a number of other blocks. The layout of the production lines and the types of machines had to be altered, and new jigs and fixtures had to be designed and manufactured. Machining of the lattice for Pile 1 was finished in October 1949 and, within a fortnight, work had started on the lattice for Pile 2 and this was completed by July 1950.

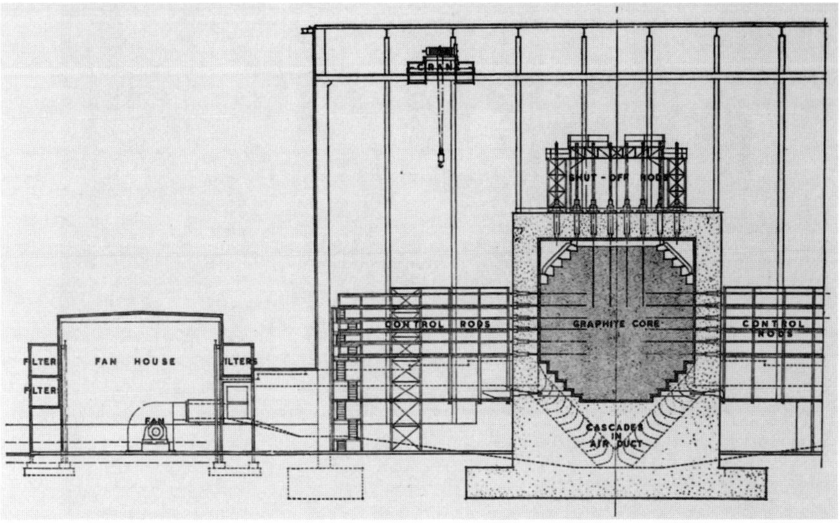

Figure 4.6. Graphite core and fan house.

The heart of the pile was the graphite moderator, which was very approximately cylindrical shaped, with its axis horizontal. The diameter of the cylinder was just over 50 feet, the length was just short of 25 feet and it contained nearly 2,000 tonnes of graphite. The lattice was pierced by horizontal channels for the fuel elements, and there were also additional channels for control rods and for various experiments.

The core of the reactor was surrounded with more graphite to act as a reflector. This was to minimise the leakage of neutrons from the pile, since neutrons escaping from the core collide with the carbon atoms in the graphite and bounce off, with some being diverted back into the core. This meant that a considerable number of neutrons which would otherwise be lost were returned to the pile. The moderator was then surrounded by biological and thermal shields which were made principally of concrete.

Air was blown through the pile to cool it, and vented through a high chimney stack. Each pile had two blower houses, one on each side of the main pile building. In addition to the main fans, there were smaller 'shutdown' fans, which kept air blowing through the pile even when it was shut down. This was necessary because the fission products which would build up in the fuel rods were highly radioactive, and their decay released a considerable amount of heat which had to be removed by the shutdown fans. A flow of air through the pile was also necessary to allow men to work on the pile face, charging and discharging fuel elements.

Figure 4.7. One of the eight fans providing cooling air.

Each blower house contained four fans, and of the eight fans, seven were usually in operation. A condition of operation was that at least one fan was in operation in each blower house. This was to prevent air being blown from one blower house across the front face of the pile and then into the other blower house. Air from the blower houses passed along air ducts and then the two streams merged at the front of the pile, flowed through the channels in the graphite lattice and then the combined airstream passed to a chimney 400 feet high.

Air contains nearly 1% argon (the third most abundant gas), which would become very slightly radioactive when passing through the pile (the argon 40 would absorb a neutron to become argon 41) and it had been calculated that, if the cooling air was discharged at 200 feet above ground level, the radioactive argon (half-life 110 minutes) would have decayed and the air would be innocuous by the time it reached ground level. A safety level of two was then introduced and this determined the height of the chimney.

During construction of the pile, Cockcroft had visited the United States and became concerned that particles of uranium could be carried up through the chimney. Amidst some controversy, he insisted that filters be fitted to the chimneys to trap any such particles. There were several problems with this, one being that the filters would have a significant effect on the rate of flow of air. More importantly, the chimneys were already half built. There were two options: either to knock them down and start again, or to put the filters at the top. Knocking the chimneys down and starting again would have wasted too much time. The filters were placed at the top, despite the inconvenience in building them, and in changing filters, and this gave the chimneys their characteristic cruciform appearance.

Effective filter design was difficult. They would inevitably cause a back pressure in the chimney which meant the pumps would have to be more powerful. Soon after the piles had been started up, it was suggested that the filters might be removed, so as to save expense in pumping power. Fortunately, it was decided to keep them in place, although their effectiveness was sometimes in doubt, as particles could and did pass through them. In the event, they caught a considerable amount of radioactive material from the 1957 fire, but even so, a good deal of material escaped.

Each pile was also provided with two auxiliary fans and four shutdown fans. The shutdown fans were intended to be used when the piles were not operating, in order to remove the residual heat generated from the decay of the fission products. The auxiliary fans took a supply of air from the main or shutdown fans and delivered it at slightly increased pressure to the charge hoist well. This was to ensure that, under all conditions, any airflow would be through the charge face into the pile and so air would not be able to flow from the pile into the charge hoist. This would have consequences during the 1957 fire.

Once the construction of the chimney had been completed, airflow tests began. The main blowers were brought on one at a time, and, after a short run with six blowers, the air supply was shut off and the pile was entered to carry out an inspection. The back face of the graphite was found to be wet and there was a considerable quantity of water in the outlet air-ducts. A steel observation box, fitted with a window, was set up in one of the outlet air-ducts and the test was repeated. As the fourth blower came into operation the water in the duct was seen to become very turbulent and, when the fifth blower was started, the waves breaking in the water started to climb the back face of the graphite. By the time the sixth blower had been brought into operation, observation was impossible, since substantial quantities of water were being sprayed into the outlet ducts. The solution was found by reducing the level of the water in the duct by some three feet.

The pile was controlled with 24 rods operating horizontally, 12 on each side. These were constructed of boron steel, the steel contributing mechanical strength and the boron acting as a neutron absorber. Mounted vertically above the lattice were 16 safety or shut-off rods also constructed of boron steel. Normally, these were held in the out position by means of solenoids, which were connected to vital electrical circuits by conventional interlocks. Any incident which involved an electrical failure broke the electrical supply to the solenoids and the rods dropped into the lattice under their own weight. The neutron absorbing capacity of the 16 rods was more than sufficient to shut down the reactor.

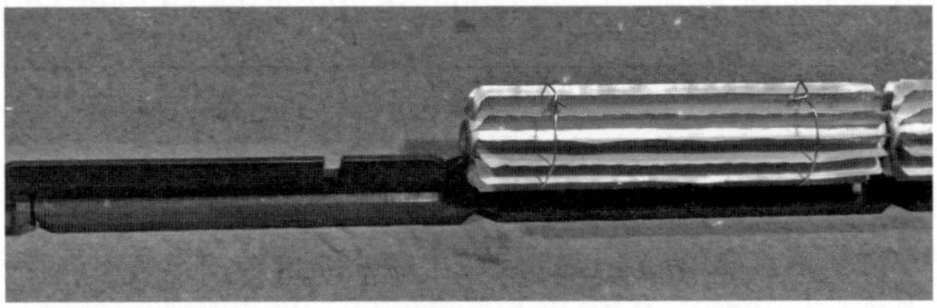

Figure 4.8. Fuel cartridge plus graphite boat.

Each cartridge consisted of a uranium rod or 'slug' 1.0 inch diameter and 11.5 inches long, completely enclosed in an aluminium can. The cans were finned to increase their heat transfer to the cooling air which was blown along the channels through the moderator. The design of these fins was a compromise: mounting the fins circumferentially led to better cooling, but offered greater resistance to the airflow; mounting them radially was not as effective but offered a good deal less resistance.[16]

Uranium in metallic contact with the inside of the aluminium container would lead to a reaction which would cause blistering and eventual bursting of the can. To prevent this, both the uranium rod and the inside of the aluminium can were coated with a thin layer of graphite before assembly. A further problem was that contact between the slug of uranium and the can altered due to the differential expansion of the two materials, leading to a reduction in the rate of heat transfer from the slug to the can and the formation of local 'hot spots'. The cartridges were therefore filled with helium to improve the heat transfer. When differential expansion occurred the helium filled the gap and ensured reasonable thermal conductivity.

Each uranium cartridge was fitted with a graphite rail or boat, which was intended to locate the cartridge in the moderator channels and also to provide an easy sliding surface. When a channel was recharged, the new row of cartridges was used to push the old cartridges out of the other end and, since each channel was nearly 25 feet long, they needed to be able to slide along the channels fairly easily. Each channel took 21 cartridges and the total pile charge was 70,000 cartridges. To prevent the strings of cartridges being blown out from the pile by the flow of the cooling air, each graphite boat was attached to its neighbours with aluminium wire staples.[17] The staples were designed so they were not able to support the full weight of a cartridge, so that when the row of cartridges was being pushed out of the pile, each cartridge would fall separately as the staple broke.

The front face of the pile was known as the 'charge face', since this was where the fuel cartridges were pushed into the channels. In front of the charge face was a platform, known as the charge hoist, which could be moved up or down so that different levels of channels could be accessed. There was a special machine to load strings of cartridges into the pile.

At the front of the pile the biological shield was effectively split into two parts. When the pile was in operation, access to the charge hoist well was not possible, but, within a short time of shutting down the pile, the reinforced concrete and steel plates constituting the charge face were adequate protection against residual radiation and personnel could work safely within the well and carry out charging operations from the charge hoist. During their seven years of operation, a total of 349,000 uranium cartridges were irradiated in Pile 1 and 338,000 in Pile 2, making a grand total of 687,000.[18]

The purpose of the charge machine was to charge the piles with cartridges of uranium, and there were two charge machines to each pile. Both machines were mounted on the charge hoist platform and between them they could traverse the full width of the charge wall. To bridge the air-gap between the inside face of the charge wall and the charge face of the graphite moderator each charge machine was fitted with a retractable snout. The machine was designed so that once it was in position, it would then remove a substantial plug from the charge face, and then, using the snout, load uranium cartridges into the four channels.[19]

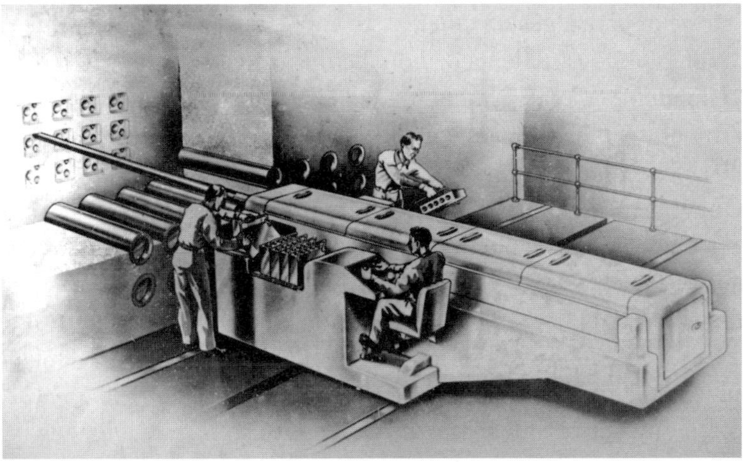

Figure 4.9. Charge machine designed to insert magazines of new fuel cartridges into the pile.

All the charge holes in the charge wall were sealed using plugs which were in position at all times except during charging, when only the charge hole concerned was unsealed. Owing to the radiation hazard the sealing plug had to be removed by some mechanical means and suitably stored during the charging operation, so the charge machines were designed both to carry out the unsealing and sealing operation and to provide suitable storage for the plug during the intervening charging period.

Cartridges tended to jam in the magazine and there was also difficulty in keeping the snout correctly located. These machines never performed satisfactorily and ultimately a drill for hand loading was worked out and used in place of the machines. It is a measure of the change in attitude to nuclear matters between then and now that hand loading uranium cartridges into a reactor should even have been considered. This is not to say safety was compromised: all workers had to wear radiation badges and dose limits were kept well below internationally agreed standards.

The design of the piles had been a compromise between various factors. First, the maximum temperature of the graphite and of the aluminium cans could not exceed certain limits. Pile 1 was initially run at 150°C, soon raised to 200°C, and by April 1952 it had become 300°C. The temperature was gradually raised until by July 1955 it had reached 395°C. In the same way, the temperature of Pile 2 was gradually raised over the years of operation. A second and important design factor was the ease with which air could be pumped through the pile. Too difficult, and the blowers would become impossibly large. One option was to make the channels relatively short, but given the pile had to be a certain minimum size this was not easy. The channel diameter was also an important consideration. A narrow channel meant a higher speed airflow, which could blow some of the cartridges out of the pile. This did indeed happen in the early days of operation before the staples were introduced to hold a string of cartridges together.

The cooling of the cans depended on the fins, and adding fins to the cans meant more aluminium in the pile. Aluminium tended to absorb neutrons and thus reduce the reactivity of the pile. When the first pile was nearly complete, new calculations by Harwell showed that its reactivity would be too low. There were two main reasons for this. One was the aluminium in the form of the cans, and the other was a factor which earlier calculations had not revealed. The neutrons tended to 'stream' along the air gaps of the channels, which effectively meant fewer neutrons for fission.[20] By now there was only one way to find out: load the pile and discover the result.

By 20 July 1950, 65 tonnes of uranium had been loaded and calculations were already indicating that the critical mass would be in excess of 100 tonnes. This was a disappointing result but there was no alternative to proceeding slowly with the loading of additional uranium and taking relevant measurements and observations. Finally, on 27 July, the pile diverged to a power of 70 W with a doubling time of

Figure 4.10. The charge face. Each plug covered four fuel channels and one isotope channel.

63 seconds and the critical mass was found to be 101 tonnes. This was well below expectations, and too low for successful operation.

The problem could be solved, but would involve doing a great deal of work in a very short time. The amount of aluminium in the pile would have to be reduced, since aluminium absorbed neutrons. To begin with, all the uranium cartridges had to be taken out of the pile again. Each cartridge — and there were 70,000 cartridges — had 16 fins. Then, by hand, each of these 16 fins would have a strip 1/16th of an inch wide trimmed from it with a pair of shears — a process which would take three weeks. At the same time a section of the graphite shop was changed over to the special task of manufacturing 70,000 graphite soles and fitting these soles to the existing graphite boats in order to increase its cross-sectional area. This would help with the neutron streaming problem.

By 14 October, the clipping of the fins and modifications to the boats were complete and it was possible to begin a new criticality experiment. On 17 October, the pile diverged and the critical mass was found to be 76 tonnes of uranium. Finally, on 22 December 1950, the pile was operated at a power of 1 MW. Gradually power was increased to 10 MW on 16 January and 30 MW on 21 January, corresponding to a cartridge temperature of 175°C.

The Chemical Plant

One of the most extraordinary achievements of the design of the plant is one which has received very little acknowledgement. The irradiated uranium was taken from the pile and kept underwater for around 90 days so that the more short lived isotopes had time to decay, then the aluminium can had to be stripped off the irradiated fuel rods. Next, the uranium would be dissolved in acid, and the resulting solution fed to the chemical separation plant. The only problem was that the British had little or no knowledge of the chemistry of plutonium, as it had been one of the areas of the original atomic bomb project in America to which the British had not been allowed access.

A small amount of irradiated material had been supplied to the Canadians by the Americans, which could then be used to investigate the chemistry of plutonium. The basic research for the Windscale chemical processes was done at Chalk River, Canada, using some 20 milligrams of plutonium. One major result of the work was the demonstration that a separation of plutonium, uranium and fission products was possible by the use of suitable organic solvents. Numerous solvents were investigated and finally dibutyl carbitol was chosen. An experimental plant was built at Chalk River based on dibutyl carbitol and an aqueous phase flowing counter-current in simple random-packed columns. Between October 1949 and April 1950 newly recruited members of the Windscale chemical staff worked at Chalk River to gain experience in the operation of the experimental plant.

The chemical plants were designed and built on the assumption that, once the processing of radioactive material had begun, access to the pipes and vessels would be impossible and as a result, neither remedial work nor maintenance work could be done. Once the first solutions had entered the pipework, the plant would become highly radioactive. In addition, great care had to be taken that contamination could not be spread from the plant itself.

The plant inside the reinforced concrete biological shield was to be fabricated in stainless steel and to be of all welded construction and a cardinal principle was that the welds would have to be as reliable as the parent metal. In the primary separation plant alone there would be some 10 miles of stainless steel piping of various sizes, together with about 150 vessels, and the total number of welds was estimated to be 50,000.

The primary separation plant received the first solutions produced from the pile on 25 February 1952, and between then and 31 July, 150 tons of irradiated uranium rods were processed. Plutonium nitrate solution was first received from the purification plant on 6 March 1952. It then had to be reduced to plutonium metal, and the Deputy Works Manager, Tom Tuohy, broke open the first reaction vessel to reveal a small lump (136 g) of plutonium at the bottom of the vessel. He later described it as being about the size of a 50 pence piece. Sufficient plutonium would be produced in time for the first British atom bomb test in October.

Plutonium would not be the only material to be produced in the piles. Another material that would be needed for the first fission bomb was polonium 210, which could be produced by irradiating bismuth with neutrons. Later, tritium, which is an isotope of hydrogen, would also be needed. In addition the opportunity was taken to produce a wide variety of isotopes for industrial and commercial purposes. The major problem with this was that all these substances would absorb neutrons and so reduce the reactivity of the pile. One way round this would be to use slightly enriched uranium in the fuel cartridges.

The original cost estimate for the site was £24 million, and the final bill came to £25.65 million. Given the cost inflation that later projects would suffer, this was a considerable feat.[21]

Figure 4.11. A complete load of 70,000 fuel cartridges ready for the pile.

The new piles were certainly not trouble free, but worked efficiently for several years.[22] Until Calder Hall became available in 1956, they were the only source of plutonium for the UK. In a much quoted phrase, Hinton described them as 'monuments to our initial ignorance'.[23] Many problems that arose had to be solved on an *ad hoc* basis and none more so than the problem of Wigner energy. The technique that was evolved to solve the problem had one major flaw, which would not emerge until 1957.

---

1 TNA: PRO AB 27/64. JD Cockcroft: Chapters, written in 1968, for book on atomic energy (autobiographical).

2 Atomic Energy Bill, House of Commons Debate (Fifth series), 8 October 1946, Vol. 427, cc. 45–46.

3 TNA: PRO AB 16/393. Africa: Suggested construction of atomic energy plant in vicinity of Victoria Falls. Note For The Record. 7 July 1947.

4 TNA: PRO CAB 134/21. Ministerial Committee on Atomic Energy: Meetings 1–5; Papers 1–21.

5 TNA: PRO AB 7/284. Factory planning for production pile. Christopher Hinton.

6 TNA: PRO AB 6/321. Production pile: Siting and policy. 'Comparison between Gas and Water Cooled Piles.' J Diamond, JV Dunworth, CA Rennie, 26 February 1946. See also TNA: PRO AB 16/391. Atomic Energy Programme: Aircooled production piles.

7 TNA: PRO CAB 134/21. Ministerial Committee on Atomic Energy: Meetings 1–5; Papers 1v21.

8 Atomic Energy Plant, West Cumberland, House of Commons Debate (Fifth series), 23 July 1947, Vol. 440, cc. 1224–1226.

9 TNA: PRO AB 19/50. Suspension of work on the third pile.

10 TNA: PRO CAB 134/30. Official Committee on Atomic Energy: Meetings 1–14; Papers 1–78.

11 TNA: PRO AB 19/50. Suspension of work on the third pile. 9 November 1949.

12 TNA: PRO AB 16/1752. Windscale; Earliest financial authority for production pile. Letter from Ministry of Works, 29 July 1947.

13 TNA: PRO AB 16/2700. HG Davey: History of Windscale.

14 Much of the following account is based on HG Davey: History of Windscale (*op. cit.*).

15 Margaret Gowing (1974). *Independence and Deterrence: Britain and Atomic Energy, 1945–52. Volume 2: Policy Execution.* London: Palgrave Macmillan.

16 TNA: PRO AB 64/90. Pile design data: Windscale; general description.

17 TNA: PRO AB 7/4890. Further incidents in the life of the Windscale piles. JL Phillips, November 1955.

[18] TNA: PRO AB 62/57. Notes for Mr HG Davey's book: Pile group.

[19] TNA: PRO AB 64/398. British Production Piles: A descriptive manual.

[20] TNA: PRO AB 15/4097. The zero-energy thermal neutron reactor programme at Harwell. FW Fenning, 2 September 1954.

[21] TNA: PRO AB 16/1106. Windscale: Financial authority for production pile. 'Windscale — Original Production Account.' 3 August 1954.

[22] TNA: PRO AB 15/5410. Some problems in the maintenance of nuclear reactors. H.G. Davey. Paper presented at UK–US Reactor Hazards Meeting 1956.

[23] As quoted in Lorna Arnold (1992). *Windscale 1957. Anatomy of a Nuclear Accident*, London: Macmillan Press Ltd, p. 17.

Chapter 5

The British Bomb

Although the civil nuclear programme was one of Britain's outstanding post-war programmes, it derived almost entirely from the military programme. Indeed, the first ten years of the British nuclear programme were almost entirely military in objective. This included the manufacture of uranium at Springfields, the production of plutonium at Windscale, quite a portion of the research undertaken at Harwell, and the work on the bomb itself at Fort Halstead in Kent, Foulness on the east coast and at Aldermaston.

The two bombs used at the end of the war against Japan were of radically different design. There was the 'gun' design ('Little Boy') which used ^{235}U, and the implosion device ('Fat Man') which used plutonium. The implosion device could be adapted to use uranium, but the gun device would not work with plutonium due to its high rate of spontaneous fission, which meant that the critical mass had be assembled very rapidly — too rapidly for the gun design to work. It was effectively a dead end.

Hence the decision was taken, even before the war had ended, to set up facilities in Britain to produce plutonium so that Britain could also make its own atomic weapons. There was debate as to whether it was worth producing ^{235}U as well, but it was thought that plutonium was a more efficient material for bomb making. There was discussion as to whether a diffusion plant for separation of uranium isotopes should be built as an 'insurance policy', but plutonium production was given priority, and it was some time before weapons grade uranium was produced. It is a moot point whether ^{235}U or plutonium could have been produced first, but the decision to go for plutonium was almost certainly the correct one in the longer term, and there were not the resources at the time to do both.

The new Labour government in 1945 inherited the nascent atomic programme as a result of its election victory, but even Attlee himself had been kept in the dark about atomic weapons. There was something of an hiatus — Cockcroft in his memoir[1] notes that 'on 25 July 1945, the Churchill government was replaced by the Attlee government and this held up decisions . . . for over two months' — but, as described elsewhere, planning soon began for the production of plutonium, even though the formal decision to develop a bomb did not come until later.

For fairly obvious reasons, the UK government is very reluctant to release information on British nuclear weapons. Even though many details may well be in the public domain, the government is still reluctant to comment on them, since this is seen as giving the details official confirmation (or denial!). There is another and less obvious reason: Britain and America have shared information about nuclear weapons since 1958, and Britain has benefited very considerably by this arrangement. The government does not want to jeopardise this relationship, and hence will not release information which might be seen in any way as prejudicial to American security. The best way to do this is to release as little information as possible. The official histories which have been written about the British atomic weapons programme have concerned themselves in the main with the logistics and policy decisions rather than technical details.

In spite of the decision to go ahead with the construction of the piles at Windscale to produce plutonium, no formal decision was taken at the time to build an atomic weapon. Towards the end of 1946, officials and the services began to become concerned about the lack of progress. Lord Portal was in charge of plutonium production with the official title of Controller of Production of Atomic Energy (CPAE). His deputy, MW Perrin, wrote a memo in September saying 'It would seem advisable to set up a separate organisation to work on the military applications of atomic energy . . . and to have a separate establishment for the co-ordination of the work' — separate meaning an establishment other than Harwell, 'where it is hoped that much of the work will be open to inspection by visiting scientists'.[2]

He followed this up with a letter to Portal:

> I have spoken to DCIGS [Deputy Chief of the Imperial General Staff] on the scrambler.
>
> He had it in mind to add a paragraph to the DCIGS paper this afternoon to the effect that no formal decision seemed to have been taken for the extent of the effort to be put in this country on atomic bomb research and development, and no organisation had been given the clear responsibility for carrying out this work.[3]

Portal jotted a handwritten response at the top of the letter: 'Good'.

Anticipating that the construction of the bomb would go ahead, William Penney was asked what would be needed in the way of facilities and logistics. He wrote a paper setting down exactly what he would need. The work would be based at Fort Halstead in Kent, and he made a rough estimate of the size of the staff that would be needed. The total scientific staff would be about 90 and the total number of skilled industrial class of worker would be about 90. It would also need a considerable number of clerical staff and draughtsman. Moulding the explosive lenses 'would take the full-time services of about 20 highly skilled fitters of the tool-making or instrument-making class'.[4]

Portal precipitated matters, noting on 31 December that 'After obtaining the views of the Chiefs of Staff, which I found to coincide exactly with my own, I had a few words with the Prime Minister'.[5] Thus in January 1947, the Prime Minister, Clement Attlee, convened a Cabinet committee and the formal decision to go ahead with the development of the bomb was taken. Penney was put in charge and immediately drew up a description of the design of the bomb[6] as recalled by those who had worked on the Manhattan Project, assisted in particular by James Tuck. The drawing shown seems to be merely that of a series of concentric spheres, but there are some points of note.

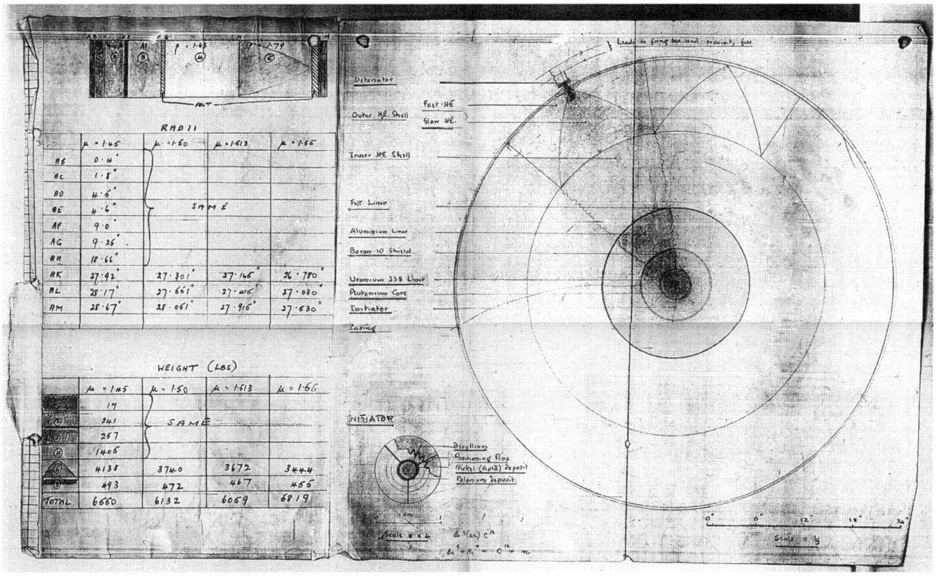

Figure 5.1. Penney's original sketch for an implosion device, obviously based on the 'Fat Man' design developed during the war.

The first is the explosive lens system. The way it is pictured here is almost certainly diagrammatic. The difficulty with the implosion device is to arrange for the shock wave from the high explosive to arrive uniformly over the surface of the plutonium sphere. This is done by using two different explosives, in which the shock wave of the explosion travels at different speeds. A lens uses the different speeds of light in glass and in air to bring the light to focus; here the different speeds of the shock waves in the two explosives can do the same. The exact geometry will, however, depend on the different speeds, and the ratio of these speeds for different explosives is noted on the drawing (the Greek letter 'μ' or 'mu' is an old fashioned symbol for refractive index).

From notes in one corner of the sketch, it appears that the speeds of the shock waves in the two different explosives were not known to Penney, or alternatively, that no choice of explosive had been made. The exact dimensions of the lens will depend on the precise value of μ, as will its weight.

The boron 10 shield between the aluminium and uranium is to block off any external neutrons which might trigger the bomb prematurely. The 'uranium liner' is not intended as being fissile, since it is merely natural uranium (a very small amount of the ^{238}U might well be fissioned by escaping neutrons but its contribution to the overall yield would be small), but instead is intended to hold the plutonium together for as long as possible before it blows itself apart, and hence is usually referred to as the tamper.

The figure of 17 lbs (7.7 kg) looks on the large side for the mass of plutonium — the amount used was probably nearer to around 4.5 kg or just under 10 lb, albeit in a somewhat modified design from the one drawn here. Inside the plutonium core is the initiator, which was intended to flood the plutonium with neutrons at the moment of implosion. This particular design of initiator, called the 'urchin' in the original 'Fat Man' design, had several drawbacks, all associated with the use of polonium 210.

When the plutonium core is compressed, the beryllium shell is mixed with the ^{210}Po, a powerful alpha particle emitter, and a reaction occurs which produces a neutron:

$$^{9}_{4}\mathrm{Be} + {}^{4}_{2}\mathrm{He} \rightarrow {}^{12}_{6}\mathrm{C} + {}^{1}_{0}\mathrm{n}$$

Polonium 210 has a half-life of only 210 days, meaning that the initiator had to be replaced regularly — there are references in Air Ministry files to 'short life initiators . . . (needing renewal every six months)',[7] and the later Red Beard weapon had 'to be re-furbished at six-monthly intervals'.[8]

The drawing was accompanied by a table outlining how each of the various components should be researched and manufactured. None of the problems would prove insuperable, and the item which determined the overall progress was, of course, the plutonium, which would not be ready until the production piles at Windscale were up and running. The final design was assembled and tested at the Montebello Islands, Western Australia, on 3 October 1952, as a test code-named Hurricane. This device was almost certainly different in many ways from Penney's original thoughts as outlined above. Penney was reluctant to make changes from a proven design, but one of the reasons given for doing so was that of safety.[9]

It has been asserted that the new design included a levitated pit — that is, the plutonium core was held suspended inside the uranium tamper. In a letter to Lord Portal, Penney said that:

. . . I should recommend that we try to make our first trial weapon of the hollow type. This means some gain in efficiency (somewhere between 20–40 per cent., if we do it right) and a reduction by about a factor of two in the pre-detonation probability. The advantage here is not so much in reducing the risk of pre-detonation as in allowing us to increase the exposure time of the uranium in the pile, and thus getting a better yield of plutonium per unit weight of uranium.[10]

This is slightly ambiguous, since there are two ways of improving the efficiency of a fission device. One is to have a solid core and suspend it so that there is an air gap between the uranium tamper and the core. The tamper accelerates across the air gap crushing the core more effectively. There needs to be a method for suspending the core within the tamper and it is claimed that caltrops were used for the purpose. A caltrops is a four pronged device so that when placed on the ground, one spike is always pointing upwards. The alternative method is to use a hollow core, and this was done in the high yield Orange Herald and Green Grass warheads.

The comment about the exposure time of the uranium refers to the amount of plutonium 240 that will be produced. If the uranium is left for longer in the pile, then more plutonium 239 is produced. Leaving it for longer still means that some of the plutonium 239 is converted into plutonium 240. This is highly undesirable in nuclear weapons since it is prone to a high level of spontaneous fission, producing neutrons which may lead to pre-detonation.

The yield of the Hurricane device is given as 25 kilotons (kT), compared with the yield of the Nagasaki bomb, which is given as 20–22 kT, and is typical for implosion type weapons.

The device tested was merely the part that explodes, often referred to as the 'physics package'. To make a bomb which can be safely transported by road, handled and serviced by service personnel, and fitted to an aircraft complete with fuzing arrangements, is another matter. The bomb case was a large aerodynamic shape based on the Tallboy bombs of the war, and the complete device was known as Blue Danube (many service code names of the period consisted of a colour followed by a random word: other physics packages would go under such names as Orange Herald or Green Bamboo). Inside the casing there would be not only the 'physics package' but all the other ancillary services such as batteries, fuzes and so on.

The Air Ministry had been making plans for a bomb for some time: a memo of 9 August 1946, sets out a requirement for an atomic bomb, although it does seem from the memo that the air staff were unaware of the exact size of the 'Fat Man' design, since they state 'For aircraft design purposes, it has been assumed that the atomic bomb may be in two sizes, either 5′ or 3′ in diameter, weighing 10,000 lb or 8,000 lb respectively'.[11] This tentative requirement would soon be refined into an official Operational Requirement (OR 1001), which in turn would become the weapon known as Blue Danube.

58 Blue Danube bombs were delivered to Bomber Command,[12] although it did not enjoy a high reputation in the RAF:

> There is evidence accumulating in Bomber Command that the unserviceability and defect rate among the components of Blue Danube are very high. The two main reasons are probably that: (a) Blue Danube is the first nuclear weapon we have made, (b) it was introduced into service at a much earlier stage in its development than it should have been for political reasons.[13] [A comment was written in pencil in the margin: 'Hear, hear!']

There were also issues with the design that made it difficult to service and maintain, as these quotes from air staff documents demonstrate:

> When assembling the bomb about 150 cable connections have to be made, 64 of which are on the two firing circuits and are most inaccessible and difficult to manipulate . . .
>
> The rubber air bags which support the H.E. ball . . . require checking every week . . .
>
> The use of batteries in the bomb affects the flexibility of the weapon as well as presenting a servicing problem. Batteries must be provisioned wherever the bomb is likely to be used, and they must be treated as a separate item as they are not part of the assembled bomb when it is in storage or being moved. Their maintenance and charging demands a large servicing effort if their complete reliability is to be assured.[14]

Figure 5.2. The Blue Danube bomb.

A 'service issue' Blue Danube was dropped at the Maralinga range in Australia by a Valiant bomber in the Buffalo test of 11 October 1956. The weapon was downrated to 16 kT and was set for a burst height of 500 feet. A live weapon dropped from an operational aircraft was a demonstration that Britain now had a fully operational independent deterrent.

A problem with Blue Danube was its size and weight, 10,250 lbs,[15] restricting its carriage to the large jet bombers known collectively as the V bombers. A smaller and lighter bomb was needed, and this was provided in the form of Red Beard, where the implosion system used was much lighter and less complex. Blue Danube had used 32 explosive lenses, Red Beard only 20 lenses. An air ministry paper noted that Red Beard 'weighs 1,600 lb against the 10,250 lb of Blue Danube',[16] and was 144 inches long with a diameter of 28 inches compared with Blue Danube's 289 inches length and 62 inch diameter. Another advantage of Red Beard over Blue Danube was the shorter arming time — one paper gives two minutes for Red Beard as opposed to 20 minutes for Blue Danube.[17]

Blue Danube and Red Beard obviously had many features in common since 'the fissile cores of Blue Danube can be converted for Red Beard in half a day's work at AWRE. They cannot afterwards be used in Blue Danube'.[18]

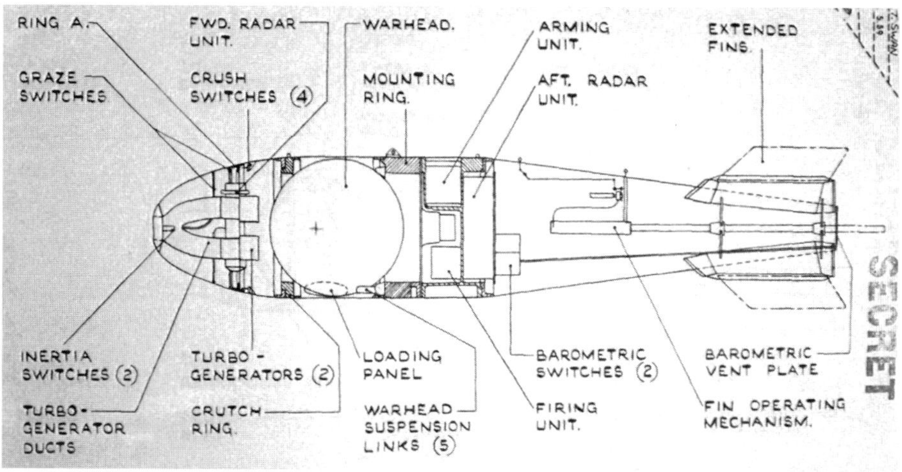

Figure 5.3. Red Beard — the successor to Blue Danube, and often described as a 'tactical' nuclear weapon.

It is quite possible that some of the fissile cores in British devices were 'composite' cores — that is, containing both ^{235}U and plutonium. Such an idea was considered quite early in the programme:

> The "mixed" bomb containing both plutonium and U.235. Various proportions could be used but the case of a bomb containing Plutonium mixed with 1.35 times its weight of U.235 has been investigated in detail and we shall assume that this proportion would be used. A "mixed" bomb can be made identical with a bomb of the Nagasaki type except for the fissile charge and the same bomb can take either a charge of pure plutonium or a mixed charge, which is larger. The explosive effect of the mixed bomb is also about the same as that of the pure plutonium bomb.

> Provided U.235 were available we could make from a given quantity of plutonium 1.7 times as many bombs as we could from plutonium alone.[19]

If this arrangement were used, then the plutonium, as the denser of the two materials, would comprise the inner part of the core. In an implosion device, the compression wave must always travel from a less dense to a more dense material; travelling the other way round causes the wave to become unstable.

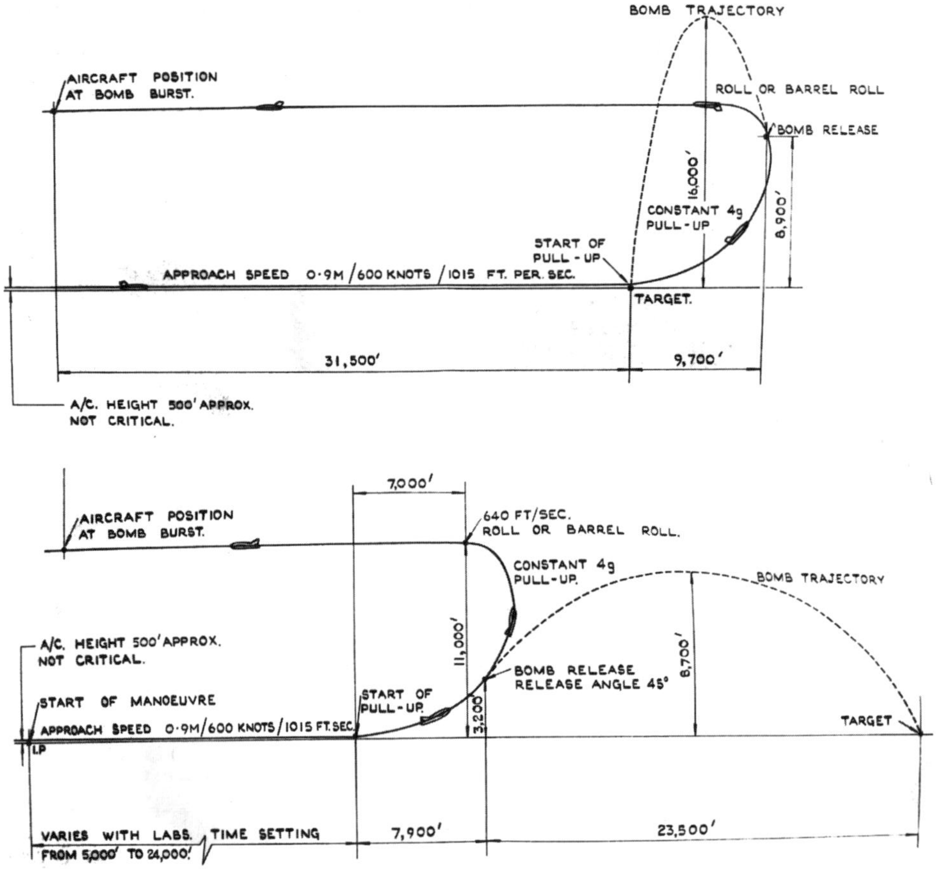

Figure 5.4. Red Beard was carried by Supermarine Scimitar aircraft flying off Royal Navy aircraft carriers. These diagrams show the LABS, or low altitude bombing system, to be used when dropping a Red Beard warhead on targets at sea — in effect, units of the Soviet Navy.

Using ^{235}U in this way might have another advantage: 'weapons grade' plutonium must have less than around 7% of the ^{240}Pu isotope, which builds up more and more the longer the fuel is left in the reactor ('burn up time', measured in MW days), since the ^{240}Pu is prone to spontaneous fission, producing unwanted neutrons. The ^{235}U can effectively dilute the ^{240}Pu in the core, allowing longer burn up times for the plutonium. This also cuts the cost of the plutonium, since the reactor fuel does not need to be processed so often.

A weakness in these early designs was the initiator. This is designed to flood the fissile core with neutrons at the moment of maximum compression. The early initiators used beryllium and polonium 210, which is a powerful alpha emitter. If the alpha particles hit a beryllium nucleus, a neutron is ejected:

$$ {}^{9}_{4}\text{Be} + {}^{4}_{2}\text{alpha} = 3\,{}^{4}_{2}\text{alpha} + {}^{1}_{0}\text{n} $$

Polonium has a relatively short half-life of only 138 days. A memo of 1961[20] refers to the 'initiator of Red Beard, which has recently been shown to be limited to an unacceptable extent'. Elsewhere there is a reference to 'short life initiators . . . needing renewal every six months)'[21] and Red Beard needing 'to be re-furbished at six-monthly intervals'[22] Neutron sources used in reactors replaced the polonium with americium 241, and it is interesting to see that among the items being charged to the Ministry of Aviation for use in nuclear weapons in 1962, americium was included in the list, with an estimated usage of £280,000.[23]

An alternative was to use an external initiator, which the same memo mentions 'can be set off independently, giving advantages in accurate timing'. It goes on to say

> The first external initiator was designed in 1957 and there have been tremendous strides since — not only has size and weight been reduced, from about 1,500 lb to only a few pounds, but reliability has been increased.

The quantity of fissile material in the core of these devices still remains classified, but a cost analysis undertaken for the Treasury makes interesting reading.[24] Thus for Red Beard, a memo stated that 22 warheads had been sold in 1959/60, containing 100.76 kg costed at £92,000 per kilogram. This works out at 4.58 kg per warhead. Since the cores of Red Beard and Blue Danube were virtually identical, it could be assumed that the core of Blue Danube was also 4.58 kg.

Megaton Weapons

Unfortunately, the first British atomic test in October 1952 was overshadowed by the first hydrogen bomb test on 1 November. This was the American Ivy Mike test, with a yield of 10–12 megatons (MT) — around 1,000 times greater than the British test. Having just tested a fission device, the British team were now given the job of designing a fusion device.

A matter of semantics needs to be noted. 'Hydrogen bomb' is often used as a synonym for a fusion device, but hydrogen plays only an indirect role in modern fusion devices. Secondly, the phrase 'megaton weapons' is often found in contemporary documents, and these were not necessarily fusion devices. In practice, there were three routes to 'megaton' weapons: firstly, a very large fission device, secondly, a device often referred to as a 'layer cake', and finally a two-stage device, using a fission stage to trigger fusion in a second stage, which is the technique used almost universally today.

The 'layer cake' design was referred to by Aldermaston as 'tamper boosting'. This is because the nuclear fusion fuel was placed between the fissile core and the heavy metal tamper which was there to contain the explosion in its early stages. This was also referred to as the 'type A', as opposed to the two-stage device, referred to as 'type B'.

The Large Fission Device

Fission devices can be scaled up from the simple implosion device already described, but above a certain size, plutonium can no longer be used because of its high rate of spontaneous fission. (The largest plutonium fission device was probably a French design of around 120 kT.) ^{235}U has to be used in its place (or possibly a combination of the two) and there are problems with having so much fissile material — several critical masses — in one device.

The first proposal for a design of this kind came in 1955 as a solution for the warhead for the Blue Streak IRBM. The only current megaton design available (Green Bamboo, never tested) was much too heavy at around 3,500 lb. Penney said he could design a pure fission warhead that would come in at the required 2,200 lb weight.[25] This design was code-named Orange Herald.

The warhead, mounted in a Blue Danube case, was the second of the first three tests at Christmas Island in the Pacific in June 1957 as part of Operation Grapple. The yield was over 700 kT, making it the largest pure fission device ever tested. According to a Ministry of Supply paper, the 'cost of [fissile] material may be £2½ million'.[26] Interestingly, an Air Ministry mentions Orange Herald as 'using up to 120 K.G. [*sic*] of fissile material'.[27] With rounding errors, this gives the cost of weapons grade ^{235}U as being in the region of £20,000 per kg.

The inclusion of Orange Herald in the hydrogen bomb tests at Operation Grapple has led to allegations that it was part of a 'nuclear bluff' — that the UK had said it was testing fusion weapons and that the apparent success of Orange Herald could be used as a cover for the partial failure of the first attempts at producing fusion devices. This theory is perhaps a little simplistic and misleading. Orange Herald was far too large to be tested in Australia, so there was little option but to test it at Christmas Island. Also, to reveal that Orange Herald was a fission bomb would lead to speculation about the UK weapons programme that the government would, not unreasonably, find unwelcome.

Having said that, a design for a pure fission warhead based on Orange Herald was later pressed into service as a 'megaton warhead' for the RAF under the code name of Green Grass. This was reduced in size so as to economise in fissile material, and was installed in the Blue Danube bomb casing. The new bomb was known as Violet Club.

As the Air Ministry put it:

> If there should be any unforeseen delay in the development of the true H type thermo-nuclear weapon we always have a second string of getting one megaton, albeit uneconomically, by using the U235 method.

This idea was followed up:

> In a meeting held in October 1956 ... DDAWRE [William Cook] proposed the introduction of an interim megaton weapon. The object was to give the RAF megaton capability at the earliest possible opportunity ... This proposal was ... endorsed by the Chiefs of Staff in January 1957 ... The Air Staff, largely on the basis of numbers that could be provided, chose a warhead ... having a yield of half a megaton. This warhead is now known as Green Grass ... The weapon itself is based largely on the present service weapon, Blue Danube, weighing of the order of 11,000 lbs with a diameter of 62 inches.

As to how many would be available: 'Maximum numbers possible will be one in 1957/58 and seven in 58/59. This would result in a stockpile of 8 by 1st April 1958'.[28] In the event, it seems that fewer were produced: 'Violet Club to cease at No. 5, which is now due for delivery on 27th November [1958]'.[29]

There were very considerable safety issues related to Violet Club.

> The Green Grass warhead has enough U235 to form an uncompressed supercritical mass in event of mechanical deformation of the sphere occurring — such as, for example, might happen if the weapon was exposed to an explosion occurring within the same storage building or very close thereto.

The design of Green Grass was unusual. It contained far too much ^{235}U to have a solid core — the critical mass of a plain sphere of ^{235}U is quoted as 52 kg, but surrounded by a reflector it would be very much less. In 1960, the Ministry of Aviation was charged for 11 Green Grass cores containing 670 kg of uranium, working out at around 60 kg per warhead.[30] Instead, the fissile material was in the form of a hollow shell which would be compressed into a sphere by the implosion system. Hence a rather unusual safety device was adopted:

> An important difference in the warhead of this weapon is that the fissile material is built into it and cannot be removed during storage. As a safety device the centre of the fissile assembly is filled with steel balls which prevent a critical state arising should the implosion system be accidentally initiated during storage ... about 1,000 lbs of steel balls will be within the bomb as a safety device before an operational take off.

Several hundred pounds of ball bearings makes for an interesting safety device. To be fair, the USAF deployed a similar weapon, the Mk 18 F Super Oralloy Bomb, which used chains made of boral (boron-aluminum alloy) inserted into the core for the same reason. As a consequence, if the weapon had to be carried on an operational flight, then it would need to be 'de-balled' before take-off by a member of AWRE, and, if it were brought back, 're-balled' immediately on landing.

A later version was developed in a new bomb casing, called Yellow Sun Mark 1. This variant at least had the advantage that it could be 'de-balled' in flight, which made it (somewhat) safer.

That was not the end of the saga:

> I have been informed that as part of the preparation for the next stage of approval of the Green Grass warhead, AWRE have recalculated the yield using their latest knowledge. The new figure is below the previous one and is around 400 kT with a possible variation of +/−15% between rounds.[31]

The definition of a megaton weapon was a rather flexible one: the yield was rounded up so that a bomb of say 600 kT became a 'megaton weapon'. Now AWRE were saying that Green Grass was only 400 kT.

This memo produced a wonderfully splenetic handwritten note from a Wing Commander with an illegible signature, dated 20 May 1959, saying:

> 2. This means that Violet Club and Yellow Sun Mk 1 are not in the megaton range at all, notwithstanding the extraordinary measures taken, and costs involved for what we had thought to be a megaton capability.
> 3. This, together with the problems to be discussed at your meeting on Friday, lead me even more strongly to the belief that production of GREEN GRASS should be curtailed. I cannot imagine any commercial organisation continuing to buy a device which so patently fails to meet the requirement, or to be misled without protest as the Air Ministry has so consistently been by AWRE.
> 4. I suggest that this is sufficiently important to be brought eventually to C.A.S.'s attention.[32] [C.A.S. = Chief of Air Staff].

That use of 'eventually' rather spoils the tone of urgent indignation!

To be fair to Aldermaston, they had clearly laid out the limitations of the warhead beforehand. The air staff (and the government) wanted to be able to say that the RAF was deploying 'megaton weapons' — which was true, even if the truth was becoming a little stretched. How effective a weapon it was is another question, since it was so surrounded with operational limitations — but also one which can be asked of nuclear weapons in general.

The 'Layer Cake' Bomb

The name derives from a device tested by the Soviet Union in August 1953, designed by Andrei Sakharov. It was so-called because it had layers of fission and fusion fuels between the fissile core and the uranium tamper. The British referred to this type of design as 'tamper boosted' or 'type B' (type A being the two-stage design).

The fuel is lithium deuteride (LiD), preferably enriched in the ^{6}Li isotope, and the neutrons from the fission react with some of the lithium atoms:

$$^{6}_{3}\mathrm{Li} + ^{1}_{0}\mathrm{n} = ^{3}_{1}\mathrm{H} + ^{4}_{2}\mathrm{He}\ (^{3}_{1}\mathrm{H}\text{ being tritium})$$

At these temperatures, tritium and deuterium react together relatively easily:

$$^{3}_{1}\mathrm{H} + ^{2}_{1}\mathrm{H} = ^{4}_{2}\mathrm{He} + ^{1}_{0}\mathrm{n}$$

The important part about this second reaction is that the neutron released in the second reaction is extremely energetic — energetic enough to fission the ^{238}U in the tamper. This fission in turn releases more neutrons to help the reaction along. Thus, a good deal of the energy released comes from the fission of the tamper. The main problem with this design is that whilst it can produce a much bigger explosion than the standard fission device (the Russian test had a yield of around 400 kT), it cannot be scaled up much further.

The UK was obviously aware of these reactions: there is a file in the National Archives which is still withheld entitled 'Lithium-six deuteride: MOA production', covering the period 1954–59,[33] as well as other files dating from 1954 onwards — which is the year that Aldermaston began its work on a fusion weapon.

There were two tests of a 'tamper boosted' design in Australia, designated the Mosaic series. The UK had promised not to test thermonuclear devices in Australia, and the boosting of these devices was relatively small. The first test used tungsten as a tamper to investigate the additional yield which would come from fusion alone. It was found the additional yield was relatively small, and so the second device used a uranium tamper. The resultant yield was greater, but even so, the technique was not thought to be effective. The tests have been the source of controversy. Mosaic G1 had a yield of 15 kT, and the yield of G2 was given as 60 kT. However, some sources have given the yield as 98 kT and asserted that this broke Britain's assurances to Australia not to test high yield devices on Australian soil.

The UK's variation on the 'layer cake' was the device known as Green Bamboo. This would have been relatively heavy at 3,500 lbs, and, interestingly, it too seems to have used ball bearings as a safety device, as the following description by William Cook, Deputy Director of Aldermaston, shows:

> Green Bamboo in the Blue Danube case. This would be a boosted weapon intermediate in the use of fissile material. Safety would be effected by filling the centre of the fissile assembly with an inert padding which could be removed when making the bomb ready just before take-off. Hence the weapon would be safe in transit but not in flight. There would be practical difficulties to the application of the principle which may not be resolved in time for early production.[34]

There is an interesting sketch preserved in the Sandys papers, dating from 1954, when Sandys was Minister of Supply. Penney sketched out a putative design for a hydrogen bomb, shown in Figure 5.5. It is something of a 'layer cake' configuration, but with a good deal of lithium tritide, which might not have been entirely practicable. This is presumably there to fuel the deuterium/tritium reaction mentioned above. There also appears to be a tube leading off to one side, where a flask of hydrogen was to be placed. In reality, the sketch shows how little the UK knew at the time about a practical design for a fusion weapon.

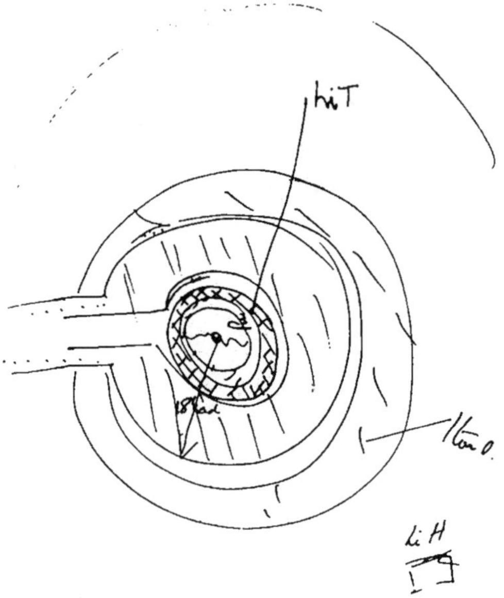

Figure 5.5. Penney's 1954 sketch of a possible fusion device.

The Two-Stage Device

Almost all modern fusion weapons are what are called 'two-stage' devices. The first stage is a fission device, often referred to as the trigger. This is used to heat and compress the fusion fuel in the second stage until it ignites. These stages are usually referred as the primary and secondary. It is also possible to have a third stage, and one of the British warheads tested in 1958 was apparently a three-stage device.

The heating and compression of the fusion fuel is not done by the blast produced from the fission reaction, but instead by the black body radiation from the fireball produced by the explosion of the primary. Any object whose temperature is above absolute zero radiates energy, and the frequencies of the radiation rise with temperature. At room temperature, all the black body radiation is in the infra-red part of the spectrum. The human body, being hotter than its surroundings, stands out well in infra-red. Around 500°C, objects may start glowing a dull red hot — the upper end of the frequency range has reached the visible part of the spectrum. The sun emits most of its energy in the visible part of the spectrum — it is white hot.

In the first nanosecond of the explosion of the fission trigger, the fireball is immensely hot, and the black body radiation it is emitting is in the X-ray part of the spectrum. The radiation travels faster than the shock wave, and the trick is to use this radiation to compress and ignite the fusion fuel contained in the secondary before it is blasted apart by the shock wave of the trigger. This is called radiation implosion.

A complication is that the fusion fuel (lithium deuteride, LiD) has a very low atomic number (low Z) and is almost transparent to X-rays, so a high Z material — usually uranium or plutonium — is used to absorb the radiation and then to heat the fusion fuel. In the process, the plutonium can be compressed into fission, to push the fusion reaction along further. The exact mixture becomes extremely complex, and the structural arrangement can be surprisingly complicated.

The British two-stage designs used a modified Red Beard fission device as the primary. Little is known about the secondary, although it was, unusually, spherical in shape. These designs were given code names involving the word 'Granite' — e.g., Green Granite — and became known generically as Granite devices.

The first tests were carried out in 1957 at Operation Grapple in the middle of the Pacific, in what was probably the largest peacetime post-war operation ever undertaken by the services (and notable for the large number of National Service personnel involved — National Service being a form of conscription for young men, soon to be abolished). All the tests were carried out as air drops from a Valiant bomber, high over the Pacific, so as to minimise fallout. The devices themselves were all fitted inside the Blue Danube bomb casing.

The first test device was named Short Granite, with a predicted yield of about 1 MT, and was dropped on 15 May 1957. The actual yield was around 300 kT, and so can be regarded as a partial success. There was obviously considerable fusion burn up, and this test could be regarded as 'proof of principle', but the yield was a good deal less than anticipated. The second test was of Orange Herald, already mentioned. The third test was of Purple Granite on 19 June, and again was only a partial success, despite having been modified in the light of the first test.

AWRE had then to rethink its designs, and tried again in November, in the Grapple X test. This had an enlarged primary and a redesigned secondary, and achieved a yield of 1.8 MT. Now Britain had a successful design for a fusion weapon.

Granite Y achieved a yield of 3 MT in a test on 28 April 1958. There were further tests in the series aimed at investigating particular features of atomic weapons, including a three-stage device. One particular aim was to try and make them immune to the effects of radiation — in particular, neutron bombardment — as this might be used in an anti-ballistic missile defence.

Despite the success of these tests, no Granite devices were ever deployed. The tests had been merely of the 'physics package', and to make a bomb that could be safely carried in aircraft and serviced by RAF personnel would have meant more testing. By the late 1950s, atmospheric testing was becoming very unpopular internationally. One solution, of course, was underground testing.

The Search for an Underground Test Site

After Grapple, there were no further British tests for several years, since pressure was building up for a ban on atmospheric testing, culminating in the Partial Test Ban Treaty of 1963. The United States had already carried out some underground testing, and even before Grapple, AWRE was investigating the possibility, as a memo from November 1956 demonstrates:

> A question of great political importance is whether an underground explosion of a high yield weapon could be made deep in the ground without radio activity escaping into the atmosphere.[35]

The idea was not taken up immediately (AWRE were rather busy with the Grapple tests during 1957 and 1958), but the idea was revived in 1959:

> An underground nuclear detonation would have the advantage that if fired at the appropriate depth it would be completely contained. There would be no radioactivity entered to the atmosphere and thus no problem arising from the movement of a radioactive cloud or the fallout therefrom. The firing of an underground shot would therefore be independent of weather conditions. It would also have the advantage that there would be no offsite effects such as noise, flash or shock . . .
>
> In selecting a site suitable for UK underground tests, the following are considered to be desirable criteria: —
>
> (a) Weapon Yield
>
> Weapons of up to 100 KT would be fired with safety. This figure . . . means that the site should give the facility of a burial depth of up to 1500-ft and preferably up to 2000-ft. Since it is known that vertical shafts cost about 3 or 4 times as much as horizontal tunnels and that vertical drill holes, although costing about the same as horizontal tunnels, are much less convenient to instrument or give control in case of snags, it is assumed that a horizontal tunnelling technique will be employed and that a convenient mountain firing site should be capable of being entered 2000-feet or more below its peak . . .
>
> Because of world-wide apprehension about the effects of nuclear explosions (in this case, unfounded) a new proving ground should be sited in an area whose ownership is clearly and unequivocally British, likely to remain so for several years to come, and whose local native population is either friendly, unconcerned or absent [*sic*].

> In practice this may restrict the choice to the UK, and certain of the more remote or backward Colonies. It is proposed that technically feasible sites should be cleared politically through the Ministry of Defence . . .[36]

Reports were drawn up detailing all British colonies, including the 'remote or backward', and it is an impressive list, as it was written before decolonisation had begun. The sun might not have yet set on the Empire, but it was certainly in its twilight days. Within the next half a dozen years, virtually all the countries mentioned would become independent.

Among the colonial territories being considered were:

Aden, The Bahamas, Barbados, Bechuanaland, Bermuda, British Guiana, British Honduras, British Solomon Islands, Brunei, Cyprus, Falkland Island dependencies, Fiji, The Gambia, Gibraltar, Hong Kong, Kenya, the Leeward Islands, Malaya, Nigeria, North Borneo, Sierra Leone, the Virgin Islands, Northern Rhodesia, Nyasaland, Pitcairn Islands, Somaliland, St Helena, Sarawak, Tanganyika, Uganda, and Zanzibar.

Most of these were rejected on grounds of excessive rainfall, as being too cold or too hot, or too low lying. Some sites were rejected on the grounds of population density, such as the Isle of Man or the Channel Isles in the UK.

A list of possible sites was obviously submitted to the Colonial Office, which came back with such comments as:

> *Mount Kenya* The area around Mount Kenya has good farming land which is owned by both Africans and Europeans, and we anticipate political difficulties here also. [The Mau Mau rebellion had begun a few years previously.]
>
> *Mount Kilimanjaro* Tanganyika is a United Nations Trust Territory and the international outcry would presumably equal that encountered by the Americans during the tests in the Trust Territory of the Pacific Islands. A further complication is that Kilimanjaro is practically holy ground to the powerful and relatively advanced Chagga tribe.
>
> *Tristan da Cunha* The prevailing weather here is very bad and landing on the island is usually very difficult. In addition we doubt the wisdom of detonating a powerful nuclear device in the peak of a volcano.[37]

That last comment rather gives the impression that the Colonial Office was not particularly impressed by the whole idea, and the Commonwealth Relations Office was also rather cool to the idea:

> I can now let you have preliminary views about the political feasibility of possible sites in Commonwealth countries for the underground testing of nuclear devices.
>
> I think it possible that the Canadians might agree to testing in the Rockies, the Australians to the use of Heard Island, and the South Africans to the use of Marian Islands. I think the South Africans, however, might be reluctant to agree to the use of a site in the Union proper. A site in the territory of South West Africa would be politically impossible, since the status of this territory is under debate at the United Nations.

> Because of the political relationships between India and Pakistan we would consider it most undesirable that tests might be carried out in the Sulaiman Range in Pakistan, even if the Pakistan government were prepared to accept this.[38]

This was as nothing compared to the response from the Home Office in the context of an underground test site in Britain:

> You asked me to write to you about certain plans under examination for carrying out underground nuclear test explosions.
>
> We feel no doubt that public opinion would be intensely hostile to the idea of conducting such explosions in this country; the fact that the possible sites are so well-known would only serve to increase public indignation. The attitude of the public would not be influenced by technical advice that the explosions would in fact cause no harm. In addition, those people who are interested in preserving the amenities of places of natural beauty would, we believe, be horrified the prospect of the construction of surface works concerned with nuclear explosions adjacent to well-known mountains, some of them in the heart of national parks.
>
> You will no doubt consult the Scottish Office and the Ministry of Housing and Local Government about the probable reactions in Scotland and Wales. We expect them to be violent.[39]

The word 'violent' rarely occurs in otherwise sedate Civil Service memos. The possible UK sites would have been the Lake District, W. Highlands and Islands, and Snowdonia.[40]

The issue came up again in a paper of the Atomic Warheads Production Committee, which had had access to data on underground sites from the United States. The committee was obviously aware of many of the political issues, but concluded that the best site from the technical point of view might be in British Columbia, a province of Canada.[41] Fortunately, the idea was never taken any further, and once nuclear cooperation between America and Britain was resumed, Britain was granted access to the underground testing site in the Nevada desert.

Anglo–American Cooperation

The success of the Grapple tests led to talks between Britain and America, yielding what Macmillan called 'the great prize' — the resumption of cooperation on nuclear matters between the two countries (formally known as the Agreement for Co-operation on the Use of Atomic Energy for Mutual Defence Purposes).

It is said that when the British and American scientists met for the first time, the atmosphere was somewhat uncertain. The British revealed details of some of their less advanced designs, and the Americans were obviously unimpressed. Sir Frederick Brundrett, who at that time was the chief scientist at the Ministry of Defence, requested a break and took the British delegation out of the room. A decision was taken to go back and discuss instead the latest and most advanced British designs. Soon it was the turn of the Americans to request a break, after which they returned to say that the laws of physics were obviously the same on both sides of the Atlantic.

Penney and his assistant, William Cook, kept the Ministry of Defence back in the UK in touch by means of telegrams, some of which are quite illuminating. At the time (August 1958), Aldermaston was carrying out further tests at Christmas Island. A 3 megaton warhead had been successfully exploded, and the further series of tests were to refine the various designs, and also to test devices which would be immune to neutron radiation — one way in which warheads might be disabled.

> The Americans categorically expressed the very strong hope that we should complete our present series of trials. This is not only because they do not wish to be the only ones continuing. They went out of their way to express admiration of achievement in reducing the weight of our megaton head and genuinely believe there may be value to them as well as us emerging from our remaining tests.[42]

The British designs used a spherical secondary stage, whereas the American devices had a cylindrical secondary. Cook noted that this was 'considered to be more amenable to calculation', but it had the drawback that 'the design runs into difficulties at light weights'. As a consequence, 40 kg of ^{235}U were used in the tamper of the secondary of the lightweight warhead to raise its yield.

There was obviously detailed discussion about both the British and American design. Cook noted that:

> No doubt that our technical achievements in thermonuclear warheads, invulnerability, and in component techniques with our resources and timescale have considerably impressed United States delegates and has been reason for more forthcoming attitude than formal procedure would dictate . . .

The agreement had a variety of consequences. Britain was offered the blueprints for two American nuclear weapons, one being the Mark 28, the other being a lightweight device, the Mark 47. Both were two-stage devices. The advantage of this to the UK was that the design was fully 'weaponised' — in other words, it had been converted from an experimental 'physics package' to a robust and easily serviced weapon which could be safely carried aboard aircraft and dealt with by service technicians. To develop a British weapon, based on the Granite devices tested at Operation Grapple that could be given safety clearance and could be armed and operated by servicemen would have taken further nuclear tests, not to mention all the political difficulties that would have entailed.

The American Mark 28 went into service in the UK under the code name Red Snow. It was fitted to the Blue Steel missile, and replaced the Green Grass warhead in the Yellow Sun free fall bomb casing, the result being known as Yellow Sun Mark 2. The Yellow Sun casing was much bigger than it needed to have been for the new warhead, and the Royal Aircraft Establishment (RAE) proposed a new casing, but this was turned down by the Treasury on the grounds of economy. Nineteen Red Snow warheads were estimated for the purposes of costing to contain 27 kg of plutonium and 173 kg of uranium 235, working out at 1.4 kg of plutonium and 9.1 kg of uranium, although this does seem to be a remarkably small amount of plutonium.[43] However, another source describes Red Snow as containing 1.6 kg of plutonium, 11 kg of uranium 235, 16 kg of lithium 6, and 2.5 g of tritium. By comparison, the lightweight (600 lbs) Mark 47 used 2.5 kg of plutonium, 60 kg of uranium, 36 kg of lithium and 4 g of tritium for a smaller yield, showing that it sacrificed efficiency for weight.[44]

It seems that the Mark 28 was the only American warhead directly adopted by the UK. 'Anglicising' the design proved more difficult than expected — different countries have different engineering standards. Later UK warheads — Polaris, its upgrade Chevaline, the three variants of the free fall bomb WE177, and the Trident warhead — have all been of indigenous design, even if drawing on American expertise.

Aldermaston had worked hard producing the Granite devices, which were now abandoned in favour of the American designs. Assimilating the American data took some time. The Mark 28 in the form of Red Snow would be used not only in the free fall bomb for the V bombers but also as the warhead for the Blue Steel stand-off missile and the Blue Streak ballistic missile, although Blue Streak was cancelled before it was deployed.

Whilst this was going on, the government was reconsidering its position on tactical nuclear weapons. There had been plans to equip the naval Sea Slug missile with a nuclear warhead, and a short range tactical nuclear missile, Blue Water, was also under development for use by the British Army based in Germany. The warhead for these missiles was designated RO 106, and was derived from the Mark 47 primary. This primary was code-named Tsetse by the Americans and had originally been designed as a kiloton warhead. The cancellation of these missiles meant that RO 106 was also cancelled. As a consequence, it appeared that Aldermaston had no longer much of a future, and there were ruminations in government as to how to cope with the inevitable decline. This might lead to another problem — the key word in the title of the agreement was 'co-operation'. The US was not going to supply the UK with designs for nuclear weapons without anything in return, which meant that Aldermaston needed to continue with a programme of research.

The Blue Streak missile was cancelled in 1960 in favour of the Skybolt missile which would be carried on the Vulcan bomber. This required the lightweight Mark 47 warhead, which apparently had a yield of 0.4 MT and a weight of 600–700 lbs. Unfortunately, Aldermaston had modified the design, using a British explosive which was less sensitive than the American explosive.[45] As a result, its yield had been reduced, and so the modified design could not be used as the primary stage in the warhead for Skybolt.

There was a further problem with the Mark 47 warhead, which is that it used a considerable quantity of fissile material — i.e., plutonium. Aldermaston came up with a suggestion for a new primary stage, which would use approximately half the quantity of plutonium.[46] This would solve two problems — it gave Aldermaston a purpose, and it provided them with material which could be used as part of the co-operative nature of the agreement with the United States.

The new device would need testing before it could be used in the missile, and the problem of a test site was also solved by the agreement — America was prepared to allow use of its underground site in the Nevada desert. The first test carried out by the British was code-named Pampas, and

> . . . was to test the application of a new implosion principle. This principle was originally investigated in an elementary form in 1958 and it has attracted particular interest in the United States. The application of the new system would offer advantages in ruggedness, safe handling and reliability, and lead to some reduction in the weight of warheads, including that for Skybolt.[47]

The test was successful, with a yield of around 10 kT. More testing was needed before the device could be used for the Skybolt warhead. Apparently the first test had not been completely satisfactory, and so a test of an improved version was necessary.

> Since the decision has been taken to develop a British firing device and not to use the American design, it is clearly desirable to have a British design which can be shown to work well.[48]

The Skybolt missile was cancelled at the end of 1962, but the work on the warhead was carried to the new missile, Polaris, which carried three re-entry vehicles and warheads.

The rationale behind these tests was summed up in a memo from Denis Healey, Secretary of State for Defence in the new Labour government of 1964, to the Prime Minister, Harold Wilson:

> More than a year ago it was agreed that the Atomic Energy Authority should initiate a three-year weapon research programme, including underground tests. The test programme, carried out with American co-operation at Nevada, is called for not only in its own right but also in order to maintain our scientific collaboration with the Americans in nuclear weapons development . . . Normally these tests are research tests; but last year one of them was an experiment to determine whether a useful saving could be made in the amount of plutonium to be used in the Polaris warheads . . .
>
> If the experiment were to succeed, a significant saving in the plutonium to be used in our Polaris warheads could be achieved.
>
> The proposals put forward by the Atomic Energy Authority for 1965/66 also include three research tests . . . the Americans want to know if we propose to continue with a worthwhile research contribution . . . If we do not test, our research

> programme will wither, with a consequential decline in scientific capability ... These tests would be treated separately from the economy experiment recommended in the previous paragraph.[49]

The last UK test was in November 1991, and the last US test was in September 1992. Both countries have now renounced weapons testing.

'Special Materials'

Atomic weapons use other materials in addition to uranium or plutonium, some of which have to be manufactured in reactors. Contemporary files usually referred to these under the euphemism, or code name, of 'special materials'. In particular, tritium and polonium 210 were used in the fission devices, and lithium deuteride used in the fusion devices.

Both tritium and polonium 210 are radioactive, and were produced in the Windscale piles — at least, until the 1957 fire. Tritium was produced by neutron irradiation of lithium, and polonium 210 from bismuth. These materials were put into specially designed cartridges and loaded into certain designated channels in the Windscale piles. In general, such cartridges were referred to as 'isotope cartridges', and lithium was always referred to by its code name of AM. Polonium cartridges were designated LM.

One of the problems of producing materials such as this in a reactor is that they absorb neutrons, thus reducing the reactivity. The Windscale piles had turned out to have a lower reactivity than calculated, and this was eventually compensated for by using slightly enriched uranium in many of the fuel cartridges.

As described above, polonium 210 was used in the initiator for the fission device. From the operational point of view, it was not very satisfactory since it needed replacing at relatively short intervals. Later devices would use what was described as an External Neutron Initiator or ENI, as well as an improved version of the internal initiator replacing the polonium with americium 241. The saga of polonium 210 and the Windscale fire is related elsewhere. In the AM cartridges, the lithium was contained within an aluminium can. Various theories have sought to implicate the AM cartridges in the fire as part of a wider cover-up.

After the Windscale fire, new production facilities had to be found. The military requirement for tritium as of 1958 was for 1.5 kg per year. There were various options to be explored. One was to use the reactors at Calder Hall and Chapelcross, and another was to build an entirely new reactor solely for tritium production. This would have been a light water reactor, and for a time was the favoured option.

The design of the new AM cartridge seems to be unusual, in that it employed highly enriched (93%) ^{235}U. The report on tritium production[50] following the

Windscale fire mentions that 'These cartridges should have associated with them a lithium containing element with an effective microscopic cross-section equivalent to the ^{238}U in present cartridges'. Further, it was recommended that the design team that had been working on the 'rehabilitation of the Windscale Pile II' should be moved to designing the new cartridges.

There was an alternative supply of tritium: the United States.

> Sir William Cook reported that the US government might be prepared to supply tritium to the UK in exchange for plutonium. The US production costs for tritium were said to be about $20,000 per gram (this is approximately the same as our own production cost estimates). It had also been suggested in discussion that the US would in effect to exchange tritium or plutonium on a free neutron basis, i.e. in the ratio by weights 1:80. (This would be a most favourable rate of exchange from the UK viewpoint, if the plutonium in question were that produced by the civil reactors.)[51]

The ultimate intention was to have a stockpile of 10 kg of tritium by 1970, with a production of 0.75 kg per year — the extra being needed for replacement as tritium decays with a half-life of 12.4 years. Although tritium was received from the United States, some was also produced in the UK. A Ministry of Defence paper produced as part of the Government Strategic Defence Review of 1998 stated that 'The Chapelcross reactors are still used for producing tritium for nuclear weapons and are not subject to international safeguards inspection'.[52] The same paper also claimed that 6.7 kg of tritium were received from the United States in exchange for plutonium.

Tritium is not used in fusion devices (other than to improve the performance of the trigger stage), but instead it can be used to increase the yield of fission devices. A boosted device, as it is called, will contain a few grams of a mixture of deuterium and tritium in the centre of the core at the moment of detonation. Soon after the start of the fission process, and when the temperature and pressure have reached high enough values, deuterium/tritium fusion begins. This releases high-energy neutrons and this burst of neutrons greatly accelerates the rate of fission in the core, making the fission process much more efficient. Typically, only about 20% of the fissile material in the core is used before the core blows itself apart. Addition of the deuterium/tritium mixture can double the yield of the bomb, although the yield that comes from the fusion itself is tiny. It is difficult to detect whether a device has been boosted from the fallout material, although sometimes small amounts of tritium can be detected.

Several of the memos referred to tritium by name, which did not please the powers that be:

> The chairman would be grateful if you would arrange for the rule to be observed in your Group that in all papers, minutes of meetings, letters etc, whether circulating inside or outside the Authority, the material which has been given the name "AM" is referred to only under that name or as "Special Material".[53]

The tritium from the United States would be supplied as part of a barter arrangement:

> There are good prospects of making arrangements with United States for the supply of $4^1/_2$ kilograms of AM [tritium] in exchange for plutonium. This would be delivered by the end of 1965. The Ministry of Defence has a requirement for a total of 10 kg of AM by 1970 and for a make-up of $^3/_4$ kilogram per year thereafter.[54]

As to the plutonium supplied, the initial agreement was:

> We have undertaken that the PU 239 content of the plutonium in these exchanges will not be less than 87% on the average of each year's deliveries. This is to ensure that it is comparable in grade to the military plutonium they will lose in producing AM for us in the Savannah River reactors.[55]

There is often confusion between the plutonium from the civil reactors — that is the magnox stations operated by the CEGB — and the plutonium from the Calder Hall and Chapelcross reactors. Calder Hall and Chapelcross were always operated by the AEA, and their initial purpose had been to produce plutonium for military purposes. This meant that the fuel had to be changed at relatively frequent intervals, so as to ensure relatively little ^{240}Pu content. The fuel in the civil reactors would have had a far greater burn up time and would have little military value. There were times when demand for military plutonium was low and the output of the AEA reactors would then be optimised for electricity production rather than plutonium production.

Another 'special material' was lithium 6. This is not a radioactive isotope. Natural lithium is a mixture of two isotopes mass 6 and 7. Lithium 6 is a very good nuclear fuel, since it can produce tritium when bombarded with a neutron. The tritium and deuterium fuse together relatively easily:

$$^{6}\mathrm{Li} + {}^{1}\mathrm{n} \rightarrow {}^{4}\mathrm{He} + {}^{3}\mathrm{H} + 4.7\,\mathrm{MeV}$$
$$^{2}\mathrm{H} + {}^{3}\mathrm{H} \rightarrow {}^{4}\mathrm{He} + \mathrm{n} + 17\,\mathrm{MeV}$$

Aldermaston was already investigating lithium 6 as early as 1953. Plans were put into place to produce up to 10 kg per year, to be increased up to 100 kg per year. There were some problems with this plan, one being that if the British government started purchasing large quantities of lithium, it would reveal that the UK was intending to produce thermonuclear weapons.

There were various methods for separating the isotopes, one being molecular distillation and another being a chemical process involving an amalgam with mercury. A distillation programme was started but with disappointing results. Eventually a conversion plant was set up at the Royal Ordnance Factory at Chorley in Lancashire. There was also another source of lithium: the United States.

> The USAEC will supply 6 tonnes of lithium six at 95% enrichment between the ratification date and the end of 1962. Substantial deliveries will be made at the start of this period, and we should therefore expect the Capenhurst plant to be no longer required after the ratification date. We also have an option on a further 8 tonnes of lithium six for delivery between 1963 and 1969. We shall pay for this material in dollars, the price being several times less than even the bare operating cost at Chorley. We therefore expect the Ministry of Supply plants to be commissioned when they are ready, brought into equilibrium production, and then mothballed. This process is expected to be complete in about 15 months' time.

Another barter arrangement was for the British to supply plutonium in exchange for highly enriched uranium for military purposes.

> We have agreed to take for weapons purposes 7½ tonnes U235 at 93% enrichment (or equivalent quantities at different enrichments) . . .
>
> The agreement does not allow us to use the material for purposes other than weapons, and if we require U235 to fuel an AM reactor [i.e. a reactor solely to produce tritium] it will have to come from Capenhurst . . .
>
> We shall pay for the U235 by deliveries of plutonium on an exchange ratio of 1.76:1 . . .
>
> We have also obtained a further option on 5 tonnes U235.
>
> Up to 5000 kg will be for research on, development, production of, or use in atomic weapons.
>
> Up to 2500 kg will be for research on, development of, production of, or use in utilisation facilities in military applications (but <u>not</u> for use in an AM reactor).

Again, according to the Ministry of Defence:

> Between 1960 and 1979 the UK supplied the US with approximately 5.4 tonnes of plutonium under the 1958 UK/US Mutual Defence Agreement (MDA) which enables transfers between the UK and US of special nuclear materials. The material was supplied in three tranches; known respectively as Barters A, B and C. Barters A and C came from the military production reactors at Calder Hall and Chapelcross, whereas civil Magnox reactors also produced some material for Barter B. In exchange, the UK received from the US 6.7 kg of tritium and 7.5 tonnes of high enriched uranium (HEU) for Defence applications.

Such exchanges have been the subject of continued political controversy, but at the time it made considerable economic sense. Britain had ample production resources for plutonium, with eight reactors available at Calder Hall and Chapelcross. Building extra facilities for the production of tritium would have involved considerable expense. Similarly, the supply of highly enriched uranium meant that the facility at Capenhurst could be closed, and production changed to low enriched uranium for civil purposes.

As to whether plutonium produced in the civil power stations was ever used for American military weapons:

> However, although in principle the 1958 US/UK MDA allowed the US to use plutonium produced in civil UK reactors for nuclear weapons, the US undertook in 1964 not to do so. Civilian programmes include californium production and reactor research. Barter C was not subject to the 1964 statement as all of the UK plutonium was obtained from the military reactors. Some of the plutonium received under Barter C was used in US nuclear weapons.
>
> The timescale between start-up of the first civil reactors in August 1961 and the time involved for irradiation of fuel, cooling, reprocessing and shipment to the US would have been considerable. In practice, therefore, it is extremely unlikely that any civil plutonium was supplied to the US before the announcement in 1964 that no civil plutonium was to be used in the US weapons programmes.[56]

Nuclear Weapons Deployed by the UK

The first weapon to be deployed was the free fall Blue Danube bomb, a simple implosion device based on the Nagasaki bomb, and which came into service in April 1954. This was replaced by a much lighter weapon of similar yield, Red Beard. Red Beard had several advantages over Blue Danube, including a short arming time and a method for in-flight insertion of the plutonium core, making it much safer. The rationale for In Flight Insertion (IFI) was given in one RAF memo as:

> This requirement has risen mainly from the need to bring back valuable and irreplaceable cores should it be found necessary to jettison a bomb. The proposal also has the additional advantage that it reduces fission hazards in the event of a crash on take-off.[57]

The memo makes no mention of the hazard to the surrounding area caused by jettisoning a bomb complete with fissile core!

The 'interim' megaton weapon was introduced as the Green Grass warhead in the Blue Danube case; this was a highly unsatisfactory weapon and only five or six were produced. The Green Grass warhead was then mounted into a new case — Yellow Sun. This at least had the option of leaving the ball bearings in place during flight.

The American Mark 28 of 1 MT yield was anglicised as Red Snow, and mounted in the Yellow Sun case to produce Yellow Sun Mark II. It was also fitted to the Blue Steel stand-off missile and would have been the warhead for the Blue Streak IRBM had it been deployed operationally.

After the Anglo–American bilateral agreement to co-operate on nuclear weapons, Britain continued to design and develop its own warheads, as the letter from Denis Healey, quoted above, indicates. The UK provided its own warhead for the three re-entry vehicles on the Polaris missile, code-named ET317 (the colour codes had been replaced by a rather more boring two-letter three-numeral code). There was a later upgrade to these when the top end of the missile was redesigned to cope with a possible Moscow Anti-Ballistic Missile (ABM) defence. This upgrade, named

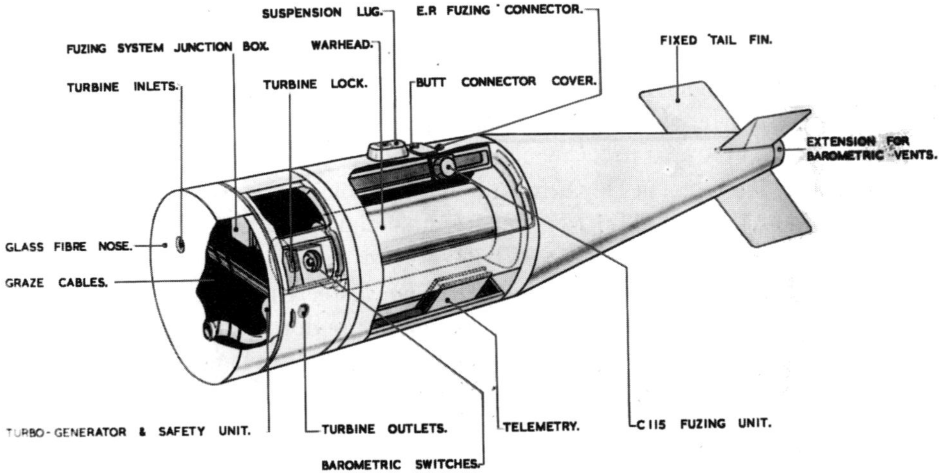

Figure 5.6. The Yellow Sun Mark II. This had originally been designed for a larger warhead. The cylindrical shape of the Red Snow warhead can be seen on the centre of the weapon.

Chevaline, involved replacing one of the warheads and re-entry bodies with a complex system of decoys. The new warhead was 'hardened' against radiation from the ABM warheads and was tested twice at Nevada.

The Yellow Sun and Red Beard free fall bombs were replaced by WE177, which came in three varieties: WE177A, WE177B and WE177C. WE177B entered service in 1966. The warhead was known as ZA297 and had a yield of 450 kT. WE177A entered service at the end of the 1960s with both the Royal Navy and RAF. Its warhead, essentially ZA297 without a fusion secondary and with a yield of either 0.5 kT (for anti-submarine use) or 10 kT, was known as PT176. WE177C entered service in the early 1970s in response to a NATO requirement for carriage on tactical aircraft based in Germany. It had a yield of about 200 kT.

The Royal Navy WE177A weapons were retired in 1992 and, in 1998, all the RAF weapons had been withdrawn and dismantled. The only warheads the UK now deploys are on the missiles carried by the Trident submarines.

---

1 TNA: PRO AB 27/64. JD Cockcroft: chapters, written in 1968, for book on atomic energy (autobiographical).

2 TNA: PRO AB 16/1905. Development of atomic weapon: policy. 'Military Application of Atomic Energy.' MW Perrin, 24 September 1946.

3 TNA: PRO AB 16/1905. Development of atomic weapon: policy. 'D.C.I.G.S. Committee. Defence Research ans Development Estimates.' MW Perrin, 12 November 1946.

4 TNA: PRO AB 16/1905. Development of atomic weapon: policy. 'Proposals for an Atomic Weapons Section in the Armaments Research Department.' WG Penney, 1 November 1946.
5 *Ibid.* Portal to Minister. 31 December 1946.
6 TNA: PRO AVIA 65/1163. Weapon principle: implosion. (Currently this file is retained by the relevant Department under Section 3.4.)
7 TNA: PRO AIR 2/13773. RED BEARD financial aspects.
8 TNA: PRO AIR 2/13774. RED BEARD.
9 Margaret Gowing (1974). *Independence and Deterrence: Britain and Atomic Energy, 1945–52. Volume 2: Policy Execution*, London: Palgrave Macmillan.
10 TNA: PRO AB 16/933. Type of weapon in first trial. WG Penney to Lord Portal of Hungerford, 18 July 1950.
11 TNA: PRO AVIA 65/1153. 10000 lb HE MC bomb: AS requirements. 'OR 1001 Air Staff Requirement for an Atomic Bomb.' 9 August 1946.
12 TNA: PRO AIR 2/13678. Requirement for British nuclear weapons. March 1959.
13 TNA: PRO AIR 2/13680. Megaton bomb (OR 1136). June 1956.
14 TNA: PRO AVIA 65/1161. 10000 lb HE MC bomb: development policy.
15 TNA: PRO AVIA 65/1153. 10000 lb HE MC bomb: AS requirements.
16 TNA: PRO AIR 2/13773. RED BEARD financial aspects. 19 December 1957.
17 TNA: PRO AIR 2/13678. Requirement for British nuclear weapons.
18 TNA: PRO AIR 2/13773. RED BEARD financial aspects. 19 December 1957.
19 TNA: PRO CAB 134/33. Atomic Energy (Review of Production) Committee: Meeting 1; Papers 1–2, December 1948.
20 TNA: PRO EG 1/312. Cost of UK atomic weapons programme. 'Nuclear Weapons: R. & D. Contract for 1961/62.' WE Berry, 8 February 1961.
21 TNA: PRO AIR 2/13773. RED BEARD financial aspects.
22 TNA: PRO AIR 2/13774. RED BEARD.
23 TNA PRO: EG 1/312. Cost of UK atomic weapons programme. 'Revised Calculation Of Charges To The Ministry Of Aviation Year 1961/62.'
24 TNA: PRO EG 1/312. Cost of UK atomic weapons programme. 'Revised Calculation Of Charges To The Ministry Of Aviation Year 1960/61.' 3 January 1961.
25 TNA: PRO AVIA 65/1193. Warhead for a medium range missile: Air Staff requirement OR 1142 Orange Herald (DAW plans action).
26 *Ibid.*
27 TNA: PRO AIR 2/13680. Megaton bomb (OR 1136).
28 TNA: PRO AIR 2/13718. Violet Club: policy.
29 TNA: PRO AIR 2/13705. YELLOW SUN: policy.
30 TNA: PRO EG 1/312. Cost of UK atomic weapons programme. 'Revised Calculation Of Charges To The Ministry Of Aviation Year 1960/61.' 3 January 1961.
31 TNA: PRO AIR 2/13705. YELLOW SUN: policy.
32 *Ibid.*
33 TNA: PRO AVIA 65/892. Lithium-six deuteride: MOA production.

34 TNA: PRO AIR 2/13680. Megaton bomb (OR 1136). 'Note on D.G.A.W.'s Suggestions for Producing an Interim Red Beard and an Interim Megaton Bomb.'
35 TNA: PRO ES 1/1349. Underground tests papers etc. Dr Corner, 16 November 1956.
36 TNA: PRO ES 1/1349. Underground tests papers etc. I Maddock, Senior Superintendent of Electronics Trials Divisions. 17 April 1959.
37 *Ibid.*
38 TNA: PRO ES 1/1349. Underground tests papers etc. TW Keeble (Commonwealth Relation Office) to VHB Macklin (Ministry of Defence), 20 May 1959.
39 TNA: PRO ES 1/1349. Underground tests papers etc. HW Stotesbury (Home Office) to VHB Macklin (Ministry of Defence), 2 June 1959.
40 TNA: PRO AB 16/4765. Atomic Warheads Production Committee. Sites For Underground Tests, 13 July 1959.
41 *Ibid.*
42 TNA: PRO AB 16/2438. Anglo-United States atomic weapons discussions, 1958: Sir Edwin Plowden's papers (Chairman of UKAEA).
43 TNA: PRO EG 1/312. Cost of UK atomic weapons programme. 'Revised Calculation Of Charges To The Ministry Of Aviation Year 1960/61.' 3 January 1961.
44 TNA: PRO AB 16/4675. Atomic Warheads Production Committee. Undated, probably July 1959.
45 TNA: PRO EG 1/686. Underground tests in Nevada and elsewhere in the USA. 'The Skybolt Warhead.' 10 August 1962.
46 TNA: PRO AVIA 65/779. WS138A warhead information. RHE Empson (D.A. Arm.) to C.A., 5 June 1959.
47 TNA: PRO EG 1/686. Underground tests in Nevada and elsewhere in the USA. R Makins to Lord President, 12 March 1962.
48 *Ibid.*
49 TNA: PRO PREM 13/123. Denis Healey to Prime Minister, 27 January 1965.
50 TNA: PRO AB 38/38 Special materials.
51 *Ibid.*
52 *Ibid.*
53 *Ibid.*
54 *Ibid.*
55 *Ibid.*
56 The United Kingdom's Defence Nuclear Weapons Programme. Plutonium and Aldermaston — An Historical Account. Published as part of the Strategic Defence Review, 2002.
57 TNA: PRO AB 16/1130. Weapons design: progress reports on operational aspects. Air Vice-Marshall Davis, 9 October 1951. See also TNA: PRO AB 16/1130. Weapons design: progress reports on operational aspects. Memo to CAE from AVM ED Davis, 9 October 1951.

Chapter 6

The Windscale Incident

> A fire in a channel must be regarded as a major disaster and must be avoided at all costs. We have at present insufficient information on the bursting of cartridges and the oxidation rates at high temperatures . . . Some work on the oxidation rates of Uranium at temperatures of about 350°C has been carried out at Harwell but information relating to the conditions existing in Pile channels is very sketchy. — November 1951.[1]

If the opening of the Calder Hall power station in 1956 represented the zenith of the early British nuclear programme, then the events of October 1957 must represent the nadir. The celebrations that accompanied the Calder Hall opening would soon look like hubris.

By 1957, attention had turned away from the production piles. Their role would be taken over by the new PIPPA reactors, and they were fast becoming curiosities of the past. The AEA was more hard-pressed than ever with its new responsibilities, particularly in regard to the nascent nuclear power programme. There were considerable shortages of personnel in key areas, and the Windscale incident would show up very clearly the administrative and logistical shortcomings of the AEA.

The combination of circumstances that led to the fire was unique. They arose from causes which at the time were not fully understood, into which insufficient research had been done, and which were no longer of great interest to the AEA, which had moved on to other projects. The piles had worked successfully for six years, and their design life had been for only ten years. The procedure which led to the disaster was one which had evolved by trial and error, and had not been studied in the depth it deserved.

The 'Wigner effect' was named after the Hungarian physicist Eugene Wigner. The purpose of a moderator in a reactor is to slow down the high-speed neutrons. These neutrons collide with the carbon atoms in the graphite moderator, and as a result of the collision, the carbon atoms can become displaced from their normal position in the atomic lattice. At low temperatures, the atoms will stay displaced and, as a result, there are certain changes in the physical properties: in particular, the thermal conductivity of the graphite is considerably reduced, and it may well expand permanently. This latter effect caused a hasty redesign of the piles in 1949. In addition, there is in effect a form of potential energy stored in the graphite, which can be liberated when the carbon atoms return to their proper place. This energy is referred to as 'Wigner energy'.

Unfortunately, the British were not aware at that time of all the details surrounding the phenomenon. At higher temperatures, the displaced carbon can fall back into place spontaneously, and energy will be released as they fall back. This energy release is called the Wigner release. If the energy released is sufficient, then the process might become self-sustaining, as the graphite becomes hotter and hotter. Eventually, of course, the process will have run its course and then the temperatures will fall again. At Windscale, the operating temperature of the piles was not quite high enough for the atoms to fall back spontaneously. As a result, there was a build-up of displaced atoms. What happened then was that some atoms started falling back at some local hotspot, releasing energy at the same time and heating the area up so that more fell back, and so on.

The first time a spontaneous release of Wigner energy occurred was after the pile had been running for some time, and was completely unexpected. It must have come as a considerable shock to the operators at the time. This is how it was described:

> During September 1952 while Pile No. 1 was shut down for remedial work, the temperature rose fairly rapidly to approximately 250°C. This temperature rise was completely unexpected and at the time caused considerable anxiety to the operating staff. Some fairly simple experiments conducted a few days later demonstrated quite clearly that this temperature rise was due to a release of stored energy in the graphite and it has been possible to account for the initiation of the release and all the subsequent events.
>
> The aspect that is of importance from the point of view of pile safety is that this release was unforeseen and the possibility that such a release was possible had neither occurred to, or had been pointed out to the operating staff. We were fortunate that nothing more serious occurred. If the release had not taken place we may have got to the state where the quantity of stored energy was such that its release could damage the fuel elements. Further if the temperature had risen further than in fact it did, it is probable that the staff would have discharged the entire pile uranium since all the evidence available to them at the time indicated either a fire or at least combustion of some sort, there being no other apparent reason for the rise in temperature and smoke was seen in the outlet ducts.
>
> The whole problem of the storage and release of Wigner energy is now being watched very carefully and the piles are deliberately annealed at regular intervals. Only one deliberate annealing has so far been carried out but this was completely successful.[2]

It is not surprising the operating staff were alarmed – indeed, it might also be said that they were lucky that this happened whilst the pile was shut down. Given the amount of energy that was obviously released, there could have been serious repercussions if this had happened when the pile was operating at its maximum output. (The smoke which was seen came from some lubricating oil which had been blown from the fans into the pile.)

Once the problem had been recognised, a solution was found, which was to run the reactor at a much higher temperature for a few hours to release the displaced atoms.[3] This was referred to as 'annealing'. During an anneal, the operating staff would periodically record the temperatures of the graphite and uranium by means of thermocouples which had been installed. The progress of the anneal was unpredictable, and the Wigner release would begin in one part of the pile and then spread erratically to other parts. The progress or path of the anneal would later be plotted out on tracing paper, and drawn out as shown in Figure 6.1:

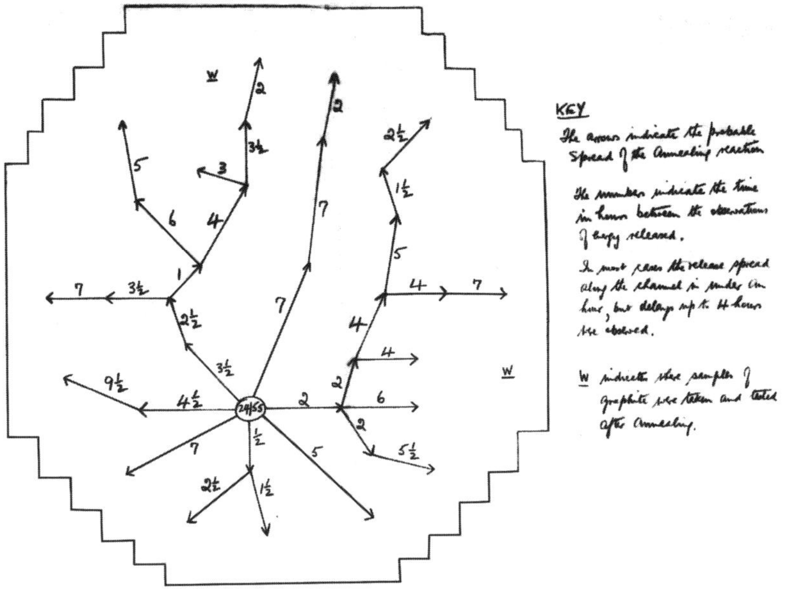

Figure 6.1. An example of an anneal. The circle marked 24/55 shows the channel in the pile where the energy release began. The arrows indicate how the energy release spread outwards, the numbers by the arrow indicating the time in hours between the observations.

This process was not always successful in annealing all the graphite in the piles: in April 1956, for example, one attempt in Pile 1 was completely unsuccessful and two others partially successful in that energy releases were recorded only from certain regions of the pile and pockets were left un-annealed. Although a Wigner release might be difficult to initiate, once started it could not be stopped, and had to be allowed to run its course. This course was entirely unpredictable — the operators were at this stage merely observers.

The procedure during an anneal was to shut the reactor down, install extra thermocouples, and apply nuclear heating until it became clear that the Wigner release had begun. During this time, the cooling fans would normally be switched off. If it appeared that the reactor was overheating, then the fans could be switched on for a short period of time. If it seemed that the release was starting to die away, then a second nuclear heating might be applied. This heating could also be directed at only one part of the pile — in other words, the control rods would be manipulated in a non-standard fashion.

The operation of the pile during an annealing was left to the judgement of the pile physicist. As the report compiled by Sir William Penney's board of inquiry,[4] written soon after the 1957 accident, put it:

> It should be noted at this point that the operation of a Wigner release is the responsibility of the Pile Physicist and his two deputies, by virtue of their specialised knowledge. The Pile Control Engineers operate on the instructions of the Pile Physicists during Wigner releases. It appears there is nothing in the nature of a Pile Operating Manual.

Given the unpredictable nature of these releases, compiling a manual was pointless. It was during one such annealing process that things went wrong. To understand the sequence of events, it is necessary to keep an image of the pile in mind. The charge face, about 50 feet high and wide, is where the cartridges were fed into the pile. There was a charge hoist, which was a platform spanning the side of the charge face, and which could be lifted up and down to access particular sets of channels. The pile contained 3,340 horizontal fuel channels which were arranged in groups of four, with access by means of a charge hole which would normally be kept plugged. The channels were 25 feet long and were open at the back of the pile. When new cartridges were fed in, the old ones simply fell into skips in water baths placed below and were then taken away. It was possible to view the back of the pile from above through inspection hatches.

As well as the main blowers, there were also small 'shutdown' fans. These would still be kept operating even after the pile had been shut down, since a good deal of heat was being generated from the decay of the fission products (of the order of a few megawatts), and so a steady airflow was needed to remove this residual heat. However, they were usually kept switched off during an anneal.

The following narrative is an edited version of the account in Penney's report, prepared soon after the fire:[5]

Just after 1:00 a.m. on Monday 7 October the pile was shut down and the main blowers switched off in preparation for the Wigner release, then the shutdown fans were switched off. After all the other preparations had been made, at 7:25 p.m. the pile was made to diverge — that is, become active — so as to generate nuclear heat for triggering off the release of Wigner energy stored in the graphite, and the power level was gradually increased.

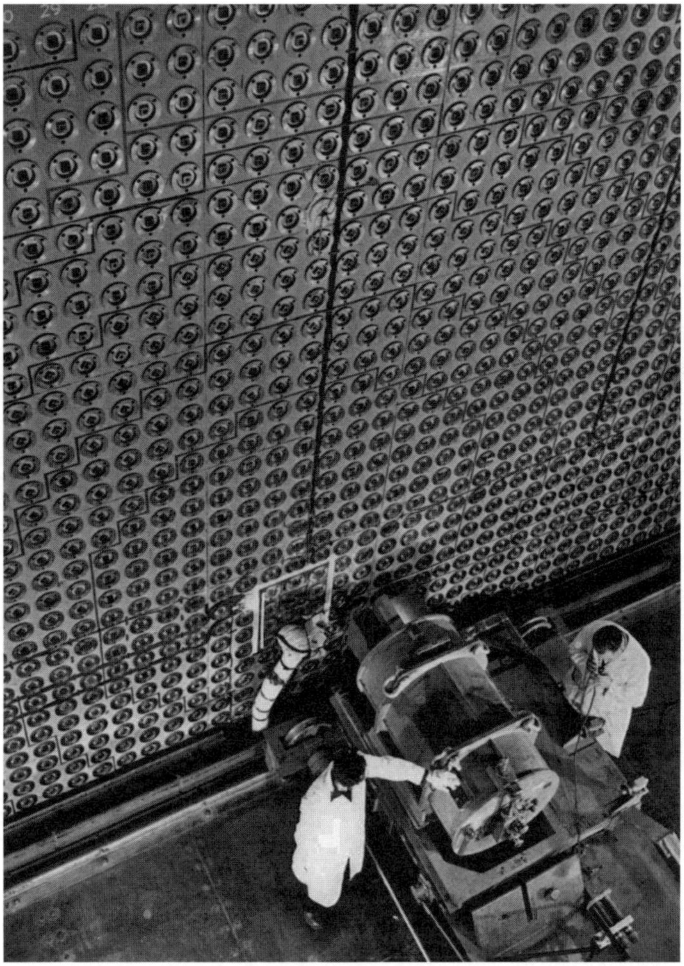

Figure 6.2. The charge face. Each plug covered four fuel channels and one isotope channel. The men are standing on the charge hoist, a platform that could be moved up and down to access different parts of the charge face. (Image courtesy of NDA and copyright NDA.)

Most of the graphite temperatures rose in much the same way as they had done in past releases, but at about 9:00 a.m., it seemed to the physicist in charge and the pile manager that the general tendency was for the graphite temperatures to be dropping rather than rising and it seemed likely that unless more nuclear heat was applied, the release would stop. The heating was kept going at a lower level until 5:00 in the evening when it was turned off, and during this period the highest uranium thermocouple readings rose to about 345°C. (The normal temperature when the pile was active was 350°C.)

During Wednesday, the uranium temperatures reached a maximum of 360°C, while at around 10:00 p.m. the highest value recorded was 340°C. The graphite temperatures showed considerable variation, but the general tendency was for the temperatures to increase following the second nuclear heating. The graphite temperature in channel 20/53, which had shown a reading of about 255°C at the time when the second nuclear heating was applied, continued to rise steadily until it had reached a temperature of 405°C.

Figure 6.3. The control room for Pile 1. It was from here that the Wigner release would be carried out. On the wall can be seen pen recorders, which would reproduce the thermocouple readings on a roll of paper. (Image courtesy of NDA and copyright NDA.)

The high temperature being recorded in channel 20/53 led the pile physicist to blow air through the reactor for short periods throughout the night. This had a cooling effect on all the graphite temperatures except in 20/53, where the temperature rise was stopped, but did not drop.

There was an activity meter fitted in the stack, or chimney, through which the air blown through the reactor was vented. Early on the Thursday morning, there was a sharp increase in its reading. This was noted by the physicist who was then on duty, but no special action was taken because he regarded it as the normal consequence of the first movement of the air through the pile and up the stack (chimney). This increase was followed by a steady drop in the curve for about two and a half hours after which time stack activity rose steadily.

The temperature in channel 20/53 continued to rise, and when air was blown through the pile to cool it, an increase in the radioactivity in the stack was noticed.

This suggested to the operating staff the existence of one or more burst cartridges, but when they tried setting up the scanning gear to find where the burst might be, the gear was found to be jammed. This was not the first time it had jammed after a Wigner release.

At this stage the Works General Manager was informed by the Pile Manager that there appeared to be a bad burst, and he instructed that the affected channel should be identified and discharged as soon as possible. Since the scanning gear could not be used it was decided to remove the charge plug and visually inspect the uranium channel showing the highest readings.

Before the personnel could inspect the charge face, an air count had to be taken to ensure conditions were safe to work in, and the operatives themselves had to change into protective clothing. The temperature of fuel channel 21/53 had been recording very rapid increases until at 4:30 p.m. it was in the neighbourhood of 450°C. The plug covering this group of four channels was pulled out and the metal inside was seen to be glowing. The graphite appeared to have its normal colour. Immediately the glowing metal was seen in the 21/53 group of channels, an attempt was made to discharge the fuel cartridges, but they were stuck fast and could not be moved.

Figure 6.4. A suit similar to those being worn by the people working at the charge face during the fire.

The main blowers could not be turned on to try to reduce the temperatures — given the high stack activity, this would probably have caused a serious neighbourhood hazard as more radioactive debris would have swept up the stack. The shutdown fans had to be kept on, however, in order to maintain tolerable working conditions on the charge hoist. But further inspection showed that as well as the 21/53 group of channels, there was a rectangular region of some 40 groups of channels — about 150 channels in all — showing red heat.

It was decided to make a fire break by discharging a complete ring of channels around the hot region. Later, a second row of channels was discharged above and at each end of the hot area; and later still, as the fire continued to threaten spread upwards, a third row was discharged above the hot area. Discharge had to be suspended at one point while skips were moved in order to avoid a criticality hazard in the water duct — in other words, so much uranium was accumulating in the skips that there was a possibility of a critical mass being formed. This would not have resulted in an explosion, but might have led to other problems, such as the water boiling off and a further meltdown or fire.

Two subsidiary measures were attempted with no success. Use of argon was considered, but it was found that insufficient was available in the works. Secondly, a tanker of CO_2 was brought over from Calder Hall, and arrangements were made for CO_2 to be supplied to the hot channels. CO_2 was fed into channel 20/56 at 4.30 a.m. but with no appreciable effect.

Meanwhile observation from the top of the pile through an inspection hole showed an obvious glow on the pile rear face at 6:45 p.m.. By 7:30 p.m. the flames were much brighter; at 8:00 p.m. they were yellow and by 8:30 p.m. they were blue.

At about this time the use of water was first considered. There were two major hazards to using water. The first was that hot steam and carbon — which is what graphite is — react together to form hydrogen gas and carbon monoxide ($H_2O + C = H_2 + CO$). When the hydrogen mixed with the air there was then the possibility of a hydrogen–oxygen explosion which would blow out the filters at the top of stack, which were keeping the worst of the radioactive particles from escaping into the outside world. Secondly, it was possible that the reactor could be made active again — a criticality hazard — due to replacement of air by water, which could act as a moderator. On the other hand, if the graphite temperatures were to rise much higher than 1,200°C then there was a danger of releasing high-temperature Wigner energy, which might well ignite the whole pile.

By about midnight the Works General Manager had decided that if all the other efforts failed to reduce the temperature, water should be used. This was a major decision, and it was supported by the Director of Production and the Deputy Works General Manager. The fire brigade was ordered to stand by with all available pumps, and work started on the preparation of equipment to enable water to be injected into the channels which had been discharged.

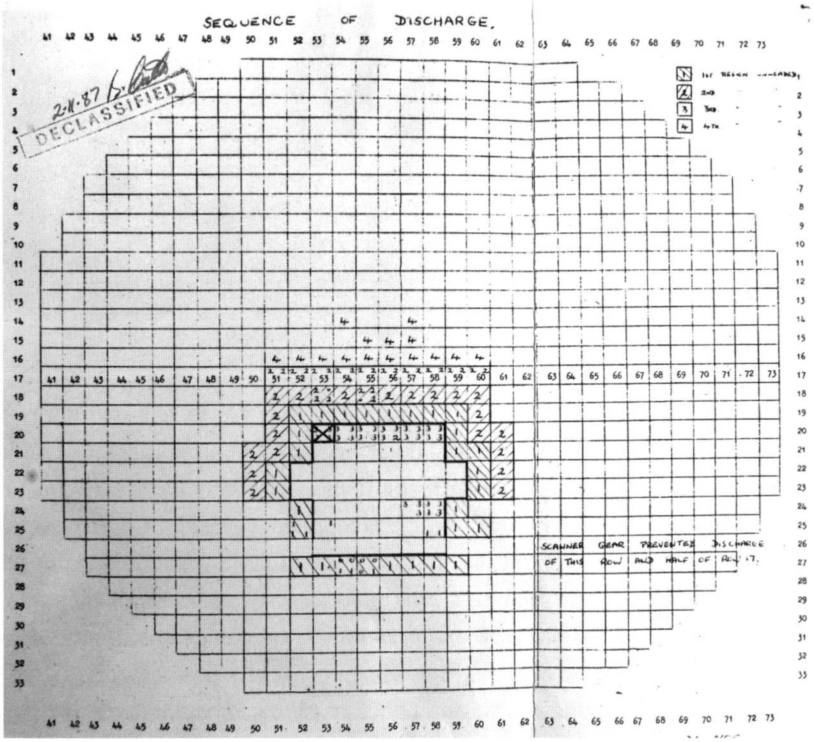

Figure 6.5. The fire was first detected in channel 21/53, marked with a cross. Attempts were made to discharge the channels above the fire, as shown.

Shortly after midnight the Chief Constable was warned of the possibility of an emergency and the men in the factory were given instructions to stay indoors and wear face masks. The graphite in channel 20/53, near the top of the "hot" area, showed a temperature of 1,000°C, and a fuel element temperature of 1,300°C was recorded by optical pyrometer. Over the next two hours, brute force efforts were successful in discharging nearly all the top row of burning elements, whilst the fire continued unabated elsewhere.

Visual inspection at 4 a.m. through two of the pile roof inspection holes still showed blue flames: the graphite appeared to be burning fiercely. A tanker of carbon dioxide had been brought over from Calder Hall, and the gas was fed into channel 21/56 at 4.30 a.m., but with no apparent effect.

After the unsuccessful use of CO_2, temperatures continued to rise. Efforts to discharge the burning cartridges continued, but by 7 a.m. it was clear that the fire was not being checked. It was then decided that water should be used, but before it was turned on all factory labour were sent under cover. Water was finally turned on at 08:55 a.m. and poured through two channels above the maximum height of the fire. No dramatic change resulted: an hour later, flames were still feathering out of the back of the pile, so at 10:10 a.m. the shutdown fans were closed off to reduce airflow through the pile and the fire immediately began to subside. At midday, two more hoses were installed, and the water flow was increased to 1,000 gallons/minute. The flow continued at this rate until 6:45 a.m. the next day, and then was gradually reduced until at 3:00 p.m. it was completely stopped, by which time the pile was cold.

The Emergency Procedures

Whilst the pile was still on fire, it was suggested that the local population should be evacuated. The Chief Constable of the county had been contacted. One of the more extraordinary features of the whole incident is that there were no plans in place to cope with an evacuation, nor were there any plans to deal with any large-scale radioactive leaks, nor even was there any real idea of the potential health hazards of any leak. There were no standards laid down as to what levels of contamination of the surrounding area by different isotopes might be hazardous. In one sense, all leaks present a hazard, but some leaks are more serious than others, and the medical staff needed to know what action should be taken given a specific leak. It seems that no estimates had been made of the effects of possible contamination on the local population before the accident, and that the teams provided to survey the area in the aftermath of the leak were totally inadequate.

There were, apparently, two vans available to carry out surveys of the immediate area, and they were sent out on the afternoon of the Thursday. The health physicist, Howells, said in his evidence to the enquiry that 'the readings we got when they came back were not particularly reliable due to contamination on the roofs of the vans'.[6]

To begin with, the Health Physics Manager had to assume that the radioactive plume consisted of the standard fission products. This was not the case on two counts. The first is that some polonium 210 had been released and this is not a normal fission product. The polonium release is described in a later section. The other reason was that many of the fission products were not volatile, and were either contained in the pile itself or had been trapped by the filters. Thus the main component of the fallout from the chimney was iodine 131. This simplified matters considerably, since the isotope has a relatively short half-life of eight days. Iodine 131 emits both beta and gamma radiation.

The next consideration was how the contamination might be absorbed by the human body. Nearby sources of gamma radiation or contamination of the skin or hair with gamma emitters would deliver radiation to all parts of the body. The other major routes would be by inhalation — breathing in contaminated dust particles — or ingestion — that is, by eating or drinking contaminated food. The decision was taken that the gamma radiation and the inhalation risk was small, and that the main risk was of ingestion. This would occur as the radioactive material fell to the ground and contaminated the grass, crops or vegetables, which were then eaten either by farm animals or directly by humans.

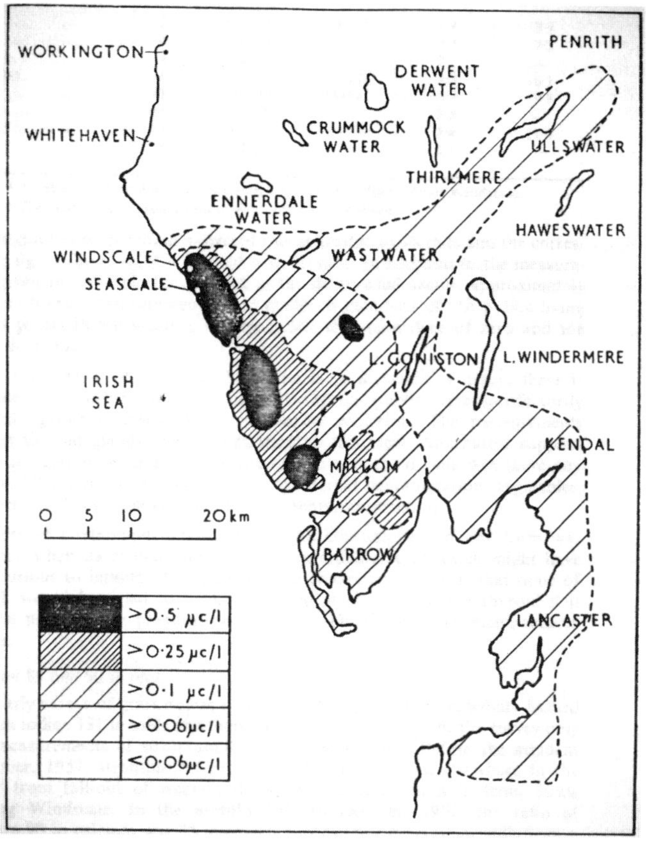

Figure 6.6. Iodine 131 fallout (from the subsequent White Paper).

It then seemed that the major problem would be the fallout of radioactive iodine onto grass, which would then be eaten by cattle, and make its way to the cows' milk. Iodine collects in the thyroid gland, and so if there were radioactive iodine contamination in the milk, it would be transferred to the human thyroid when the milk was drunk. The next step was to find out how much radioactive iodine had found its way into the milk in the vicinity.

When it became clear to the medical officer at Risley, Dr MacLean, that iodine was likely to be the major problem, he then had to work out what dose might be considered acceptable. There was no accepted limit at that time, either in the UK or internationally. He was able to find a report which had been produced with civil defence in mind, in which a figure of 200 R to the thyroid was stated to be the level at which damage to the tissues could be caused. He made a fairly arbitrary guess that one tenth of that dose — 20 R — should be the upper limit.

This was for an adult, and the main problem lay with the milk being fed to babies.

> In making our assessment of the problem, we found ourselves short both of philosophical and of qualitative information. We felt that the situation in Cumberland hardly be regarded in the same light as a normal planned effluent disposal operation but, equally, it lacked the widespread catastrophic character of a nuclear attack. Furthermore, we realise that the main performer in the piece was not the familiar "Standard Man" and, with indecent haste we had to conceive our model child. For these reasons our assessment was personal and arbitrary and it was perhaps fortunate that it agreed quite well with that of your Special Committee.[7]

The 'model child' mentioned was scaled down from the 'Standard Man'. The reasoning behind the figures was as follows:

> The total dose delivered by a concentration of 1 microcurie of iodine-131 per gramme of thyroid is 130 rads. The mass of the adult thyroid is given as 20 grammes and that of a child has been taken to be 5 grammes. One microcurie in the adult thyroid thus delivers 6.5 rads, whilst the same amount in the child delivers 26 rads. The child's thyroid was assumed to retain 45% of the ingested iodine with an effective half-life of 8 days. The total intake required to give a total dose of 20 rads is thus:
>
> $$(20/26) \times (100/45) \text{ microcuries.}$$
>
> The milk consumption of a child was assumed to be one litre per day and the rate of decrease of activity in the milk supplies was assumed to be that due to radioactive decay alone, the mean life being 11.5 days. The limiting concentration of iodine-131 in milk was therefore:
>
> $$(20/26) \times (100/45) \times (1/11.5) \text{ microcurie per litre} = 0.15 \text{ microcurie per litre.}$$[8]

This was one step up from guesswork, although Dr MacLean and his colleagues spent several hours on the telephone to other medical specialists, attempting to get confirmation of their calculations. As it happened, their assessment was fairly close to the mark, and the acceptable level of activity in the milk was set at 0.1 μCi per litre.

Back at Windscale, Howells requested that samples of local milk be analysed, and on the basis of those results rang Superintendent Nixon at Whitehaven police station to ask him to stop the issuing of local milk. Interestingly, the AEA had no legal basis for doing this. The initial ban was applied to 17 farms, but as more samples were analysed, the ban was extended to a coastal strip two miles wide and seven miles long, and then, as further samples were taken, extended further to a total of 200 square miles. Over the course of the milk sampling programme about 3,000 half pint (0.25 l) samples of milk were analysed.

In the less heavily contaminated areas the ban lasted for 25 days, but in the more heavily affected areas the ban was extended to 44 days.

Radiation Received by the Workers

The workers on the charge face wore protective suits which covered the entire body and had a filter for breathing air. This would have stopped most of the body contamination, although at least one worker had to go home with his hands and hair in a protective bag. Too much scrubbing was obviously not good for the skin.

The ICRP (International Commission on Radiological Protection) tolerance level for workers in the nuclear industry was 3.0 R (30 mSv) at the time. According to the personal dosimeter the workers were carrying, two received 4.5 R during the accident, one received 3.3 R, and there were four others in excess of 2 R. According to Penney's report:

> When the plugs were being removed from the charge wall to find the limits of the area of the fire and to eject burning cartridges, some men looked for a few seconds through the open plug holes towards the pile face from a distance of several feet back from the charge wall. A few men were not wearing head film badges, although they were wearing the normal type of film badge. These men may have got a dose of radiation to their head, somewhere between 0.1 R and 0.5 R, in addition to the whole body dose recorded by their film badges.

Tom Tuohy, Deputy Works Manager, deliberately discarded his radiation badge so as to give the management no opportunity to withdraw him from the action. Certainly Tuohy's actions during the fire went far beyond his duties, and he almost certainly received a radiation dose well in excess of the recommended limit. It would hardly have been politic to award honours to someone for their actions during the emergency, but Tuohy's actions probably merited greater recognition. He became Windscale General Manager from 1958 to 1964, then Managing Director of the UKAEA Production Group until 1971. He was the first Managing Director of BNFL, then Managing Director of the new uranium enrichment company, Urenco, at Capenhurst, taking early retirement in 1974 at the age of 57. He was awarded the CBE in 1969. He lived to the age of 90, and so obviously did not suffer any ill effects from his exposure.

Figure 6.7. Tom Tuohy. (Image courtesy of NDA and copyright NDA.)

Perhaps the last word on the topic of the possible health risks to those who were working in the plant at the time of the accident can be given to a study which was a follow-up of the mortality and cancer rates among the workers known to have been involved in the incident. A study was made of the 470 male workers involved in tackling the fire or the subsequent clear, the conclusion of which was that:

> This analysis of the mortality and cancer morbidity experience of those Sellafield workers involved in the 1957 Windscale fire does not reveal any measurable effect of the fire upon their health. Although this study has low statistical power for detecting small adverse effects, due to the relatively small number of workers, it does provide reassurance that no significant health effects are associated with the 1957 Windscale fire even after 50 years of follow-up.[9]

The Report

It was essential that the cause of the fire be established as quickly as possible. By 15 October, a committee of enquiry had been set up with Sir William Penney as Chairman. Its terms of reference were 'to investigate the cause of the fire at Windscale No. 1. Pile on 10th October, 1957, and the measures taken to deal with it and its consequences.'[10] The other members of the board were Sir Basil Schonland, the Deputy Director of Harwell, Professor JM Kay of Imperial College London, and Professor J Diamond of Manchester University. Kay and Diamond were both engineering consultants to the AEA; Diamond had been working on the original proposals for nuclear submarine propulsion from 1945 onwards. DH Peirson, Secretary to the AEA, also acted as secretary to the enquiry.

The board saw its task as one of investigation, and so the witnesses would be able to give evidence without fear of any subsequent disciplinary action. Accordingly, no legal or professional representation was provided for the witnesses. In retrospect, this was something of a mistake, as certain comments made in the report were later used to criticise personnel without them being able to give an effective reply. No individuals were ever officially named directly, although some newspapers did name names.

The enquiry lasted for ten days, starting on 17 October, and 37 people were interviewed, some more than once. In addition, documents, reports, graphs, logbooks and maps were also produced for the enquiry. The proceedings were recorded on tape and by a shorthand writer. The report itself was finished by 26 October, a remarkable feat in the circumstances. It can be challenged in places today, but given the speed with which it was produced, it stands up remarkably well.

The report reached the Prime Minister on 28 October. There was then the question of what to do next. The AEA was prepared to see the report published, but the Prime Minister disagreed. Instead, a White Paper based on the report was prepared for the subsequent debate in Parliament.[11]

What Caused the Fire?

There are three possibilities for the cause of the fire. The first is the graphite itself, the second is a burst uranium cartridge, and the third is an AM cartridge. (AM was the code name given to tritium, and the cartridges contained lithium metal canned in aluminium.)

Penney and his enquiry team came to the conclusion that it had been a uranium cartridge that had started the fire, although the evidence was relatively slight.

There is no evidence that the AM cartridges were responsible, although several buckled and distorted AM cartridges were found when Pile 2 was cleared.[12] On the other hand, buckled and distorted is not the same as being inflammable.

A more considered report was made three months later:

> The shutdown dampers were opened on three separate occasions with no detectable change in the stack activity filter . . . The total volume of air which passed through the pile is thus two to three times the normal volume of the pile void, the outlet ducts and the chimney. Under these conditions the rate of airflow down the uranium channels is approximately two feet per second, and it is very difficult to believe that gaseous activity in the uranium channels would not be taken up past the stack filters.

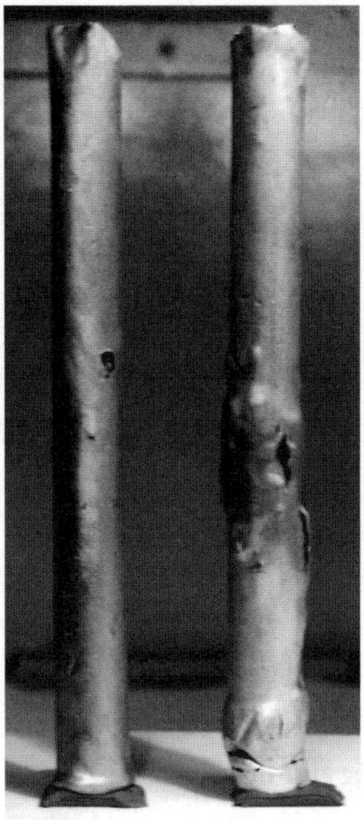

Figure 6.8. Distorted AM cartridges found later when Pile 2 was being cleared.

> I feel the burst cartridge detector gear can actually detect a serious burst in the reactor even if it is jammed in position . . . There was no apparent centre of fire but rather we had a large area of the pile, perhaps ten feet by eight feet, over which all the channels were very nearly the same red hot temperature. At the edge of this zone the temperatures fell very rapidly over perhaps a distance of two pitches from being red hot to quite undamaged.
>
> The AM cartridges could not, however, have been the sole cause of the fire. The amount of energy released in the burning of AM is not in itself sufficient to raise the temperature of the adjacent AM cartridges more than a few degrees centigrade.[13]

The unprecedented nature of the incident meant that a very considerable research programme was devoted to finding out exactly what went wrong and studying the problems of graphite in reactors in very considerable detail — particularly since the new power reactors would all have graphite moderators, even if they were not air-cooled. There is no doubt that the efforts given to this work had serious consequences on much other development work going on at the same time.

One of those working on the problem was Alan Cottrell,[14] who was also looking at the possibility of re-opening Pile 2. He came out strongly against this as a consequence of the work done on the oxidation rates of irradiated graphite. His argument was that at the temperatures needed for a Wigner release, highly irradiated graphite could not, as he put it, 'be guaranteed against runaway oxidation'. There was a good deal of highly irradiated graphite in Pile 1, and thus one possible cause of the fire could have been 'runaway oxidation' of the graphite. This could, of course, then ignite the uranium or AM cartridges.

Thus, there are the three possible causes, and for each one there is evidence in favour and evidence against. It is unlikely that the true cause will ever be established for certain, even when the reactor is finally taken apart.

'Errors of Judgement'

The report from Penney's enquiry concluded that 'We have come to the conclusion that the primary cause of the accident was the second nuclear heating'. The report does not say that there was anything unusual in a second heating. The members of the enquiry team were fully aware that a second heating had been used in the past, when Gausden, manager of the pile group at Windscale, told them in his evidence that:

> You cannot lay down a set pattern for Wigner release. It is really one big experiment every time we do it. We have found that on a number of occasions in the past that graphite temperatures tend to fall and that the release can be started up again by putting in some nuclear heating.
>
> The other important point is one that was made time after time: there was no set pattern for the Wigner release, with the corollary that this was not a routine procedure.

Although this was not stated as such in his report, Penney obviously felt that this second heating was a mistake, and that temperatures in the pile had not been falling. The record of the thermocouples[15] half an hour before the second nuclear heating are shown in Table 6.1.

There were 66 thermocouples in all, although only 64 were operational.

This was not the complete picture, since it was not only whether the pile was cooling again that mattered, but where it was cooling at all. In other words, temperatures may have risen in a particular area as a Wigner release began and then started dropping back down again.

There was no such thing as an operating manual or any operating instructions for a Wigner release; it was left almost entirely to the pile physicists in charge on that particular event. Indeed, there would be no one person overseeing the whole

Table 6.1. Rise and fall of temperatures in the pile.

Rising	Doubtful Rising	Steady	Falling
27.3%	13.6%	39.4%	16.7%

operation, since it ran through several shifts. Gethin Davey, the Windscale General Manager, says of the releases that:

> Before Pile No. 1 was commissioned and brought into operation, a Plant Manual had been written, and Operating Instructions, Safety Regulations and Emergency Procedures had been produced which covered every aspect of pile operation with the exception of the release of Wigner energy which, of course, was an unknown phenomenon at that time. After September 1952 various draft instructions to cover the Wigner energy release were introduced but a final and comprehensive instruction was never produced for the simple reason that no two releases were alike.[16]

Penney's report was not interested in allocating blame, but in finding out the cause of the fire. Indeed, it would have been unfair to point a finger at any one individual, since those giving evidence to the enquiry had no representation, either legal or from a professional association.

The White Paper[17] describing the incident began with a memorandum by the Prime Minister. Towards the end of the memorandum, he states 'the accident was due partly to inadequacies in the instrumentation provided at Windscale for the maintenance operation that was being performed at the time of the accident, and partly the faults of judgement by the operating staff, these faults of judgement being themselves attributable to the weaknesses of organisation'.

This is a distinctly ambiguous comment, and there is little in Penney's original report to back this up. The comment about 'faults of judgement' is qualified by the remark about the weaknesses of organisation, but journalists are often not interested in the qualification. Certainly this remark was picked up by the press, and attempts were made, particularly in the *Daily Express*, to name the 'guilty men'. The publicity was sufficient for those concerned to make representations via their trade union, the Institution of Professional Civil Servants. The institution engaged in a long correspondence with the AEA on behalf of its members. Unfortunately, rather than concentrating on a few single important issues, the institution covered a whole series of complaints about the White Paper, many of which were not especially relevant.

Some of their complaints however, did have considerable validity:

> The word "controlled" used in the first para is really quite the wrong word. The release is not controlled it is a deliberate release to which is attached a maximum temperature.[18]

The institution was quite correct: once a Wigner release had been started, there was no way of controlling it. This was dismissed as 'a fine drafting distinction which is of little relevance to the interests of the I.P.C.S.'.[19]

When the institution complained about the lack of an operating manual for Wigner release, the Authority noted that 'these potentially dangerous operations

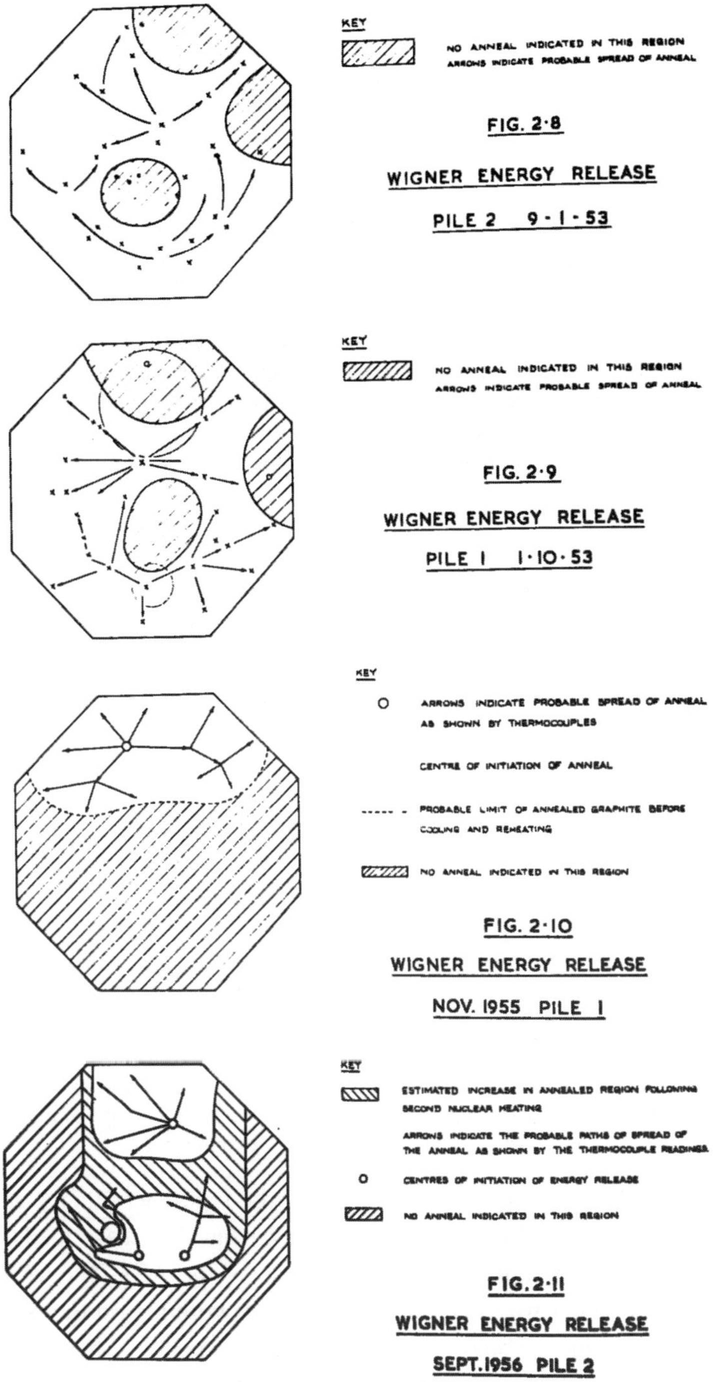

Figure 6.9. The results from some previous anneals, showing how random and unpredictable the process could be.

were left in the charge of comparatively junior staff relying mainly on verbal instructions and traditions'.[20]

The heart of their complaint lay in the allocation of blame.

> . . . the Chairman in his minute to the Prime Minister says quite explicitly that the accident arose partly from faults of judgement by the operating staff. This is a clear and categorical assertion in condemnation of three people. In the terms of the report it is a condemnation of the physicist in charge, in terms of the actual giving of the order for the second nuclear heating it is a condemnation of the Pile Manager and the consultant physicist . . . It must be remembered that these officers have had enormous amount of experience of these piles and the consultant physicist for example has seen every one of the anneals in both piles . . . Notwithstanding the enormous experience resident in these three officers, the Chairman has seen fit to condemn their judgement. This is really a quite shattering thing to do in respect of young men in the practice of their profession. It is a course that ought not to be taken to set when one is absolutely sure of the grounds for the assertion.

The institution had a good case, but given the circumstances, was not likely to get very far with it. On the other hand, the treatment of the three concerned did lead to a great deal of bitterness in the staff at Windscale. An anneal of the Windscale piles could never be described as 'controlled' or 'routine', particularly given the inadequate instrumentation. They were at best a matter of trial and error, with the potential for disaster. It would have been more fitting for the government to have admitted this from the outset.

A Cover-Up?

It has been alleged that Harold Macmillan, the Prime Minister, made a decision for political reasons to cover-up the true story of the fire. This allegation is based in part on the decision not to publish Penney's full report, but to issue a separate White Paper. In the section headed 'Memorandum by the Prime Minister', Macmillan justifies his decision by describing Penney's report as

> a technical document dealing with the design and operation of a defence installation. It also presupposes considerable knowledge of the technology of this particular pile. It would not be in the national interest to publish it.

Macmillan's justification for not publishing the report was that it concerned a top-secret military establishment, but other motives have been ascribed to him. The first is that the report is quite critical of aspects of the AEA, the second is that negotiations were under way with the United States with regard to cooperation on nuclear matters. A report which suggested incompetence at the heart of the British nuclear programme would not have been welcomed. Furthermore,

> . . . the McMahon Act in the United States severely restricted any exchange of nuclear information with the UK and its amendment was seen by the Prime

> Minister as an important objective which would influence both nuclear and other defence considerations. To have published details of certain of the Windscale operations would confirm the suspicions of some US observers that the UK could not be trusted to protect nuclear military secrets.[21]

These suppositions are somewhat undermined by the arrival in Britain of a seven member American team from the USAEC at the beginning of December for a three-day conference.[22] The 15 member British team included Cockcroft, Owen, Schonland, Davey and Tuohy, who discussed the entire incident with their opposite numbers, so the idea that a technical 'cover-up' was possible can probably be dismissed. On the other hand, Macmillan may well have had the public relations aspect in mind: whilst he might have been prepared to come clean in private, he preferred not to give his critics, particularly those in the United States Senate, any opportunities for criticism. The minutes of an AEA meeting soon after the incident are revealing:

> The Chairman said that, in accordance with the Authority's decision at their last meeting, he had submitted to the Prime Minister the Report of Sir William Penney's Committee of Enquiry on the accident at Windscale No. 1 Pile and had discussed with him the points raised during the Authority's consideration of it. The Prime Minister had taken the view that it would not be in the public interest to publish the Report in full. He thought that it would be wrong to publish so much detailed technical information about a defence installation. Even if it had been considered that there was no security objection to the publication of so much technical detail, they would still remain the danger that it would be quoted out of context and misused in other ways by hostile critics. In particular it would provide ammunition to those in the United States who would in any case oppose the necessary amendments of the McMahon Act which the United States authorities intended to propose in order to make possible the desired degree of closer collaboration between the United States and the United Kingdom in the military applications of atomic energy. It would also adversely affect the collaboration between the two countries in other defence fields. The Prime Minister had therefore asked Sir William Penney's Committee to produce a simplified version of the Report in language which would not be open to these objections.[23]

It is certainly true that aspects of the pile production were sensitive matters from the security point of view. The AM cartridges, which were a possible candidate for the cause of the fire, were designed to produce tritium, and this was certainly a sensitive issue — when an internal memorandum referred to the production of tritium, the author was reminded in a subsequent memo that the code name AM should always be used. Tritium itself is not used in fusion weapons (the 'hydrogen bomb') directly, but to improve the efficiency of fission devices. It is used in fusion weapons in the sense that a fission device is used as the trigger for the fusion process.

Penney's report also goes into detail of the construction of the pile, and bearing in mind that this event occurred during the height of the Cold War, it is not surprising that these details were suppressed in the interests of security.

There is a final issue. Penney's report contained considerable criticism of the management structure surrounding the production piles. He does not say that the AEA had been negligent, but that is certainly an inference which could be drawn from several of his criticisms. On the other hand, the White Paper does report many of Penney's strictures. Penney's report was published as an annex to the White Paper in an amended form, and in paragraph two he states:

> The immediate cause of the accident was the second nuclear heating. This was applied before it was necessary and the nuclear heating was put in at too rapid a rate. The second nuclear heating was applied because it was thought that the Wigner release was dying away and that parts of the graphite structure were therefore going to escape being annealed. The instrumentation of the pile was not sufficient in quantity or in distribution throughout the pile to enable a reliable judgement to be made.

The last sentence is the crucial one: if the instrumentation was inadequate (and there is no doubt it was), then, as Penney says, a reliable judgement is not possible. The blame, if one wishes to allocate blame, lies with those who decided that annealing the pile was possible given the existing instrumentation. On the other hand, the only other option would have been to close the piles down, which would have been seen as unacceptable, or suspending operations to install more thermocouples — not an easy task given the highly radioactive state of the core.

If anyone might have been aiming at a cover-up, it would have been the AEA, whose Chairman at the time was Sir Edwin Plowden. There was a meeting of the AEA soon after they received Penney's report. Various points were made during the meeting:

> It could reasonably be inferred from the Committee of Enquiry's Report that this accident might well have been very much worse and that a similar or worse accident might have occurred upon a number of occasions during the last few years. It would also be clear to any reader that this accident, or any comparable accident which might have occurred earlier, could be directly attributed to serious defects in the Authority's organisation and to equally avoidable defects in the instrumentation of the Windscale piles.
>
> Publication of the Report would severely shake public confidence in the Authority's competence to undertake tasks entrusted to them and would inevitably provide ammunition for all those who had doubts of one kind or another about the development and the future of nuclear power.[24]

At least the AEA was being realistic about the causes of the accident. Despite this, the minutes of the meeting went on to say:

> So far as the Authority themselves were concerned, it was important that there should be no apparent attempt to gloss over the facts. Any expressions of regret must be so worded as to suggest not mere polite compliance with convention, but rather the genuine regret of the Authority and must be accompanied by a forceful statement of intent to take steps to ensure that the state of affairs which had led

the present incident be speedily and effectively amended so that nothing similar ever happen again.[25]

The Future of Pile 2

The question remained as to what to do about Pile 2. Extra instrumentation and new safety devices had been recommended for the reactor before it could be restarted, and the cost of these was estimated at £500,000. There was also the question of the irradiated uranium that had been left in the pile when it was closed down.

> The reactor at present contains 88 tons of natural uranium, compared with its normal loading of 109 tons, and also its full complement of 55 tons of enriched uranium. To meet essential military requirements for low irradiation plutonium next year, it is desirable to discharge and process much of this fuel, whatever decision is taken about the future of the reactor.
>
> The balance remaining would be 44 tons of natural uranium (irradiation 70 MWD/T) and 12 tons of enriched uranium (irradiation 370 MWD/T). In value this is about one quarter of a full charge.
>
> The cost of the new charge ex-works is as follows:
>
> Natural uranium $£15,000 \times 109 = £1.6$ M
>
> Enriched uranium $£35,000 \times 65 = £2.3$ M.[26]

There were also isotope cartridges in the pile which would certainly be worth recovering.

Additionally, there was the question of annealing the pile — firstly, whether it was worth doing, secondly, how to do it. There was even discussion as to whether the pile could still be run without any annealing at all.[27] One option was to use electrical heating as for BEPO (see Chapter 10), but this would also mean de-fuelling the reactor beforehand.[28] Figure 6.10 shows the modifications which would be necessary.

The decisive argument came in a paper of August 1958,[29] written by Alan Cottrell (then the Deputy Head of Metallurgy at Harwell), summarising the results of the various research programmes that had been set into motion as a result of the accident:

> It now seems unlikely that Windscale B.P.P. 2 [Pile 2] can be annealed by a method that is both safe and effective. The difficulty is not one of controlling the release of Wigner energy — we are in fact fairly sure of being able to do this — but that the latest oxidation results show that some blocks of graphite cannot be guaranteed against runaway oxidation even at 350°C. To produce an effective anneal, which would give the reactor several years of life afterwards, the temperature of the graphite would have to reach about 300°C. With such a narrow interval between this temperature and the runaway oxidation temperature of certain blocks almost

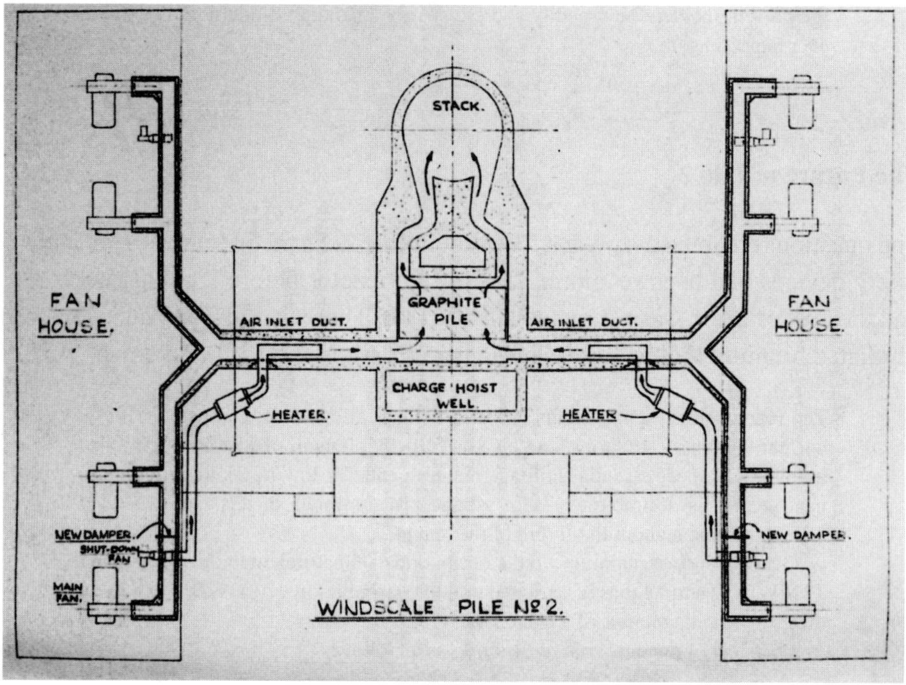

Figure 6.10. Using electrical heaters to anneal Pile 2.

> every block would have to be sampled individually before the safety of the Wigner release could be affirmed, which is surely impracticable.

After setting out the evidence obtained he concluded:

> . . . on the present evidence of oxidation rates, there is a strong risk of uncontrolled oxidation setting in if the graphite temperatures are allowed to exceed 300°C in a Wigner release. To reduce this risk to negligible proportions the maximum release temperature would have to be reduced to below about 250°C. This may perhaps be technically feasible, by adjusting the conditions of the two-stage annealing method, but the release to such temperature would not have enough effect on the stored energy plateau to ensure a long working life of the reactor afterwards.

The production piles had been intended to have a life of ten years. By 1957, Pile 2 had been operating for six years. Now that the reactors at Calder Hall had become available, the need to use Pile 2 to produce plutonium was much less acute. Isotope production was another matter: improvements in weapon technology meant that polonium would no longer be needed, but instead the demand for tritium had increased considerably. Producing tritium in the Calder Hall reactors would be possible, but it was thought that new fuel rods containing 93% uranium 235 would be needed, and this was considered unacceptable. The alternative was to build an entirely new reactor, which would be water-cooled and water-moderated, and which could produce 1.5 kg of tritium a year. The weapons programme required a stockpile of 10 kg of tritium by 1970, and a production of around 0.75 kg would be needed each year for replacement purposes. The preferred option was to exchange British plutonium for American tritium (the cost of production of tritium in the United States was estimated at about $20,000 per gram[30]).

Given the nature of the disaster in Pile 1, there would have to be some very good reasons for continuing with the operation of Pile 2. The pile was cleared of all the fuel and isotope rods, before being closed. Both piles were put into care and maintenance until the mid-1980s when significant safety improvements were undertaken.

The Clean Up of Pile 1

Soon after the fire had been discovered, efforts were made to create what might be described as a 'fire break' by pushing out the fuel cartridges from the channels above and to the side of the pile. This was a distinctly hazardous process. At one stage, scaffold poles were used to clear the channels. The fuel cartridges were red hot, and in some cases welded themselves to the end of the poles, so that when the pole was withdrawn, the cartridge came with it, and had to be kicked away from the charge hoist. A diagram drawn up for the Penney enquiry shows the area that had been cleared (Figure 6.5).

As a result of the fire, there was widespread contamination of the pile buildings and surrounding areas. Much of this activity was due to the overflow of the water which had been pumped into the pile and which was heavily contaminated with fission products, causing beta and gamma contamination over large areas of ground in the neighbourhood with localised spots up to 1 mSv/hr, and similar levels in many buildings and on roofs. Rainfall washed some of this activity into drains in the area.

In the buildings of Pile 1, spread of activity was largely due to leakage of water from the core — this being the water used to quench the fire and cool the pile. This affected blower house B4 in particular, where levels of up to 0.5 mSv/hr of gamma radiation and 0.7 mSv/hr of beta radiation were found over large areas of the floor some days after the incident. The stack filters of Pile 1 contained around 100 TBq of activity and gamma radiation levels at the door to the filters on the lower parapet were 600 mSv/hr five days after the incident, decaying to 10 mSv/hr after two weeks and 1 mSv/h after four months.

The interiors of Pile 2 buildings, being somewhat shielded from the fallout, were not highly contaminated, although spots up to 0.1 mSv/hr of beta and gamma radiation were found in the blower houses.

During the months immediately following the incident, extensive decontamination was carried out, particularly of ground areas on the 'non-active' i.e. north, side of the water duct and pond. The blower house filters were removed, the air ducts sealed off; the stack filters of Pile 1 removed and the filter bed blanked off. All the fuel was discharged from Pile 2 and as much as possible from Pile 1.[31]

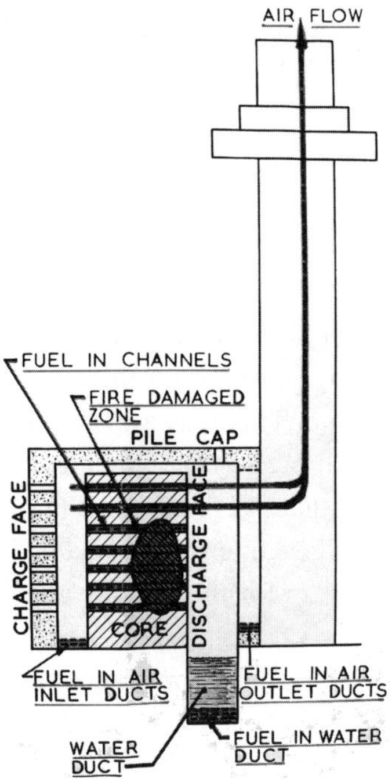

Figure 6.11. As well as fuel left in the core, many fuel elements had ended up in the air ducts and the water duct as shown.

Having cleaned up much of the ground and roads, decontamination of the blower houses, control rooms, and roofs etc. began, so that by 1960 most of the pile area had been cleared. It seems that very little more was done until the 1980s, when a new programme started to investigate the site. A report from 1961 was all the information that was available to the team working on the site. A summary of the data then available was given:

> Pile 1 still contained an estimated 22 tonnes of irradiated uranium, of which 17 tonnes (some 8000 cartridges) were still in the core; 2.5 tonnes (1000 cartridges) were estimated to be in the air ducts; and another 2.5 tonnes (1000 cartridges) in the water duct.[32] Much of the uranium still in the core would have been completely

> oxidised by the fire. There were also isotope channels containing Li/Mg alloy, bismuth oxide etc that have not been discharged. Finally, considering the fire that had taken place, it was unlikely that there will be much residual stored Wigner energy.[33]

Pile 2 was emptied of all fuel and isotope cartridges and there would be few discharged cartridges in the ducts. Since it was a Wigner release that started the fire in Pile 1, Pile 2 had not been annealed and it was presumed that it still had significant stored energy.

The opportunity was also taken to use remote television cameras to inspect the rear of the pile, and half-burnt fuel cartridges could be seen protruding from the fuel channels. Phase 1 decommissioning on the pile included sealing of the outlet air ducts connecting the core space to the chimney, removal of the fuel cartridges from the air outlet and outlet ducts, isolation of the water duct from the cooling pond, and cleaning out, draining and sealing of the water duct.

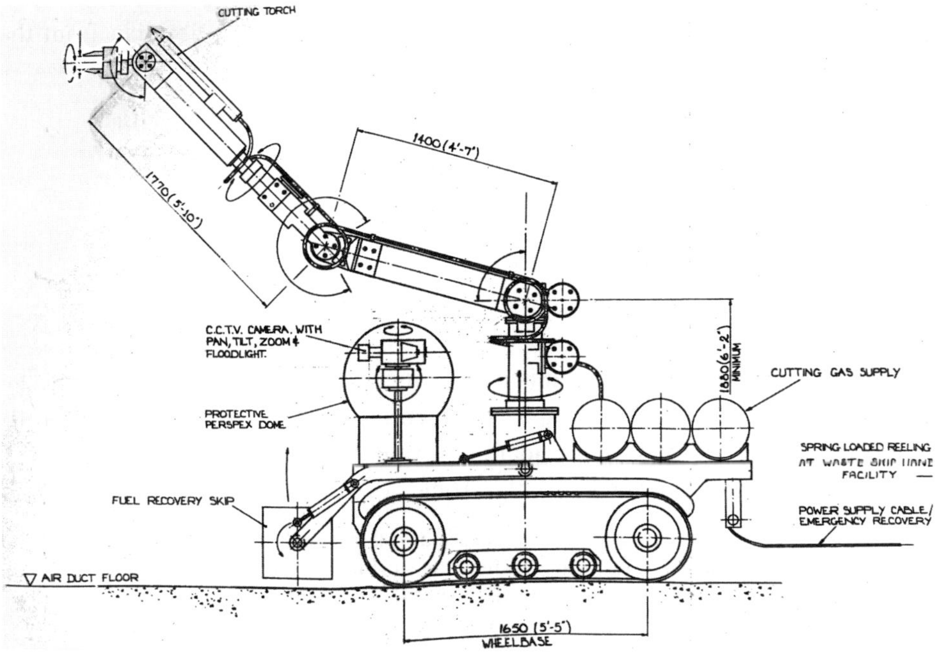

Figure 6.12. Remotely operated vehicle used to examine the inaccessible parts of the pile.

In October 2010, the decision was taken to defer the decommissioning in favour of higher priority projects, and to restart around 2017 or 2018, with the aim to have Pile 1 fully decommissioned by 2041 and Pile 2 by 2050.

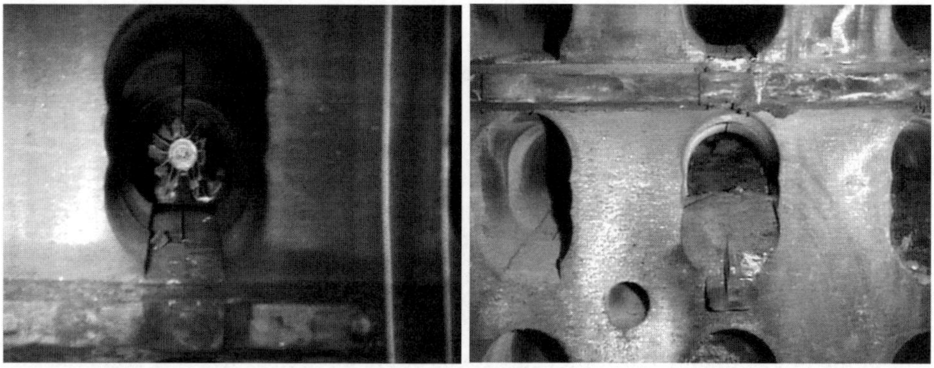

Figure 6.13. Views of the back of the pile — the discharge face. On the right can be seen the remains of a fuel cartridge; on the left, the material within the channel appears to have melted.

Polonium Fallout

In March 1983, the *New Scientist* magazine published an article entitled 'Polonium: Windscale's most lethal legacy', written by John Urquhart, a librarian from the University of Newcastle-upon-Tyne. The article began:

> It is 25 years since the nuclear accident at Windscale in October 1957. Until recently there has never been any suggestion that the radioactive releases that took place then produced any serious health effects. Attention has centred throughout on the releases of radioactive iodine and its subsequent ingestion over a wide area of Britain and Western Europe . . .
>
> However, the damage to health may have been much more severe than this. Indeed, it could represent the worst environmental disaster that Western Europe has known this century.[34]

This was something of a sensationalist claim, and not the kind of statement that one might expect to find in a magazine which includes the word 'scientist' in its title. After a description of the incident (an American account is quoted as it was apparently the 'most independent'), the article goes on to say:

> But there is one isotope released in the accident that is highly mobile, that does have a high take-up by the human body, has a half-life of 140 days, and — though this was only revealed this week by the NRPB [National Radiological Protection Board] after New Scientist's enquiries — was released in significant quantities. It is polonium . . .

In a separate box within the main article, further claims are made:

> The results of the Windscale fire have important implications in the general theory of the effects of nuclear accidents. Both Britain and the US have used polonium in the atomic bombs they have exploded. Even if each bomb contained only 500 Ci, less than one tenth of a gram, the hundreds of tests could have contributed significantly to world leukaemia and cancer levels. Further information on the

> quantities used will be needed from the military authorities, but 500 bomb tests scattering 500 Ci of polonium 210 implies an average deposit concentration of 0.1 nCi per square metre over the world's surface. That is 10 mrem for each person in the world or an extra 50,000 deaths.
>
> Clearly further investigation into the whole of the Windscale accident must be urgently pursued. The British are in effect now the nuclear laboratory of the world.

The article concluded by saying 'John Urquhart has published a fuller version of this article in the *Journal of Nuclear Information*'.

The Secretary to the NRPB wrote an extended response:

> In his article "Polonium: Windscale's most lethal legacy" John Urquhart has rightly drawn attention to the omission from consideration of polonium 210 in the National Radiological Protection Board's report on the 1957 Windscale reactor fire.
>
> However we consider his evaluation of the implications of the polonium 210 release to be grossly in error. We give here the main reasons for doubting the validity of Urquhart's population dose estimates, and for rejecting the conclusions of the accompanying contribution "Looking for an increase in deaths from cancer".
>
> Dose assessment: the account of dose calculation contained in Urquhart's article does not allow the method he used to be completely understood, and it has proved impossible to obtain the "fuller version" of the article, either from the *Journal of Nuclear Information*, which does not yet exist, or from the author himself. Despite these difficulties, it is clear from the New Scientist article that the approach used produces a considerable over estimate of the population dose.[35]

He then went on to give his reasoning:

> 1. The data used as a source of information on dosimetry are not valid for application to the Windscale fire release because they apply to polonium 210 in the environment in equilibrium with its precursors in the uranium 238 decay chain. This situation is quite different from the Windscale fire, in which the single isotope polonium 210 was released.
> 2. The method used to obtain the population effective dose due to polonium 210 in the environment by scaling the population thyroid dose due to iodine 131 . . . is not valid because of the different exposure pathways involved.
>
> The degree of over estimation in Urquhart's calculation is not certain, but we consider it likely to be a factor of about 100.
>
> We also reject Urquhart's claims that population thyroid exposure due to the presence of tellurium 132 and molybdenum in the release were not considered in the Board's study. They were included in our report: tellurium 132 was estimated to contribute about 5 per cent to the total thyroid collective dose and molybdenum 99 was found to make a negligible contribution.
>
> Cancer incidence: we consider the contribution "Looking for an increase in deaths from cancer" to be extremely poor.
>
> 1. The histogram on page 874 shows ratios of observed-to-expected leukaemia deaths for different ages. The numbers given in the boxes are not the numbers of leukaemia deaths as the presentation suggests — they are nearer

the total of all causes of death. Their exact meaning is unclear because the definition of the population of which they are based is ambiguous.

2. The article challenges the statement by the Cumbrian Area Health Authority that the local leukaemia rates do not significantly differ from national rates. On the contrary, the first statement on p 875 supports the health authority's statement event although the multiple myeloma data appear to have been included in the column "RES neoplasms" as well. There is no significant change in leukaemia rates in the two periods.
   The increase in multiple myeloma was reported by the health authority and is being investigated.
3. The increase in male cancer rates in South-West Cumbria are in line with national trends over the same period.
4. The reference to elevated cancer rates between 1974–80 among those aged between 15–24 applies to the population of whom 50 per cent were born after the Windscale accident. The appropriate comparison should have been made by following through a cohort who would have been exposed by the accident. Such an analysis is part of the larger long-term programme of the NRPB devoted to a geographical study of malignancy in the UK.

There was a further letter published in *New Scientist* from CR Hill of the Institute of Cancer Research in Sutton, Surrey, which began:

> John Urquhart's article . . . must have given many of its readers the impression that polonium is an abnormal constituent of man's environment and with an impact that is therefore unpredictable.
>
> In fact it has been known since the late 1950s . . . that 210 Po is widely distributed in the environment, and in man, as a result of atmospheric fall-out of the decay products of natural radon-222 . . . of the order of 10^6curies in total of the surface world land mass . . . It is in this context that the estimated release of 370 curies of 210 Po should be viewed.[36]

Why had polonium been ignored up to this point? Part of the answer lies in the fact that polonium 210 is not a natural fission product of uranium. Instead, it was being manufactured in the pile — cartridges of bismuth oxide were inserted into the isotope channels, and neutron bombardment produced polonium.

Polonium was needed as the initiator for the early fission bombs. It was a powerful alpha emitter, and when placed in close contact with beryllium, neutrons were produced. Owing to the short half-life of polonium 210, these initiators needed replacing at fairly frequent intervals. Later designs of bombs may have had internal initiators using americium, but polonium was still needed for the early devices still in service.

Certainly Harwell was aware of the release of polonium at the time of the accident, as this memo demonstrates:

> The levels of polonium and iodine on filter papers, exposed for a three-day period during the incident, at Harwell and also in the Netherlands show approximately the same ratio of I 131 activity to alpha activity [polonium 210 is an alpha emitter], namely, 25:1. The continuous inhalation maximum permissible levels are in the

> ratio 60:1 or 12:1 depending on whether the polonium is insoluble or soluble respectively. There is thus no difference from polonium and iodine judged on a continuous inhalation basis.
>
> Based on data in the draft 1956 ICRP Manual, the maximum permissible single intake of these isotopes (producing a maximum permissible body content) is 0.6 μCi for I 131 and 0.14 μCi for polonium 210 — a ratio of 4:1. On this basis, the iodine should present a greater risk by a factor of about 6.[37]

The memorandum then considered whether polonium might be taken up by cows and decided that: '. . . Accordingly, pending reference to our agricultural and biological experts, we can conclude that the hazard through milk is also considerably less for polonium than iodine in this incident'.

A paper entitled 'District Surveys Following Windscale Incident'[38] was presented at a United Nations conference in Geneva in September 1958, and reference is made to polonium in the paper. The reference is hardly conspicuous however — on the fifth page of the article appears the statement: 'Smaller quantities of other fission products such as caesium-137, strontium-89 and 90, ruthenium-103 and 106, zirconium-95, niobium-95 and cerium-144 together with polonium-210 were also released'.

One of the problems is that the number of extra deaths, if they occurred, would be very difficult to recognise in the general mortality rate. One thing is for certain, though: this was not 'the worst environmental disaster that Western Europe has known this century'.

---

1 TNA: PRO AB 7/1286. Paper on the operation of the Windscale piles.

2 TNA: PRO AB 7 18254. Incidents in the life of the Windscale Piles. AA Farmer and JM Hill.

3 TNA: PRO AB 86/78. Committee of Inquiry: Exhibit 54, paper WTSC/R 180, Wigner energy release, pile 1. GM Insch, July 1954.

4 TNA: PRO AB 38/51. Windscale incident, 10 October 1957. 'Report on the Accident at Windscale No. 1 Pile on 10th October, 1957.'

5 TNA: PRO AB 38/51. Windscale incident, 10 October 1957. Adapted from 'Report on the Accident at Windscale No. 1 Pile on 10th October 1957', Chapter II, 'Events Leading up to the Accident.'

6 TNA: PRO AB 86/22. Windscale Accident Inquiry: transcript of evidence; Tuesday, 22 October 1957.

7 TNA: PRO AB 86/25. Windscale Accident Inquiry; Report of the Inquiry, with papers and correspondence belonging to Sir William Penney. Letter from Dr MacLean to the Medical Research Council, 31 October 1957.

8 HJ Dunster, H Howells and WL Templeton (2007). 'District Surveys following the Windscale Incident, October 1957', *Journal of Radiological Protection*, 27, 217–230.

[9] D McGeoghegan, S Whaley, K Binks, M Gillies, K Thompson, and DM McElvenny (2010). 'Mortality and cancer registration experience of the Sellafield workers known to have been involved in the 1957 Windscale accident: 50 year follow-up', *Journal of Radiological Protection* 30(3), 407–403.

[10] Atomic Energy Office (1957). *Accident at Windscale No. 1 Pile on 10th October, 1957*, [White Paper] London: HMSO (Cmnd 302).

[11] *Ibid.*

[12] TNA: PRO AB 86/26. Windscale Accident Inquiry; papers and correspondence belonging to Sir William Penney. DER Hughes to JM Hill, 2 April 1958.

[13] TNA: PRO AB 38/51. Windscale incident, 10 October 1957. JM Hill to Sir Leonard Owen, 17 January 1958.

[14] Sir Alan Howard Cottrell (1919–2012) was a metallurgist and physicist. He worked at Harwell from 1955–1958. He later became Chief Scientific Advisor to the Government from 1971–1974. He was Master of Jesus College Cambridge from 1973–1986, and Vice Chancellor of the University from 1977–1979.

[15] TNA: PRO AB 86/26. Windscale Accident Inquiry; papers and correspondence belonging to Sir William Penney. H Kronberger to Sir William Penney, 25 April 1958.

[16] TNA: PRO AB 16/2702. HG Davey: History of Windscale: correspondence (extract from AB 16/2702).

[17] Atomic Energy Office (1957). *Accident at Windscale No. 1 Pile on 10th October, 1957*, [White Paper] London: HMSO (Cmnd 302).

[18] TNA: PRO AB 86/26. Windscale Accident Inquiry; papers and correspondence belonging to Sir William Penney.

[19] *Ibid.*

[20] *Ibid.*

[21] TNA: PRO HP 3/22. National Radiological Protection Board assessment of the radiological impact of the Windscale Reactor Fire, October 1957: the collective radiation dose received by the population; allegations regarding European contamination levels; question and answer briefs on the Windscale Fire.

[22] TNA: PRO AB 62/35. Incidents: Windscale pile 1: removal of pile stack filters. 'Visit of US Safety Group to Risley 2–3 Dec. 1957.'

[23] TNA: PRO AB 86/25. Windscale Accident Inquiry; Report of the Inquiry, with papers and correspondence belonging to Sir William Penney. Minutes of the 20th meeting of the AEA. 4 November 1957.

[24] TNA: PRO AB 86/25. Windscale Accident Inquiry; Report of the Inquiry, with papers and correspondence belonging to Sir William Penney.

[25] *Ibid.*

[26] TNA: PRO AB 38/35. Windscale Pile No 2: correspondence. 'Windscale Reactor No. 2 Situation Report.' RV Moore, 11 September 1958.

[27] TNA: PRO AB 62/46 Windscale Pile No 2: possible restart of pile 2 and final sealing. 'Comments on Fleck "Wigner Release" Working Party Report.' GB Greenough, 22 April 1958.

[28] TNA: PRO AB 38/172. Windscale incident. Dr. Kronberger's file.

[29] TNA: PRO AB 38/34. Windscale Pile No 2: correspondence. 'Release of Wigner Energy in Windscale Pile No. 2.' AH Cottrell, August 1958.

[30] TNA: PRO AB 38/38. Special materials. 'Notes on a Discussion of Tritium Production Held by Sir William Cook at Risley on Tuesday, 11th November, 1958.'

[31] TNA: PRO AB 62/71. Windscale piles: situation April 1961. TN Rutherford.

[32] TNA: PRO AB 44/114. Decommissioning and radioactive waste management operations (DRAWMOPS): Windscale Piles. 'Windscale Piles 1 and 2.' HK Hardy, 2 September 1980.

[33] TNA: PRO AB 38/2181. Windscale Nuclear Laboratories: decommissioning of Piles 1 and 2. 'Windscale Nuclear Power Development Laboratories.' HK Hardy. Original report 'The Windscale Piles — Situation April 1961.' TN Rutherford.

[34] J Urquhart (1983). 'Polonium: Windscale's most lethal legacy', *New Scientist* 97(1351), 873–875.

[35] RH Clarke (1983). 'Polonium Deaths', *New Scientist* 98(1355), 243.

[36] CR Hill (1983). 'Natural Polonium', *New Scientist* 98(1354), 178.

[37] TNA: PRO AB 6/2352. Windscale incident. 'Relative Hazards of Po210 and I131 in Windscale Accident.' WG Marley and NG Stewart, 6 November 1957.

[38] HJ Dunster, H Howells and WL Templeton (1958). 'District surveys following the Windscale incident, October 1957', in: *Proceedings of the Second Annual United Nations International Conference on the Peaceful Uses of Atomic Energy: Volume 18, Waste Treatment and Environmental Aspects of Atomic Energy,* Geneva: IAEA, pp. 296–308.

Chapter 7

The Fast Reactor

The fast reactor appeared very attractive to British scientists and engineers in the 1950s, partly because it seemed to offer something for nothing: it could, in theory, produce more fuel than it consumed. To understand why, we must revisit the meaning of three words: fissile, fissionable and fertile.

A fissile material is one whose nuclei are easily split by neutrons and can thus be used as part of a chain reaction. A fissionable material is one whose nuclei can be split only by very energetic neutrons, and it is difficult to make the material take part in a chain reaction. A fertile material is one that can be easily converted into a fissile material.

^{238}U is both fissionable and fertile. The nucleus can be split only with very energetic neutrons, of at least 1 MeV energy. When the ^{238}U nucleus is hit by a low energy neutron, the neutron is absorbed to form ^{239}U, which then decays to ^{239}Pu. This was the point of the Windscale piles.

A fast reactor is so called since the neutrons within the reactor have not been slowed down — thus they are 'fast' neutrons. A fast reactor does not need a moderator. The purpose of a moderator is to slow down the neutrons, and a reactor which uses a moderator is often called a 'thermal reactor'. In addition, the way in which the nucleus breaks apart varies with the speed of the neutrons, and more neutrons per fission are produced from fast neutrons compared with slow neutrons. More neutrons mean that fertile material can be converted to fissile material faster.

There are problems with the design of a fast reactor. The first is that the nuclear cross-section of uranium 235 — that is, the apparent size of the nucleus — appears to be smaller than a fast neutron compared with a slow one, and hence there needs to be more fissile material in the reactor. Unlike a thermal reactor, such as Calder Hall or the magnox reactors, a fast reactor cannot be built using natural uranium, but needs highly enriched uranium 235 or plutonium as fuels.

Since there is no moderator, the size of the core is very much reduced. A paper of 1953[1] made the following estimates for the core of a fast reactor:

Table 7.1. Estimations for the core of a fast reactor.

Mass of ^{235}U/kg	200	250	300	350
Mass of ^{238}U/kg	400	600	850	1100
Fraction of ^{235}U in fuel	0.33	0.29	0.26	0.24
Enrichment factor	46	41	36	24
Height/diameter of core/inches	17	19	21	22.5

In this example the core is taken as being a cylinder whose height is equal to its radius, so that something in the order of 50–100 MW of heat are being produced in a cylinder approximately 50 cm high and 50 cm wide — a volume of approximately 0.1 m^3 or 100 litres.

By comparison, the core of the Dounreay fast reactor (DFR) was 20.5 inches wide and 21 inches high and generated 60 MW of heat.[2] The core of the prototype fast reactor (PFR) core was 57 inches across and 36 inches high, generating 600 MW.[3] Removing this amount of heat, as can be imagined, leads to problems finding an effective coolant.

Water can be ruled out immediately, as the hydrogen atoms will act as a moderator, defeating the purpose of the reactor. Gas-cooling can be ruled out on the grounds that there was simply too much heat to be removed from a very small space. This leaves liquid metals, and here again the choice is limited. Lithium, with its low atomic mass, would also act as a moderator. Mercury, liquid at room temperature, has many disadvantages: low boiling point, low thermal conductivity and a large neutron cross-section. It was used in the experimental American Clementine reactor, but not since. Several Soviet submarines used a lead/bismuth alloy, but the mixture is corrosive, and bismuth is a neutron absorber, decaying to the highly active polonium 210 isotope.

Sodium is a possibility, as is the use of a sodium/potassium alloy (alloys have a lower melting point than their main constituent). The DFR used a sodium/potassium alloy and the later PFR used 1,500 tonnes of liquid sodium as coolant. Liquid sodium is not an easy material to work with and a very great deal of development work was needed.

As mentioned, one of the major attractions of a fast reactor was that it seemed capable of generating more fuel than it consumed, and the 1953 paper set out the arithmetic behind this as follows:

Table 7.2. Number of neutrons produced per fissile atom destroyed.

	Uranium 233	Uranium 235	Plutonium 239
Fast fission	2.60	2.35	2.95
Thermal fission	2.35	2.05	1.95

(These numbers are only averages in the sense that the nucleus can split in many different ways, but to take plutonium as an example, the average number of neutrons produced from the fission of 1,000 atoms of ^{239}Pu is 295.)

Thus the fast fission of plutonium produces the most neutrons, making it the best candidate for the fuel in a fast reactor, particularly if the reactor is to be used to 'breed' more fuel. In 1953, adequate supplies of plutonium seemed to be some way in the future, so the calculations were carried out assuming ^{235}U was the fuel.

In the proposed reactor, the fissile uranium 235 atoms are destroyed and plutonium produced by the capture of neutrons in uranium 238 (^{238}U can be split by fast neutrons but not by slow ones, so there will be some extra neutrons produced from ^{238}U fission). The paper went on to outline what it called a 'neutron balance sheet'.

> This can be drawn up to account for the neutrons produced when 100 atoms of uranium 235 are destroyed (93 by fission and seven by capture to produce uranium 236). At the same time about six atoms of uranium 238 undergo fission. The balance should then read:

Credit		Debit	
By fission of U235:	233	To fission of U235:	93
By fission of U238:	15	To produce U236:	7
		To fission of uranium 238:	6
Total:	248	Total:	106
Balance in hand:	142		

> In order to replace the 100 uranium 235 atoms destroyed, it will be necessary to allocate 100 neutrons on the balance of 142 neutrons for the production of plutonium 239... This leaves a balance of 42 neutrons out of which one must allow for capture in structural materials in the core, blanket, and shield. The remaining neutrons are then available for capture in uranium 238...

It was this which made the fast reactor so attractive, not only in the early 1950s, but later in the power programme. By the mid-1960s, reprocessing of the magnox fuel meant that there was an excess of plutonium. Part of the thinking in later years was that the thermal reactors could produce plutonium which could be burned in fast reactors, making the two complementary.

Safety

The worst accident which one could envisage happening to a fast reactor arises from the combination of two effects. The first is the small thermal capacity of the reactor core and the high rates of heat removal which are necessary. This means that if the coolant flow is interrupted the fuel may melt, even if the nuclear reaction is stopped, because of the heat generated by the fission products which are formed during operation. The second effect is that if the fuel melts, then the channels through which the coolant flows may well become blocked.

Figure 7.1. Dounreay: The PFR is housed in the building by the shore; the DFR dome can be seen in the distance. (Image courtesy of NDA and copyright NDA.)

Thus the reactor core must be designed in such a way that if it melts it cannot agglomerate into a closely packed lump. This is a fundamental design requirement, but it still leaves the possibility of an accident involving the melting of fuel, with probably a sodium fire at the same time. Since this could mean the release of the fission products or radioactive sodium into the atmosphere, some form of containment might well be necessary, which is why the DFR was built within a sphere: the sphere was intended to contain up to 99% of any radioactivity which might escape from the reactor core during an accident.

One advantage of the large volume of sodium in the primary circuit is that it is able to absorb the residual heat within the reactor when it is shut down with only a slow rise in temperature. This means that the reactor can cope with many of the common faults, such as loss of power supplies, which may have temporarily interrupted the circulation of coolant.

A further advantage of the system is that the sodium is not pressurised, unlike the carbon dioxide in the gas reactors or water in the various water-cooled reactors. This reduces the possibility of leaks considerably, and makes the system safer when there is a leak.

ZEPHYR, ZEUS and ZEBRA

The physics and engineering of fast reactors would provide a considerable challenge. Before full-scale designs could be attempted, a great deal of work was needed. Much of this was done using zero-energy reactor experiments — hence the ZE-, for zero-energy, in the names of the reactor experiments. They could be used to study the physics of the design without generating significant quantities of heat.

ZEPHYR was the first of these reactors.[4] A contemporary press release describes it as follows:

> ZEPHYR, the zero energy fast reactor at Harwell, became critical for the first time on February 5, 1954. This is the first fast reactor to be built in the United Kingdom. The objects of ZEPHYR are to obtain operating experience with a fast reactor and to gain information (for example about control systems, nuclear constants and materials and methods of reactor construction) which can only be obtained by the actual operation of a reactor. This information will be of major importance to the design work on an experimental power producing fast breeder reactor which is being undertaken jointly by Harwell and Risley.
>
> The fast reactor has characteristics which make it likely that most of the uranium atoms in natural uranium can be consumed by the process known as breeding. Consequently, if this type of system can be developed a nuclear energy electricity generating system should operate with a much smaller supply of fuel than in the case of natural uranium or slightly enriched uranium thermal fission reactors. The advantages of the fast reactor are therefore bound up with the cost and availability of uranium ores.
>
> Reactors previously built and now in use in Britain — two at Harwell and two at Sellafield — use uranium rods enclosed in graphite which acts as a moderator to slow down neutrons produced by fission. Plutonium is created by such piles and those at Sellafield were built for this purpose, but the principle of breeding is to create more fissile material than is consumed.

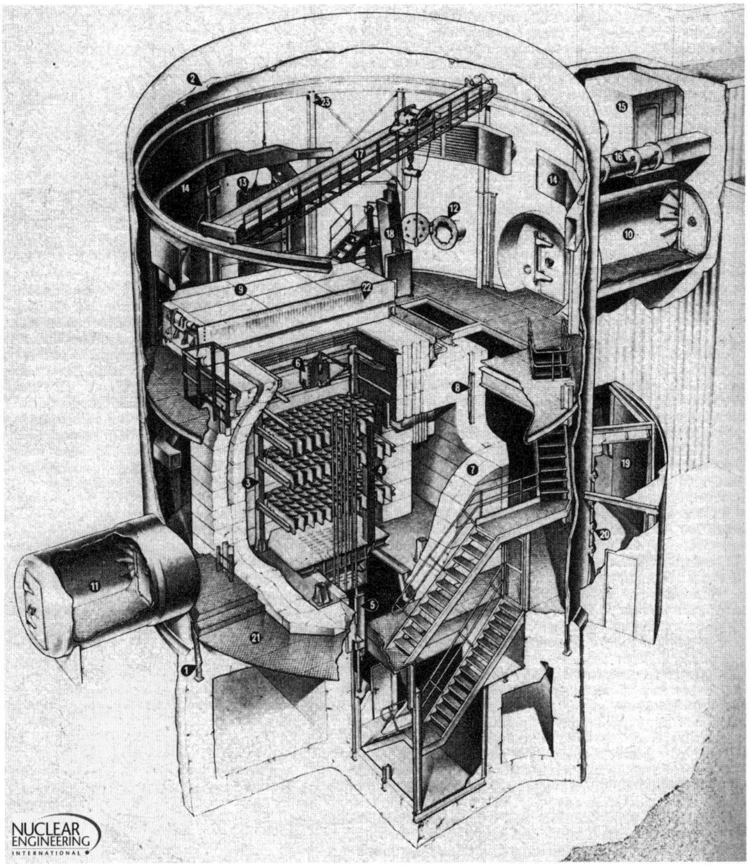

Figure 7.2. ZEBRA was built at Winfrith to test out various different core configurations. It illustrates how much effort was put into research and prototype reactors.

> The construction of a fast reactor requires pure, or nearly pure, fissile material, so the construction of ZEPHYR could not be undertaken until this material was available. The fuel used is, in fact, plutonium enclosed in a metal can. The core of a fast reactor, i.e. the central portion containing the fuel elements, is very small and in the case of ZEPHYR only about the size of a top hat. The core is surrounded by a more massive envelope or blanket of uranium which either reflects back any neutrons escaping from the core or absorbs them so as to produce fresh plutonium. In this way very few neutrons are wasted.
>
> The designation zero energy means that the reactor is to be operated at a very low power level so that it will not get highly radioactive and will not require cooling. As a result it should be possible to make modifications to the reactor from time to time in the light of experience which has been gained.[5]

The core, which the press release describes as being ‘the size of a top hat’ was actually a cylinder 15 cm long and 13 cm in diameter.

ZEPHYR was a considerable success in that it managed to demonstrate a breeding factor of two — that is, two plutonium nuclei were created for every one destroyed. Despite its success, extrapolating from ZEPHYR to a full-sized 100 MW reactor would have been a step too far, and so a second reactor, ZEUS, was designed to simulate as closely as practicable the size and composition of the proposed fast reactor to be built at Dounreay (the DFR). It was an important source of reactor physics information for the DFR design and, later, for use in the early operation of DFR.

The successor to ZEUS was ZEBRA (zero-energy breeder reactor assembly), which was built at Winfrith. The core of ZEBRA was made of many small pieces which could be taken apart and reassembled to test out new designs. ZEBRA could use either highly enriched uranium or plutonium in its core.[6]

Dounreay Fast Reactor

Hinton was one of the chief proponents of the fast reactor. It is noticeable that in a 1950s film produced by the AEA promoting Calder Hall,[7] there is a short piece near the end when Hinton talks to the camera. He dismisses Calder Hall (the subject of the film!) as being like 'an old slow speed reciprocating steam engine' compared with a fast reactor which he likens to a modern gas turbine.

Although Risley was already developing the gas-cooled design called PIPPA, Hinton pushed ahead with work on the proposed fast reactor. A Fast Reactor Design Committee (FRDC) was set up as early as October 1951, but initial progress was slow, as it took time to refine the ideas as regarding coolant and safety, and much of the underlying nuclear physics was still uncertain.

Not only was the physics uncertain, but so was much of the technology. Liquid metal-cooling was an entirely new area, and testing a complete sodium loop in a research reactor would take a minimum of perhaps two years. Instead, the reactor itself would be the test bed for all the new technology, and it was intended that as many parts of the reactor as possible could be replaced if necessary.

The coolant chosen was a sodium/potassium mixture. Pure sodium melts at 98°C and pure potassium at 64°C. Mixtures always melt at a lower temperature than their main constituents. The mixture with the lowest melting point is called a eutectic, and for sodium/potassium, this is 22% sodium and 78% potassium with a melting point of −12°C. An alloy of 70% sodium and 30% potassium was chosen which had a freezing point of only 40°C. Although the intention was to use pure sodium in commercial fast reactors, this experimental reactor might well have been running at very low power ratings for considerable periods; hence the decision to use the alloy with its lower freezing point.

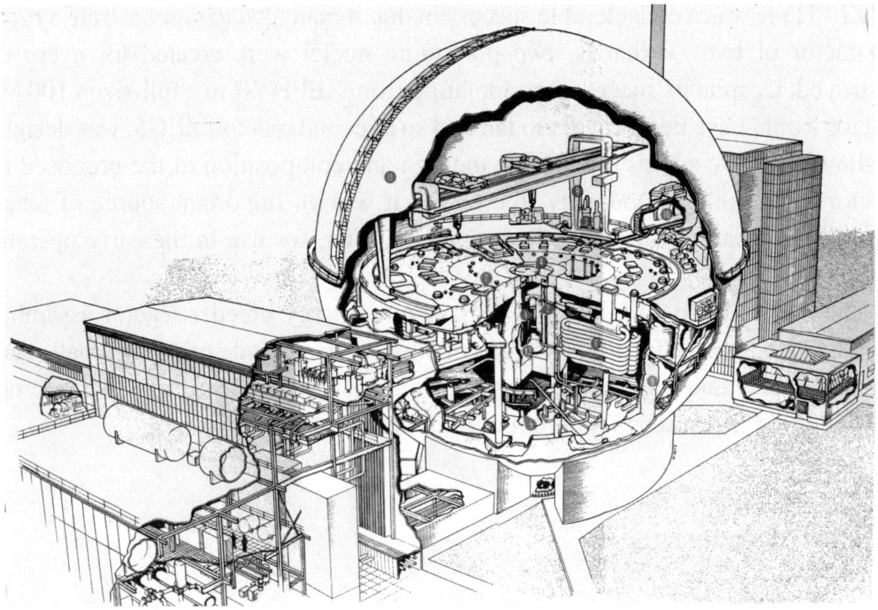

Figure 7.3. A cutaway view of the Dounreay fast reactor (DFR).

There were two coolant circuits: the primary circuit took heat directly from the core, and passed it to a secondary circuit which then transferred the heat to the steam. This was to prevent radioactivity escaping from the core. The first circuit contained radioactive liquid metal and therefore was contained entirely within the reactor vault. The second circuit, which contained 64 tons of liquid metal, was protected from neutron bombardment by the graphite shielding of the reactor. This circuit extracted the heat from the primary coolant and then brought it out through the reactor vault to the secondary heat exchangers.

The secondary circuit was then used to heat the steam for the turbines. One major problem was the NaK/steam heat exchanger. In the gas-cooled reactors, the hot gas flowed through pipes which ran through the boilers. This had obvious problems for a sodium-cooled system. Water and sodium/potassium react together very violently even at room temperature, and one of the products is hydrogen, which can form an explosive mixture with air, so any arrangement where the two could mix as a result of a leak had to be avoided. A different system had to be devised:

> The scheme chosen used tubes carrying sodium and, separately, tubes carrying water or steam. Heat was transferred between the tubes via a matrix of close packed 3 mm thick copper washers with holes to carry the tubes. A leak from either a sodium tube or a water/steam tube would be to air and readily detectable and a sodium-water reaction would not be a credible accident... In the event,

> the expensive choice was justified. The plant suffered a number of water-side leaks and one liquid metal leak, all of which would have been more serious had a conventional shell and tube design been chosen.[8]

Twenty four separate cooling circuits were used to extract the 60 MW of heat from the core: the pumps for the liquid metal coolant were electromagnetic and so had no moving parts. A further design decision was to avoid any valves in the system: this had implications for the design since one-way valves would not be available, which might lead to flow reversal in a circuit where the pump had failed.

Preventing a coolant accident was an important consideration. The 24 cooling circuits were grouped into 12 pairs, which were completely independent of each other. A failure of one circuit would not then lead to a serious incident. In addition, the primary circuit vessel was surrounded with a leak jacket, and there was sufficient NaK coolant in the circuit to ensure that if it sprang a leak and emptied into the jacket, the core would still remain submerged. Since fast reactors were a new technology, a conservative approach was taken to much of the design of features such as the cooling system.

There were no control rods in the reactor, but instead there were 12 groups of ten fuel elements which could be moved in or out of the core. Lifting them up into the core increased the reactivity. This was done with a magnetic clutch, so that no external connections were needed. In addition, if the electricity supply to the reactor failed, then the rods would fall back out of the reactor, shutting it down. There were also three rods containing boron-10 which could be used as a back-up.

The fuel elements were unusual in that they consisted of hollow cylinders, which were fabricated as a form of sandwich: on the outside was niobium metal and on the inside vanadium metal, with the uranium sandwiched between the two. The reasoning behind this was that if there were a catastrophic loss of coolant, the vanadium would fail first, meaning that the molten uranium could flow down inside the outer niobium tube. Making the cylinder hollow improved the head transfer as the coolant could flow down the middle of the tube as well as the outside.

Removing fuel elements from the reactor also posed problems. The nitrogen gas which was used as a blanket gas above the coolant was highly radioactive (being contaminated with fission products) and had to be prevented from escaping. The fuel elements themselves had been immersed in a radioactive NaK coolant and after removal were sealed into a stainless steel lead lined can. The lead lining would melt due to the residual heat of the element and alloy with any sodium. The canned element was then transported in a transit flask through the airlock and immersed in a molten lead bath to dissolve any traces of sodium from the outside of the can and to ensure the lead inside had melted. The can was then immersed in a cooling pond for 120 days before being processed.

The reactor was housed in a gigantic pressure vessel, which, together with the Windscale AGR dome, became one of the iconic figures of the British nuclear programme. The reactor sphere was 135 feet in diameter and was constructed from sections of mild steel plate varying in thickness between 1 and $1^7/_8$ inch thickness, the steel plate being cold pressed hydraulically into shape before being welded. The sphere had a surface area of about 1.5 acres (around 6,000 m^3) and weighed over 1,500 tons. The total length of the welded seam was over two miles.

> The sphere serves two purposes. Firstly it will localise the spread of fission products formed during reactor operation, should they be accidentally released within the sphere. Secondly it has been designed to withstand any pressure variations that might occur as a result of a liquid metal fire within the sphere. The reactor sphere is in fact one of the largest pressure vessels ever built.
>
> Access to the sphere is through an airlock 40 feet long and 16 feet in diameter with airtight doors at each end. The small hand operated emergency airlock is fitted diametrically opposite the main one to allow exit to the Heat Exchanger Building should any failure of the main doors occur.[9]

Figure 7.4. The DFR dome.

Work at the site started in March 1955, and most of the construction work on the establishment had been completed by the end of 1958. It cost around £28.5 million to build, using a workforce of around 3,000 men, half of them coming from the local area, and produced an electrical output of around 14 MW, some of which could be exported to the Scottish grid. The heat output was 60 MW, and the amount of highly enriched uranium available at the time was an important factor in deciding the size of the reactor core.

The reactor turned out to be comparatively easy to control, with no surprises, partly as a result of the preliminary work done with the test reactors, but soon after operation had been begun, two major problems emerged.

> During the initial physics experiments in November 1959, unpredicted reactivity changes were noticed when the coolant flow rate was varied. Levels in some of the liquid metal coolant expansion tanks rose higher than expected. A resistivity meter, installed in a bypass circuit indicated the presence of nitrogen blanket gas in the coolant.
>
> Determination of the cause of entrainment was not assisted by the instrumentation which was then available. Preliminary hydraulic calculations showed that there was a possibility that the coolant level was being lowered by vortexing in the vessel to a point just below the shields. An introscope was fitted over the core centre and it was seen that, although a swirl did exist, the level in fact rose by over 2 feet. This level rise could not be accounted for hydraulically and a large part of it was obviously due to an accumulation of blanket gas in the vessel.[10]

Major modifications had to be carried out to prevent the blanket gas being caught up into the coolant. In early 1961, further tests were carried out to see whether entrainment was occurring elsewhere.

> It was soon established that entrainment was also occurring by way of tubes in parallel with the reactor core. There were 18 such tubes, there being the 12 control unit mechanism tubes and which serve to guide thermocouples to locations beneath the core and breeder.
>
> The modifications to prevent these tubes acting as sources of gas entrainment occupied a period from March to September 1961. The relatively simple operations on the thermocouple tubes were complicated by the necessity for remote operations in an inert atmosphere, and the control unit modifications were prolonged because each of the 12 units had to be removed and decontaminated before work could begin on it and the shielding arrangement of the vessel top restricted work to one unit at the time. The actual modifications were also rather complex and involved a certain amount of development work.[11]

The second problem involved impurities that built up in the sodium metal, blocking some of the pipes:

> Sodium is an extremely reactive metal and on exposure to the atmosphere very readily forms compounds, the two of concern being the oxide and the hydride which are only soluble in sodium to a limited extent. Their formation in the primary coolant circuit has two disadvantages: they react with fuel and canning materials and they collect as solids, ultimately causing blockages in the cooler parts and at restrictions. This was realised at the design stage and provision was made for by-pass circuits incorporating cold traps to remove impurity, making use of the lower solubility of sodium oxide and hydride in sodium at lower temperatures.

A fraction of coolant in the return pipe from the heat exchanger to the reactor is diverted into the cold trap, entering at about 200°C, and passes through a heat exchanger. The liquid metal is cooled and some of the oxide precipitates, being collected on ring packing in the trap. After filtering the purified coolant is heated in the regenerative heat exchanger and returns to the main circuit. During operation of the reactor a number of these by-pass circuits became blocked and the traps were unable to obtain the required degree of purity. When the reactor was shut down in December 1961 it was decided to carry out a major clean-up of the whole coolant circuit.

The clean-up cycle consisted of heating the coolant in the reactor to about 250°C by electrical heaters specially installed, so that it would dissolve the deposited impurities, transfer it to a dump tank outside the reactor, where it was cooled to about 80°C and deposited much of the dissolved impurity. After filtering, the coolant was returned to the reactor to repeat the cycle. 12 cycles where needed to reduce the impurity to an acceptable level, taking three months in all.[12]

The Commercial Fast Reactor

Soon after the completion of the DFR, the Consortia (Atomic Power Projects, The Nuclear Power Group, and the United Power Company Limited) made a study of the possibilities of a commercial fast reactor (CFR), and in June 1963, produced a

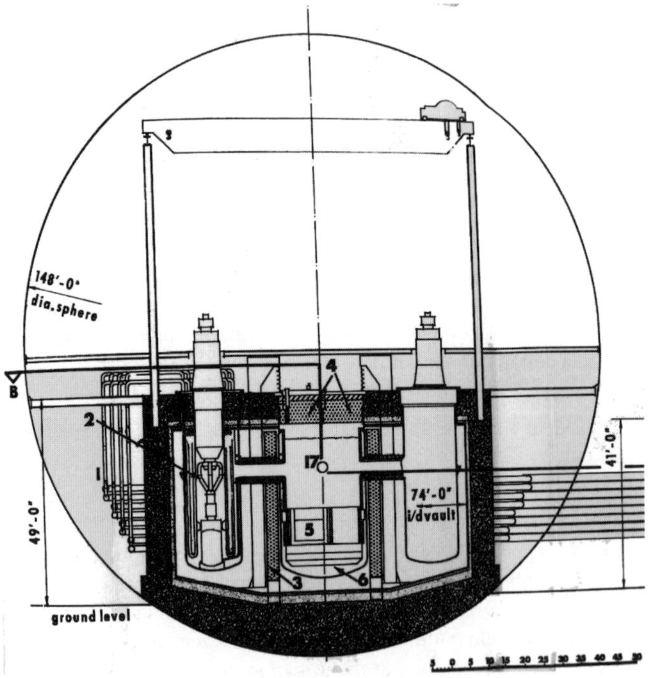

Figure 7.5. A sketch of a possible commercial fast reactor (CFR).

report[13] for the AEA's Reactor Policy Committee. In the summary, it noted that there are 'major uncertainties which must be resolved before sanction for the prototype is sought'. If a prototype was given the go-ahead and was successful, then it would be possible for the first civil reactor to be on power by 1986.

BL Goodlet, the Deputy Chief Engineer at Harwell, when describing the origins of PIPPA and Calder Hall, said of Hinton's enthusiasm in 1951 for the fast reactor that 'Personally I thought that the engineering problems of the FBR [fast breeder reactor] were at the moment insoluble and was glad to see them off our plate'.[14] Given that the prediction for the first operational CFR was the mid-1980s, Goodlet's comment was remarkably accurate.

The Consortia thought that the capital cost of a fast reactor would be roughly comparable with that of the AGR and the SGHWR. As to fuel costs, plutonium was thought to be a much more economical proposition than enriched uranium. The plutonium would come from the magnox reactors, and the cost of extracting it from the spent fuel was estimated at around £1/gram of plutonium.

This was followed by a further study by the consortia, assisted by the AEA and with the involvement of the CEGB. A working party was set up in October 1963 and met at approximately monthly intervals. The purpose was to design and give estimated costs for a $2 \times 1,000$ MW(E) civil fast reactor station. This would act as a reference design.[15] The design was being constantly revisited: a detailed report was produced by The Nuclear Power Group in January 1973, with a further status report in October 1974.[16] None of these would lead to a successful commercial design.

The Prototype Fast Reactor

In February 1966, the go-ahead was given to construct a prototype fast power reactor at Dounreay which was intended to be an intermediate step between the experimental fast reactor which had already been built and a fully-fledged large commercial fast reactor.[17] It had a design output of 250 MW (E) and was intended to demonstrate the operating characteristics of much larger stations design to produce electrical power in excess of 1,000 MW. It was thought that commercial fast reactors would be more economical since their capital costs would not be higher than those of other reactors, but their fuel costs would be much lower since they could convert about 75% of the total energy available compared with about 2% from the likes of the gas-cooled reactors. They would also be able to use the stocks of plutonium which would be produced by the gas-cooled reactors.[18]

The design of the PFR was finalised after extensive studies of future commercial designs, such as the one described above. The design of the core of the reactor was dictated by the need to test designs of fuel suitable for the commercial fast reactor, and this in turn fixed the core height of the PFR and the size of the fuel sub-assembly. There was also the need to gain operating experience with engineering components on a scale that could be extrapolated with reasonable confidence to the larger commercial scale. The output chosen, 250 MW(E), was judged to be the smallest that could reasonably meet these requirements.[19]

The DFR used metallic uranium as the fuel, but this would not have been suitable for commercial stations which ran at higher temperatures and greater burn up rates. Instead, a mixture of uranium oxide and plutonium oxides would be used, giving rise to a fuel known as MOX, for Mixed OXide. The choice of mixed oxide fuel with its relatively low thermal conductivity meant that the basic fuel element had to be a pin smaller in diameter than that of the metallic pins used in the DFR. A sealed pin was used, which would retain all the fission product gases released from the fuel in a plenum; the alternative being a vented pin which would release the gases into the reactor but which would avoid the risk of creep rupture due to build-up of internal pressure.

Another deliberate design decision was to produce steam at the pressures and temperatures (516–566°C) used in coal or oil-fired stations. This meant that the electricity generating side of the plant would be a standard unit, but it also meant that fuel element temperatures would be high: 650°C or so, hence the need for an oxide fuel. Sodium has a boiling point of 880°C, which made it an ideal coolant.

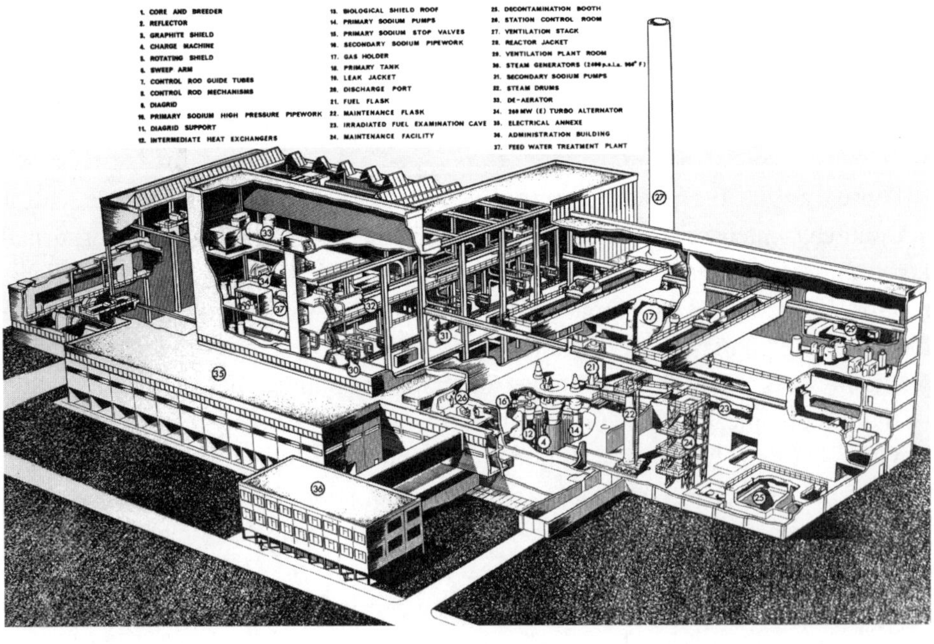

Figure 7.6. A cutaway view of the prototype fast reactor (PFR).

Construction was nearly complete by the early summer of 1973, and the commissioning stage had begun. After the primary circuit was sealed off, it was pre-heated with hot argon and filled with sodium during August. The primary circuit was then tested with a core of dummy fuel subassemblies and the primary pumps were run progressively up to full speed.

Fuel loading started in January 1974 and PFR was first taken critical on 3 March 1974. During the rest of 1974, the reactor was operated at low power levels while the steam circuits were being commissioned. The PFR turbine was commissioned with steam from the steam generating units early in 1975, and was first synchronised with the grid on 2 February 1975.

The development of a commercial reactor depended crucially on the performance of the prototype. The DFR had been a demonstrator to see whether the technology

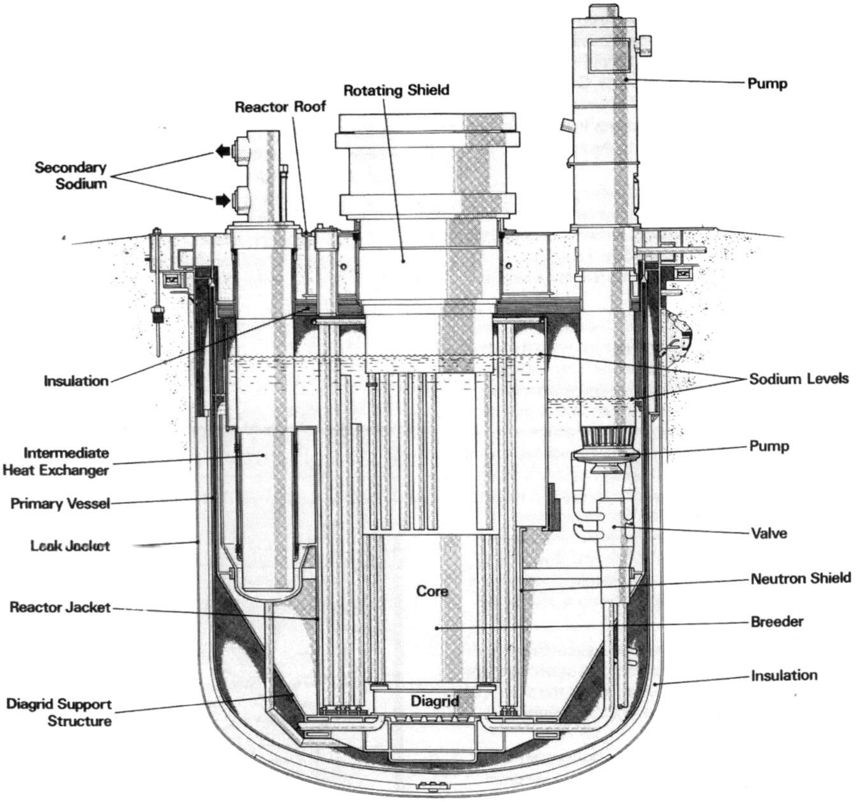

Figure 7.7. The core of the PFR. This was sunk into the ground in case of a sodium leakage. There was sufficient spare volume to prevent any leakiing out onto the ground outside. The rotating shield could be moved aside for refuelling. The sodium pump is on the right. On the left is the sodium heat exchanger. Liquid sodium in the secondary circuit was then pumped out to boil water for the steam for the turbines.

Table 7.3. Load factor for the PFR[20] over several years.

	Annual (%)	Cumulative
1978	14.7	—
1979	9.9	12.3
1980	No data	—
1981	10.5	11.6
1982	6.0	10.3
1983	8.0	9.8
1984	20.3	12.0
1985	40.8	16.9
1986	43.4	20.6
1987	41.1	23.0
1988	29.7	23.8
1989	47.9	26.2
1990	24.5	26.1
1991	35.7	26.9

would work. The PFR was supposed to be the final step before full commercial exploitation. By their very nature, prototypes will need modification. This means they will have to be shut down periodically while those modifications are being made. Thus their load factors — the ratio of the energy produced to the total energy possible — will not be as high as with a commercial station.

These figures are not impressive. Being a prototype, it could be expected that the reactor would be shut down from time to time for inspection and modification, and operating a new design would also have an impact on the load factor, but with time and experience this should improve. The load factor never even reached 50%, the highest being just over 40% ten years after the reactor had first been connected to the grid, and the technology was obviously far from being mature from a commercial point of view.

The fast reactor was still being mentioned as being a possible part of the power programme through the 1970s, but it was becoming clear that hopes for a successful commercial design were still some way into the future. It was also becoming extremely expensive — in 1988, the annual bill had reached £105 million. This was giving the government second thoughts, as the following announcement on 21 July 1988, in the House of Commons by Cecil Parkinson, the Secretary of State for Energy makes clear:

> The programme involves the major facilities at Dounreay in Caithness — the prototype fast reactor, known as the PFR, which started operation in 1974...
>
> In the current financial year, net expenditure on the programme is planned at £105 million, of which the CEGB is contributing £28 million. Of that total, some £50 million represents the net cost of the Dounreay operations.

Figure 7.8. The PFR control room.

> The Government have carried out a review of the programme in the light of the expectation that commercial deployment of fast reactors in the United Kingdom will not now be required for 30 to 40 years. Our overall aim in the review has been to retain a position in the technology for the United Kingdom at economic cost. . . .
>
> We recognise that there is continuing benefit to be secured from operation of the prototype fast reactor. We have therefore decided to fund the reactor until the end of the financial year 1993–94. This will enable operating experience to accumulate for a further five years. We have also decided to fund the reprocessing plant at Dounreay until 1996–97, to process spent fuel from the reactor. Our decisions will ensure continuing and substantial employment at Dounreay into the late 1990s.
>
> In addition to the work at Dounreay, we have decided to maintain a core programme of fast reactor research and development of £10 million a year. The present research programme will be phased down to that level over the next 18 months . . . Moving to the core programme could mean the loss of over 1,500 jobs over the next two to three years at sites other than Dounreay.

By 1988, construction of Sizewell B had already begun. Not only were no commercial fast reactors ever built; no further power reactors were ever built in the UK after Sizewell. The PFR was finally closed in March 1994.

---

[1] TNA: PRO AB 15/3451. Nuclear design of fast reactors. TM Fry and CA Rennie.

[2] TNA PRO AB 17/65. Dounreay Fast Reactor and Associated Plant.

[3] TNA: PRO AB 17/69. Prototype Fast Reactor.

[4] TNA: PRO AB 6/1088. Zero energy reactors: ZEPHYR programme.

[5] TNA: PRO AB 16/908. Reactor programme: policy pre Authority.

[6] TNA: PRO AB 17/302. Reactors UK. See also TNA: PRO AB 6/2306. Zero energy reactor ZEBRA.

[7] UKAEA: 'Calder Hall. Report to Geneva upon progress at Britain's first Atomic Power Station July 1955.'

[8] Conception and design history of DFR.

[9] TNA: PRO AB 17/63. The Fast Reactor (Revised Edition).

[10] TNA: PRO AB 17/65. Dounreay Fast Reactor and Associated Plant.

[11] *Ibid.*

[12] *Ibid.*

[13] TNA: PRO AB 41/579. Committee on the Authority's Reactor Programme: papers and reports. 'Report On Consortia Appraisal Of The Fast Reactor For The Attention Of Members Of The Reactor Policy Committee June 1963.'

[14] TNA: PRO AB 6/2563. Calder Hall book; source material.

[15] TNA: PRO AB 48/795. Commercial Fast Reactor (CFR).

[16] TNA: PRO AB 43/371. The Nuclear Power Group: Commercial Fast Reactor (CFR) design work. 'CFR 1 Design Status Report October 1974.'

[17] TNA: PRO AB 6/2313. Prototype Fast Reactor. Press release: 'New Fast Reactor Approved.' 9 February 1966.

[18] TNA: PRO AB 17/68. Dounreay.

[19] TNA: PRO AB 17/219. Fast Reactors in Britain.

[20] Data from the Power Reactor Information System (PRIS) maintained by the International Atomic Energy Authority (IAEA) and available at <http://www.iaea.org/PRIS>.

Chapter 8

PIPPA and Calder Hall

In retrospect, the move from the air-cooled piles of Harwell and Windscale to the gas-cooled reactor design that would become Calder Hall seems obvious. In reality, the gas-cooled reactor nearly fell victim to internal politics within the Atomic Energy Department (as it then was). At the end of the 1940s, there was a variety of competing designs for power reactors and the one that had the greatest appeal to the majority of the design engineers — including, crucially, Hinton — was the fast reactor. There were others who felt that the problems of the fast reactor would be too difficult to solve in the short or medium term (in the event, only two fast reactors were built, one experimental and the other a prototype), and that a gas-cooled reactor offered the quickest route to a working power design to produce electricity, even if the design was not the most elegant possible from either the engineering or the nuclear point of view. The two men who led the effort on the gas-cooled reactor were BL Goodlet and RV Moore. Goodlet later described how the design came to be accepted, and the following paragraphs are based on his account.[1]

The idea of getting useful power from a reactor using only natural uranium had been under consideration since the late 1940s. A report had been commissioned from the Parolle Company of Newcastle upon Tyne, who manufactured turbines and electrical generators for power stations. This was a study of the steam plant for a nuclear power station assuming that there was hot gas coming from the reactor at a temperature of 350 °C. The reactor itself was treated as a 'black box' — in other words, there was no attempt to produce any specific reactor design.[2]

The next step was to consider how the conditions in the report could be met, and the starting point was that the pile would be graphite-moderated and gas-cooled since that was the type of pile which was best known in Britain at the time. Indeed, there was little other option. If it were not a fast reactor, it would need a moderator of some kind. Heavy water was expensive and difficult to obtain. Using light water was a possibility, but this would need some enrichment of the uranium (and indeed this option was studied extensively, only to be later dropped). Hence graphite seemed the only option as a moderator. At this stage, the project had no priority, with only four people working on the design.

In June 1951, Goodlet, who was one of those working on the design, went to a meeting at Risley at which both Cockcroft and Hinton were present, and where Hinton said that he proposed to study the design of a fast reactor. Goodlet was doubtful as to the practicality of a fast reactor and expressed his doubts on the subject to Hinton. He later wrote that 'Personally I felt that the engineering problems of the FBR [fast breeder reactor] were at the moment insoluble and was glad to see them off our plate'.[3]

Hinton pressed on with the fast reactor, and began expressing his opposition to the natural uranium project on the grounds that it would be a simple waste of effort. Goodlet and Moore wrote a paper for the 1951 Harwell Power Conference[4] in which, as Goodlet put it, 'stated difficulties in the hope of eliciting suggestions for solving them'. Goodlet goes on to say,

> This paper had a very bad reception. We were accused of undue pessimism and the whole project was belittled as being retrograde and a wasteful diversion of effort. We were strongly urged to stop work on the scheme and only the Director's "casting vote" saved the project from the dustbin.

In particular, the reactor was criticised by Hinton and others at Risley as being low-rated, large and clumsy. It seemed that the gas-cooled reactor would be dropped from the power programme for 1952.

Two improvements made the design much more practicable: the first was the production of pure high-density graphite which had a much lower neutron capture, and the other was to use magnesium as the canning material.[5] Graphite of high-density and low capture cross-section plus magnesium cans would make a radical change in the picture. A critical size for the reactor of about 18 feet was suggested. To prevent the project been squeezed out of the reactor programme, Goodlet put up a proposal for building a nuclear power plant at Harwell to supply the establishment's electricity load plus waste heat. This idea appealed to Cockcroft and the idea was given the go-ahead.

Unfortunately, it became clear that the critical size calculations on which the project was based were in error and that either the uranium would need enriching or the diameter of the pressure vessel would have to be increased by ten feet. Increasing the size of the pile would make the calculations more difficult, but would be more worthwhile than having to resort to enrichment.

By this time, engineers from Parsons and the BEA (British Electrical Authority) had joined the team at Harwell. By September 1952, it was becoming quite clear that the engineering difficulties associated with the breeder reactor were proving unsolvable without a good deal more preliminary research, and the basic ideas and information necessary for a practical design were not available. The postponement of the fast breeder meant the needs for power designs were becoming more acute.

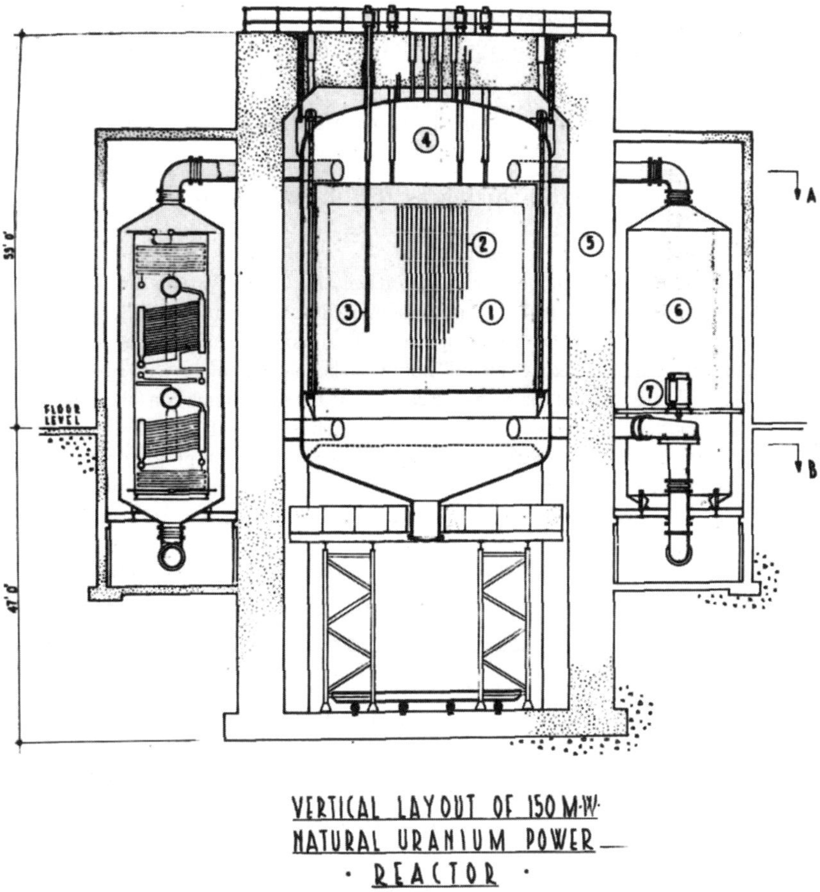

Figure 8.1. Goodlet's 1951 sketch for a carbon dioxide cooled natural uranium reactor. The cylinders either side are the heat exchangers, where steam would be generated.

The Military Requirement

In the meantime, another problem was also becoming more serious: the increased requirement for plutonium for military purposes. The existing piles were not sufficient. One option was to restart work on the third pile, which had been abandoned in 1950, but another possibility seemed to be to combine the design for the new power reactor with a production reactor. This would be the origin of PIPPA and, by extension, Calder Hall.

The two Windscale piles had been designed to produce 90 kg of plutonium a year between them, although in reality production was somewhat less. This was not enough for the military. As early as December 1948, 'The Chiefs of Staff have asked for at least 200 atomic bombs by the beginning of 1957'.[6] (The paper also noted that

90 kg of plutonium was 'equivalent to 15 bombs'. This gives a figure of 6 kg per bomb.) If the piles started producing plutonium in 1952, then it would take 13 or 14 years to produce enough for 200 bombs — although the figure of 200 seems to be somewhat arbitrary. Certainly, it bore little resemblance to the size of the bomber force.

There was an alternative, which was to use what were described as 'mixed bombs':

> The 'mixed' bomb containing both plutonium and U.235. Various proportions could be used but the case of a bomb containing Plutonium mixed with 1.35 times its weight of U.235 has been investigated in detail and we shall assume that this proportion would be used. A "mixed" bomb can be made identical with a bomb of the Nagasaki type except for the fissile charge and the same bomb can take either a charge of pure plutonium or a mixed charge, which is larger. The explosive effect of the mixed bomb is also about the same as that of the pure plutonium bomb. Provided U.235 were available we could make from a given quantity of plutonium 1.7 times as many bombs as we could from plutonium alone.[7]

This option would become available once the high enrichment section of the gaseous diffusion plant at Capenhurst had come into full-scale production. Most of the highly enriched ^{235}U was used in high yield nuclear weapons – in particular, the Orange Herald and Green Grass warheads.

Four years later, the military were still insistent that more plutonium was needed:

> In July 1952 the Chiefs of Staff stated that they wished the plutonium output to be doubled within a period of three years to meet strategic requirements. The only way in which this requirement could be met within this time limit was by the construction of "Chinese copies" of the Windscale piles. The time which would be required for design work etc for the construction of other types would necessarily involve delay. It was considered, however, that it was undesirable to devote effort to repetition work and if the Chiefs of Staff could accept a longer period before the additional plutonium becomes available it would, it was hoped, be possible to construct piles which, whilst producing the required quantity of plutonium, would also produce useful electric power. The Chiefs of Staff were accordingly informed of the situation and asked to accept a longer period before the additional plutonium became available. They agreed that a period of four years would be acceptable.
>
> Design studies were accordingly immediately commenced on a natural uranium reactor enclosed in a pressure shell, the heat produced being transferred by a gas under pressure through a heat exchanger to a conventional electric power generator.[8]

This new design was to be named PIPPA, a rather forced acronym of pressurised pile producing industrial power and plutonium.

> In the course of the design studies it appeared, however, that the greater heat at which these piles would operate would produce plutonium of a quality which by itself would not be suitable for weapon manufacture, but which, mixed with the plutonium from the Windscale piles, would be satisfactory.

There is some oversimplification here: it is not the 'greater heat' that was the problem, but the extra irradiation resulting from higher activity and a longer period between replacing the fuel elements.

> In the early stages of development it was thought that the maximum quantity of PIPPA plutonium which could be mixed with the Windscale plutonium would be the amount derived from one pile. It was accordingly decided that at that stage we should proceed immediately with the construction of one PIPPA and that further consideration should be given to the means by which the balance of the requirement to meet the program could be made available.
>
> In the meantime work proceeded on the calculations which would determine the acceptability or otherwise of plutonium from a second PIPPA. This work has now been completed and it is clear that by the operation of the Windscale piles and two PIPPAs at agreed levels the plutonium requirements of the Chiefs of Staff can be met ... The Atomic Energy Board accordingly decided ... that, as there were now no technical reasons why the balance of requirement could not be met from a second PIPPA, to advise the Defence Committee that the way was now clear to proceed with the construction of the second PIPPA if they so desired to meet in full the additional requirement of the Chiefs of Staff. The time which has elapsed in reaching a solution of the many technical problems which have arisen precludes consideration of any alternative to this proposal if requirements are to be available within the time-limit set by the Chiefs of Staff.

The point was also made that more plutonium would be needed in the future if the idea of a fast breeder reactor programme was to be taken up:

> In [a Cabinet paper of 1953] a tentative programme for the large-scale development of nuclear power industry was set out in some detail. This long-term plan envisages the construction of plutonium producing reactors to provide initial fuel for "breeder" reactors. Plutonium will be required within the next few years for the experimental breeder, a site for which is now being sought...

The comment as to the plutonium from the PIPPA 'would not be suitable for weapon manufacture' might need some explanation. It was not, as the note maintains, because of 'the greater heat at which these piles would operate', but the effects of more intense and longer neutron irradiation. Some isotopes of plutonium are more suited to atomic weapons than others. The isotope produced from uranium 238 by neutron absorption is plutonium 239. If the plutonium 239 is struck by a further neutron, it will either fission or it will absorb the neutron to become plutonium 240. 27% of the neutron collisions result in the formation of the ^{240}Pu isotope.

^{239}Pu will fission spontaneously, producing neutrons as a result — around ten neutrons per second per kilogram. ^{240}Pu has a much higher rate of spontaneous fission, producing around 1,000,000 neutrons per second per kilogram. This is highly undesirable in a nuclear weapon, since the neutrons produced by this spontaneous fission can lead to premature detonation of the bomb and hence a reduced yield. Weapons grade plutonium would normally contain less than 7% ^{240}Pu. It was intended that the fuel elements in the PIPPA design would remain in the reactor for very much longer than in the Windscale piles and thus extra ^{240}Pu would accumulate. One way around this would be to mix the output from the PIPPAs with plutonium from Windscale.

Figures (see Table 8.1) were given for the neutron activity of the plutonium obtained from the different plants. The first figure given for the Windscale piles is the 'burn up' in the reactor, which could be expressed as a percentage — 5% of the atoms have been 'burned up'. This is not easy to measure, so an alternative definition is used, which is the amount of thermal energy produced per ton (or tonne) of fissile material. Thus 200 MWD is 200 megawatt days, equivalent to $200 \times 10^6\,\mathrm{W} \times 86,400\,\mathrm{s} = 1.7 \times 10^{13}\,\mathrm{J}$. By modern standards, these burn rates are very low. A 1% burn up is very approximately equal to 10,000 MWD/T.

Table 8.1. Neutron activity of plutonium.

From Windscale:	
45 kg @ 3.0×10^4 n/sec/kg	200 MWD/T
45 kg @ 4.5×10^4 n/sec/kg	320 MWD/T
And from PIPPA:	
45 kg @ 6.0×10^4 n/sec/kg	259 MWD/T

This suggests that the plutonium obtained from the Windscale piles contained between 3 and 4.5% ^{240}Pu, whereas that from the PIPPAs was around 6%. One of the objectives of the second and third British atomic tests, code-named Operation Totem, held at Emu Field in South Australia in October 1953, was to test plutonium with a higher proportion of ^{240}Pu, both tests being successful.

The main features of PIPPA were determined by three basic decisions, which were firstly to use natural uranium as fuel, secondly to use graphite as the moderator and thirdly to use a gas under pressure as the coolant.[9]

The decision to use natural uranium was taken on grounds of availability and cost. Some of the cartridges in the Windscale piles contained slightly enriched uranium, but it was decided to go ahead with a design that did not require enrichment.

Heavy water was not considered as an alternative moderator since the design of a heavy water power reactor was being actively pursued elsewhere in the Commonwealth (Canada) and it was not available in the UK. Importing it would have been expensive at a time when the balance of payments, particularly in regard to dollar expenditure, was a constant government pre-occupation.

The problem with a liquid coolant such as water (and there were no real alternatives at the time) was that both the water and the pipework would tend to act as neutron absorbers. This would mean having to use enriched uranium, and one of the objectives was to be able to use natural uranium. Using a gas eliminated the pipework; choosing the correct one would eliminate neutron absorption.

The gas used for heat transfer had to be circulated through the reactor core channels, the heat exchangers and the connecting pipework. It was essential for the power needed to pump the gas round the system (the blowing power) to be only a small fraction of the heat power released in the pile. The laws of thermodynamics dictated that only about 25% of the pile heat could be turned into electrical energy. If the blowing power were 10% of the heat power, it would be 40% of the electrical power and hence the net electrical power output would be greatly reduced.

The blowing power for a given rate of heat removal varies roughly inversely as the square of the absolute pressure of the gas, so that the blowing power needed at seven atmospheres pressure is about 1/49 of what it would be at normal atmospheric pressure. This might seem slightly counter-intuitive, but the rate of heat removal will depend on the mass of gas flowing past per second. A higher pressure means a greater density of the gas and so a greater mass flow for the same gas velocity. In addition, the fans moving the gas will act more efficiently on a denser gas. Thus the gas had to be pressurised, which in turn meant that the whole reactor needed to be enclosed within a very large steel pressure vessel.

The hoop stress for a cylinder is given by $(P \times r)/t$, where P is the pressure, r the radius of the cylinder and t its thickness. Much experience had been gained with pressure vessels over the previous century through the use of steam boilers in ships and locomotives, so this was not new technology — although the size of the pressure vessel was unusual. The thickness of the steel wall was set by the practicality of installing it in place and welding it, and it was felt that two inches thickness was the effective limit.

Given a two inch thick steel wall and a gas pressure of seven atmospheres, the designers calculated that the maximum diameter of the pressure cylinder would be 39 feet for a reasonable working stress. The lower limit for the diameter was set by the minimum size of a natural uranium reactor generating negligible power, which would have been about 26 feet.

In all the graphite reactors built up to that time, the axis of the core and fuel rods had been horizontal, but it was decided that for a reactor within a pressure vessel, which is bound to change its dimensions slightly under pressure and temperature, a vertical axis was the better option. The graphite core was built up out of individual machined blocks to a diameter of 36 feet and a height of around 27 feet, with a total mass of about 1,500 tons. This would be supported by a steel honeycomb grating about 4 feet in depth.

One of the problems with a reactor of this kind is minimising neutron loss — in other words, selecting materials which will not absorb neutrons. The major culprits are the graphite (or its impurities), the coolant and the metal cans holding the uranium fuel.

Graphite purity had improved considerably in the previous few years resulting in greatly improved criticality conditions. The second large source of neutron capture was the material used to can the uranium metal.

The four possibilities considered were beryllium, magnesium, aluminium and zirconium. Beryllium was considered hard to obtain and difficult to fabricate into a complicated shape such as a can with cooling fins. Zirconium, in the hafnium-free state essential for use in a reactor, was not available in quantity at that time in the UK and was incompatible with carbon dioxide, the chosen coolant. The choice of canning material therefore lay between aluminium and magnesium. Magnesium had not been used up until then partly because its low capture cross-section had only become known in 1948. Aluminium would absorb considerably more neutrons. The other objection to magnesium had been that the earlier reactors were air-cooled and its rapid oxidation was a problem. When ignited, it burns very vigorously in air. In the case of PIPPA, however, where the cooling gas was carbon dioxide, the use of a magnesium alloy offered considerable advantages and was the final choice.

The three features of pure graphite, magnesium alloy cans and carbon dioxide cooling meant that the critical size of the reactor was reduced to an extent that would have seemed impossible a few years previously without enriching the fuel.

Once it had been decided that a graphite-moderated gas-cooled reactor was the best proposition for immediate development, a thorough survey was made of all probable and improbable cooling gases. Whilst this survey showed that helium was best technically, there were problems with the supply of helium, since it would have to be imported from the USA under restrictions imposed by the MacMahon Act. The only worthwhile alternative was carbon dioxide. Although carbon dioxide is somewhat inferior to helium as a coolant, it had the virtues of being abundant, cheap and easy to handle. The fact that it was not chemically inert necessitated intensive experimental work to prove the practicability of using it (the failure to apply this experimental experience to the design of later magnox power reactors was to prove a considerable embarrassment).

In the PIPPA design, the following substances would be in physical contact inside the reactor: uranium and magnesium alloy; magnesium and carbon dioxide; carbon dioxide and graphite; carbon dioxide and mild steel and, in the event of a can failure, carbon dioxide and uranium. It was essential to be certain that no unwanted chemical reactions could occur in spite of the high temperature and radiation conditions. Since the steam in the heat exchangers was at a higher pressure than the carbon dioxide, there was also a possibility of steam leaking into the carbon dioxide, and so the reactions with wet carbon dioxide also needed investigating.

One of the outstanding advantages of using magnesium for canning is that, unlike aluminium, which had been used previously, no chemical reaction occurs between it and uranium even under pile radiation. This considerably simplified the design of the fuel elements.

Magnesium does not oxidise appreciably in air below about 350°C, but above this temperature oxidation begins and at 550°C the heat of the reaction is sufficient to cause ignition. In carbon dioxide, the reaction is very different. With dry gas, no significant action occurs below 550°C, this being reduced by about 50°C if the gas is wet. Above this temperature, the protective film of oxide breaks down completely and rapid corrosion occurs.

There was also the possibility that alloying magnesium with other metals might improve the corrosion properties, and the results were tested at Harwell. One alloy, containing 0.05% beryllium, 0.1% calcium and 1% aluminium, showed remarkable resistance to corrosion. No measurable attack occurred below 600°C in wet air, which is the most generally corrosive environment.

Another problem was the interaction between carbon dioxide and graphite, which is another form of carbon. The reaction is: $CO_2 + C \leftrightharpoons 2CO$. In a closed circuit cooling system as used in PIPPA, graphite is initially removed into the gas phase until an equilibrium state is reached when no further removal occurs. This does not mean that the reaction ceases, because different parts of the reactor at different temperatures and under different intensities of irradiation cannot all be in equilibrium with the particular steady state composition reached by the gas. Parts of the core will therefore lose graphite to the gas stream, resulting in a transfer of graphite from one part of the core to another.

Experimental tests were carried out on the reaction and the conclusion was that the carbon dioxide graphite reaction would result in a very slow mass transfer of graphite from one part of the core to another, so altering, over a long period of time, the density of the graphite by small amounts, but not enough to be significant — the Calder Hall reactors were to run for nearly 47 years without graphite erosion being a problem.

A further potential problem lay in the interaction between carbon dioxide and steel. At first sight it might seem that dry carbon dioxide being less oxidising than oxygen or air, it would not attack iron, but above 250°C, a dark brown velvety scale formed at a rate comparable to that in air. It was thought, however, that with a corrosion allowance of 1/16 inch, this scaling effect would not affect the life or safety of the pressure vessel.

An awkward problem might arise if the scale flaked off or became caught up in the gas stream. Although the scale would not be thick, the large areas of steel, especially in the heat exchangers, could produce considerable quantities of dust and particle from the scale. There would be more than 400,000 square feet of steel in contact with the gas, and about half this area would be at a temperature higher than 250°C. If metal was removed even at a rate of 0.001 inch a year, there would be would be some 34 cubic feet (approximately 1 m^3) of scale produced. Provision would have to be made for filtering a small bleed off from the main gas stream, so that dust and scale of any origin could be continuously removed.

An attempt was made to estimate the economics of the plant. The costs (and the authors were honest enough to describe the estimates as 'guessed'!) were £3.5 million for the reactor, £1.5 million for the heat exchangers, £2.5 million for the power plant, and £1 million for the site. This was not unreasonable, and the cost of the power plant could certainly be established quite accurately, as it was very similar to those of conventional stations.

However, before PIPPA was given final approval, it was stipulated that the design should be approved by industry, as a note from Goodlet, the Deputy Chief Engineer at Harwell, shows:

> I understand that Mr. Anderson's terms of reference are to make a study of *all* our projects for producing electrical power from nuclear energy and, in the light of that study, to recommend whether PIPPA should or should not go ahead.[10]

Mr Anderson came from the firm of the Parolle Electrical Plant Company of Newcastle upon Tyne, and his report was entirely favourable.[11] Parolle was owned equally by CA Parsons and A Reyrolle. (Charles Parsons had been the inventor of the steam turbine and had created a sensation when his *Turbinia* turbine-powered launch appeared unannounced at the 1897 Naval Review at Spithead, completely outpacing the naval picket boat sent to intercept it.)

The conclusion of Anderson's evaluation were that when 1 tonne of natural uranium costing £17,000 had been irradiated for 3000 MW · days, the result would be 17.3×10^6 kW · hrs of electricity, 1.99 kg of fissile plutonium, and 0.27 kg of non-fissile ^{240}Pu.

Goodlet went on to say:

> I must however remark that I expect the Parsons organisation to give us help as well as criticism... You will note that B.E.A. [British Electrical Authority] are looking after the entire power plant including the Heat Exchanger....
>
> I therefore propose to ask the Parsons team to attack the two problems that have as yet not been handed out to anybody, viz:
>
> (a) Design of the CO_2 blower and pipework.
> (b) The design and manufacture of the full scale heat transfer test rig...
>
> Could you make it quite clear Parsons that this urgent work *must* be done and if they are not prepared to do it we shall have to look elsewhere. We have no use in the team for people who are going to enquire, discuss and criticise without doing useful work.

At that time, coal for electricity cost £3 (60 shillings) a ton, and Goodlet estimated the cost of a kW.hr of electricity generated from coal as being around 0.33 d. The

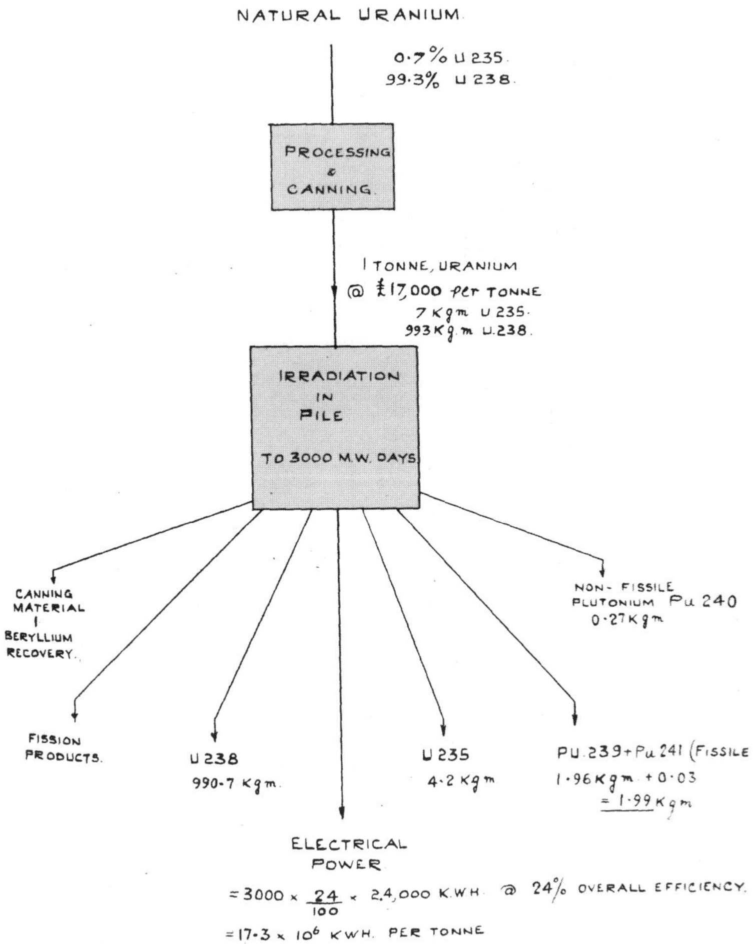

Figure 8.2. Assessment of PIPPA made by Mr Anderson from the firm of the Parolle Electrical Plant Company of Newcastle upon Tyne.

cost of the uranium per unit of electricity sent out (uranium was then £17,000 per ton) depended on how long the fuel was left in the reactor — the 'burn up'.

Table 8.2. Cost of uranium.

Burn up (MW Days/tonne)	300	600	1000	2000	3000
Cost per kW · hr (d)	2.26	1.13	0.68	0.34	0.226

The degree of burn up depended on the purpose of the reactor: if it was producing weapons grade plutonium, then the burn up had to be low to keep the amount of ^{240}Pu low. If, on the other hand, the reactor was intended merely to produce power, then the longer the fuel was kept in the reactor, the cheaper the electricity became.

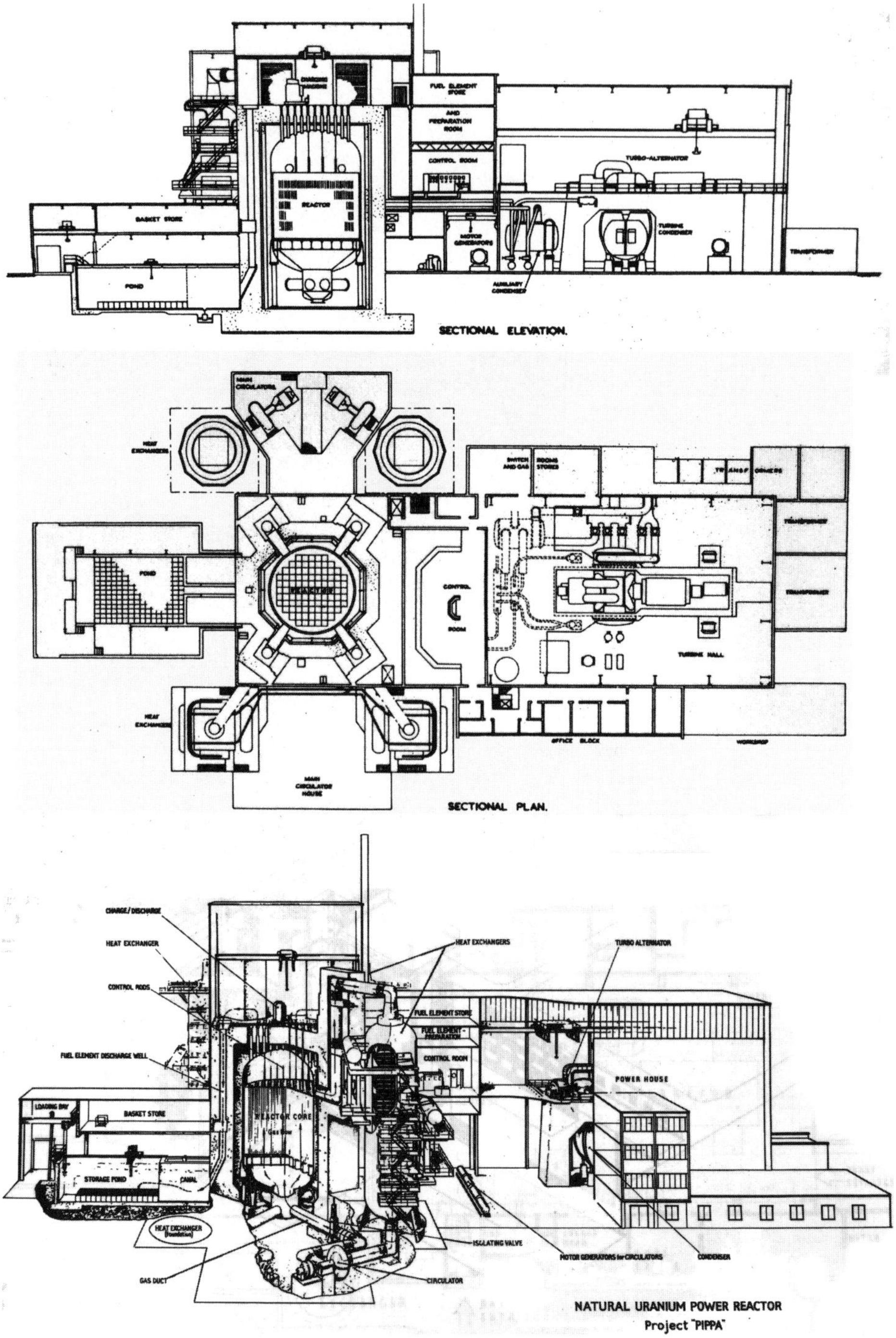

Figure 8.3. The finalised PIPPA design. Calder Hall differs from this as each of the two power stations was built with two reactors each, making a total of four reactors. The Chapelcross power station in Scotland would be a nearly identical copy of Calder Hall, also with four reactors.

There were also capital costs. Goodlet's estimates are shown in Table 8.3

Table 8.3. Estimated capital costs.

Interest	5% of £5 million	£250 k
Sinking fund	0.0872 × £5 million	£435 k
Running charges		£115 k
Total Annual Fixed Charges		£800 k

Assuming full power operation for 8,000 hours per year, this gave the cost per kW.hr of the fixed charges as 0.68 d (8,000 hours a year is a load factor of 91%, which is perhaps a slightly optimistic assumption). Adding the fixed costs to the cost of the uranium at 3,000 MW.days/tonne gave a figure of 0.92 d per unit. By comparison, the cost of electricity from current coal power stations was 0.65 d.[12]

Thus it seemed that the PIPPA design would fulfil both functions: it could produce electricity at a reasonably economic price, and it could produce plutonium for the military needs. The decision to build a PIPPA station had been approved in principle by the defence committee of the Cabinet in February 1953, and an announcement was made in parliament to the effect that:

> It is proposed to build on the Calder Hall site, adjacent to the Windscale Works, Sellafield, an atomic reactor... which will produce both plutonium and electrical power. Work on the site is scheduled to begin on 1st May, 1953, and it is expected that work on the main structure would begin about 1st October, 1953.

The design which would become Calder Hall was slightly different from the original PIPPA design, which had been optimised to produce electricity. The new design would be optimised to produce plutonium, since plutonium production was proportional to the heat output of the reactor. To get more heat from the reactor, the difference in temperature between the gas flowing in and flowing out had to be increased. The upper limit was fixed by the fuel elements, but the inlet temperature could be reduced. It was decided to reduce the inlet temperature from 180°C to 140°C, which had the effect of reducing boiler efficiency and thus electrical output. The overall efficiency of the original Harwell design had been 24.6%, whereas the efficiency of the new PIPPA design was only 19.2%.

The Steam Cycle

The hot gas from the reactor was passed into a section of the heat exchanger where good quality steam could be generated at the highest possible pressure. The gas leaving this section of the heat exchanger would still be comparatively hot and could then be passed through a second section of the heat exchanger in which rather low-grade steam would be generated, the steam conditions depending on the temperature of the carbon dioxide. The steam of these two grades was then to be fed to a turbine having high-pressure and low-pressure cylinders. The high-pressure steam would produce about 65% of the power generated, but the low-pressure steam would provide a useful contribution and would raise the overall efficiency of the plant considerably.

Figure 8.4. One of the carbon dioxide blowers which circulated the gas through the reactor.

The dual-pressure steam cycle had an important advantage in connection with controlling the plant as a whole, especially if it was necessary suddenly to shut down the reactor for any reason. It was important that the temperature of the reactor did not change rapidly since this would cause thermal stresses which might damage the structure. The plant control, therefore, was arranged so that the temperature of the core was kept nearly constant whatever the load, except of course when the reactor was shut down slowly to allow fuel elements to be replaced. Constant temperature was achieved in two ways; first, the rise in temperature of the gas as it passed through the core was kept constant, regardless of the rate at which heat was being generated, by varying the speed of the gas circulators and hence the rate at which the gas flowed through the core; and second, the temperature of the gas entering the core was kept constant, regardless of the heat supplied to the boilers, by varying the steam pressure in the low-pressure section of the boiler (the higher the pressure, the lower the amount of heat removed from the gas and therefore the higher the emergent gas temperature). This double control resulted in a closer control of temperature, and was considerably more efficient than a system which depended only on varying the gas flow.

Associated with the control system was the dump condenser, which was a drum filled with tubes through which cold water flowed. The steam which passed into the drum was condensed by the cold tubes, and a valve enabled all or part of the steam from the boiler to be diverted to the dump condenser instead of going to the turbine. Thus the steam load of the boiler could be kept constant regardless of the electrical load and the reactor could continue to operate at full power even when the turbo alternators were idle. The dump condenser also enabled the turbines to be started and run up with the reactor at power.

Building Calder Hall

Construction of what would be called Calder A began in August 1953, and its sister station, Calder B, was started in August 1955. Calder A was officially opened by the Queen on 17 October 1956, although prior to the official opening there had been a 'working up' period of about six months during which the operation of the pile was thoroughly tested. This gives a construction period of just over three years which, given the novel nature of the new plant, was a very creditable achievement, and was the fastest building time of any British nuclear power station (the AGR station at Dungeness was to take over 20 years!).

The BEA had been involved from quite early in the study, and had even delayed construction at a site at East Yalland near Barnstaple in Devon to allow borings to be taken in the hope that the new plant would be constructed there.[13] On the other hand, given that the main purpose of the new plant would be to produce plutonium, it made much greater sense to situate it next to the Windscale plant.

The original design had been for one pile only, but not long afterwards a second one was authorised, which changed the layout of the plant — the reactors would now be housed in separate buildings, with the turbines and electric alternators in a third building between the other two.

The major construction work began with excavations for the reactor foundations. The reactor with its shield and associated buildings weighed in the region of 22,000 tons. These would rest on a reinforced concrete raft 11 feet thick by 130 feet long by 104 feet wide which added nearly another 10,000 tons to the total weight on the subsoil. It was essential that this raft should not move or settle when completed or the biological shield on it might crack. The concrete, therefore, had to be of high and uniform quality throughout, and had to be placed in such a way as to minimise movement and shrinking.

It was also essential that no impurities which might absorb neutrons should be allowed in the completed core. The graphite blocks would therefore machined

Figure 8.5. Calder Hall under construction. One of the Windscale pile chimneys can be seen in the background.

under conditions comparable in cleanliness with the aseptic conditions of an operating theatre. Each completed block was marked with its identifying number, vacuum cleaned, and packed in a cardboard box for transport to the reactor. The reactor pressure vessel was cleaned inside and protected from corrosion by air conditioning. After this had been done, stringently clean conditions were maintained inside throughout the stacking and other work. All the workmen had to change their clothes completely before entering the sealed vessel and spectacles, wristwatches, and similar personal property were checked to ensure they were not inadvertently left inside the reactor. Certain metals such as brass were prohibited. Of the three shifts working through a 24-hour day on stacking, one was given over wholly to inspection.

Gethin Davey, the Windscale Works Manager, describes the commissioning of the reactor thus:

> The reactor was handed over by the Construction Group to the Operations Group on the 18th May, 1956. The loading of all the special instrumentation required in the reactor core for the measurements during the loading to critical size began immediately. At the same time exhaustive tests were being carried out on safety circuits and control rods, together with complete checks of all reactor equipment, electrical supplies and valve settings against schedules which had previously been prepared. This work continued late into the night and it was in the early hours of the following day that the order has given to prepare the first hole to receive fuel.

It had been decided to use the charge/discharge machine in the normal way during the loading to critical size — principally to get maximum practice at this important operation. However considerable difficulty was experienced especially during the preparation of the hole and some delay occurred before the first fuel element was loaded into the reactor. During the 19th May loading proceeded slowly due to mechanical troubles on the charge/discharge machine and it was finally decided to increase the rate of loading by using specially designed hand grabs. All cartridges were lowered down to the charge pans and accepted there by a loading team which carried the cartridge to its channel and lowered it using the special hand grab. A very significant increase in the loading rate was achieved in this way.

At various stages in the loading the personnel were withdrawn from the vessel and the control rods raised carefully to the fully out position, then very accurate readings were taken of the reactor power level from the special instrumentation in the reactor core. These measurements of power level were plotted graphically in a way that enabled a prediction of the critical size to be made. By the 22nd of May 380 channels had been loaded and the graphs were predicting a critical size of about 407 channels. Great interest was now aroused as the theoretical prediction of critical size was about 475 channels and the much smaller critical size which appeared likely meant that the reactor would have much greater reactivity than had been suspected. Loading proceeded very carefully above 380 channels and the control rods were withdrawn for measurements of the pile power more frequently so that the critical size could be predicted with increased accuracy. By late in the afternoon it became clear critical size would be 405 channels. At 404 channels the control rods were carefully withdrawn and the pile power was observed from the recordings of the special instruments in the reactor core; the power rose very slowly and gave no sign of stabilising at a steady value as it would do if the reactor was still sub critical. However relaxation times are very long as criticality moves very close and it becomes difficult to determine whether the reactor is just under or just over the critical size. It was therefore decided to load another 4 channels. At 20.09 hours on the 22nd May, 1956 control rods were withdrawn. The power rose continuously at a steady rate and the following entry was made in the reactor commissioning log book:

"412 channels loaded, reactor definitely divergent, doubling time 64 seconds."

The reactor was shut down by pressing the emergency button when the pile power had reached 1 kW. The critical size was certainly much smaller than had been predicted and calculations were immediately started to determine how much extra reactivity would be available. It was clear from even the simplest of calculations that the steel absorber which had been provided would definitely be required following the loss of reactivity due to xenon and temperature was as calculated.

The following five days were spent carrying out a series of measurements to determine certain reactor physics parameters, flux distribution, reactor physics effects of empty channels and steel channels, initial rough calibration of a control rod and determinations of the absolute power level to calibrate the instruments. This work was completed on 27th of May and preparations were made to start the loading of the reactor to full size. The most important preparation consisted of restoring the control rods' withdrawal speed to its normal value and careful tests were made to ensure this had been done.

The loading to full size was carried out using the charge machine in the normal way. This resulted in a slower loading rate but valuable experience was gained in the operation of these machines. Loading was carried out with only a limited number of control rods inserted in the core and the measurements were taken again using the special instrumentation. The critical size, as a function of a number of control rods loaded, could thus be determined in the same way as the initial critical size had been. These measurements were most valuable for they enabled an estimate to be made of the number of control rods required to maintain the reactor in a safe condition when it was fully loaded. By 11th June full loading of 1696 channels had been achieved and 52 control rods were installed for calibration. This number of control rods was again much smaller than had predicted. Theoretically, it seemed that they were rather more effective than had been expected and this was subsequently confirmed during the control rod calibration.

The control rod calibration using the new technique was successfully completed by 15th June. The measurements of the air pressure which just balanced the reactor with the control rods fully withdrawn gave another accurate determination of the total reactivity of the core. They confirmed the estimates that had been made on the basis of the measurement at critical size...

The next phase was successfully completed on the 29th of June. It consisted of an extended run of the gas circuit fully pressurised, the blowers running at full speed and the circuit heated to about 120°C by means of Windscale steam and blower power. This was the first time CO_2 had been used in the gas circuit and extensive surveys were made around the plant to detect any leakage. As many plant items as possible were tested during this time...

This phase was completed on the 4th July and after the circuit was purged to remove the CO_2, the vessel was opened. After complete health physics surveys, personnel entered the vessel to start an exhaustive inspection. It was immediately noticed that the tops of some of the cartridges had come off and were lying on the charge pans and examination of some of the channels revealed that many top cartridges had loose tops. A method of locking the cartridge tops was evolved and was immediately followed by some very quick measurements to determine the attenuation of neutron flux through the pressure vessel biological shield...

The test of the burst cartridge detection gear was started on the 7th July. Almost immediately it was noticed that the background readings from the equipment had increased to a high level. This background was not responsive to power changes and contamination of accounting equipment was suspected. A variety of attempts were made to discover the source of this background — but the trouble persisted. It was then suspected the trouble was being caused by radioactive argon reaching the annular hole in the phosphor through which the wire passes for counting. This was checked by opening the gear to the atmosphere which immediately reduced the background by allowing fresh air to displace activated air drawn from the reactor. Some air from the reactor was isolated in the counting and the half-life of the background was determined: this showed the characteristic 110 minute half-life of argon 41. It was decided that this problem of activated argon be cured by arranging for a bleed of clean gas past the phosphor in the counting head which would prevent the diffusion of the active coolant gas...

On 1st August after the final preparations had been made the control rods were withdrawn for operation at power. Power was increased very gradually and exhaustive measurements of all temperatures, radiation levels and mechanical movements were made. By 5th August the reactor power was 70 MW at a fuel element temperature of 300°C and finally by 27th August number one turbo generator was successfully commissioned followed on 3 September by the commissioning of number 2 alternator.

The total time taken at this stage was four months compared with a programme time of six months. The commissioning of Reactor 2 began in December 1956 and it was in full operation by February 1957. Calder Reactor 3 achieved full power operation in June 1958 and Reactor 4 completed the whole station in April 1959.[14]

Figure 8.6. The finished product. The two power stations, A and B, were laid out as mirror images. There is another set of cooling towers just out of sight on the left. Each station has a central turbine hall with one reactor either side.

The Opening Ceremony

In the early 1950s, there was a mood of optimism in the country. The accession of the new Queen led to talk of a 'new Elizabethan age'. Rationing had finally been abolished, Mount Everest had been climbed for the first time, by a Commonwealth expedition. The world's first jet airliner, the Comet, made in Britain, had just gone into service (although a series of crashes meant that it was not the commercial success it might have been). The opening of the world's first commercial atomic power station which would feed electricity directly into the National Grid suited this narrative very well.[15]

The opening of Calder Hall would have been an event in itself; the Royal visit was to make it memorable. Plowden obviously had a sense of theatre, and realised that it could be more than just a simple opening ceremony.

> There will be about 450 specially invited guests, including Members of both Houses, senior Civil Servants, industrialists and scientists, a number of prominent Cumberland residents, representatives of Commonwealth and foreign countries

> and members of our own staff. There will be about 200 representatives of the world press, television etc. . . .
>
> Standing accommodation will be available for several thousand local people and in addition for about 1000 Cumberland schoolchildren in such a position that they will have a good view of Her Majesty at the opening ceremony. Loudspeakers will enable them to hear the speeches.[16]

The caterers would be busy: there would be a buffet lunch for the more important visitors — a total of 380 — and lunch in the canteen at Windscale for another 292, making a total of 672 lunches to be provided.

The AEA estimated the total cost of the ceremony at £16,330, broken down thus[17]:

Table 8.4. Cost of the opening ceremony of Calder Hall.

Buffet lunch (350)	£2,650
Queen's table (30)	£400
Flowers	£120
Drinks	£170
Tentage	£1,540
Press & staff lunch in canteen including drinks	£300
Transport, train and coach parties including food and hotel accommodation	£3,600
Royal Dais	£2,000
Stands	£4,550
Exhibition	£500
Contingencies	£500

Unfortunately, the Treasury was only prepared to allow a budget of £16,000.

There was also the tricky question as to who would be on the table having lunch with the Queen.

> The Financial Secretary of the Treasury has suggested that invitations should go to the Leader of the Opposition and his deputy. This could clearly not be done unless invitations were sent to the Prime Minister and Mr Butler, and Mr Clement Davies [the leader of the Liberal Party] would then presumably have to be included for good measure . . . As to guests other than for the luncheon table . . . the claims of the local MP, Frank Anderson, must be regarded as very strong. He is, of course, a great nuisance, but he will probably be a worse nuisance if he is slighted by not being invited on this occasion.

There was a long correspondence with the Queen's private secretary in which he was kept fully informed of the smallest detail:

> You may wish to have details of the design and colouring of the Royal dais. It is essentially an umbrella-shaped canopy over a roughly circular raised platform. The tubular steel structure will be painted white and samples of the covering

> materials for the canopy and of the carpet are enclosed. The colour desk in front of Her Majesty will be painted duck-egg blue and this colour will be repeated on the lining of a circular pond which has been constructed around the dais.

No detail was overlooked. The Lady-in-Waiting, who would accompany the Queen, was informed as to the details for the 'Royal Nose-powdering' (a euphemism for the toilet arrangements).

The Queen was scheduled to arrive at Calder Hall at 10:15 in the morning. A gale the previous night had threatened to blow away the canopy and all the marquees which had been erected for the guests, but fortunately they survived. On her arrival at Calder Hall, presentations were made, and just after 11:00 the Queen began her tour of the plant.

Figure 8.7. The Queen preparing to throw the switch to connect Calder Hall to the National Grid.

The opening ceremony itself took place at noon. Reactor number 1 had been brought up to power before the ceremony, and the electricity generated was temporarily supplied to the Windscale works. When the Queen performed the ceremony, the power generated in the plant was transferred by remote control to the National Grid, making electricity generated from nuclear energy available to the public for the first time. A meter on the roof of the Administration Building would record how much electricity was being fed into the grid.

Figure 8.8. The Queen on her tour of Calder Hall. Top left photograph: on the left is HG Davey. Immediately behind the Queen, on the left, is RA Butler. Top right photograph: The Queen with HG (Gethin) Davey, Calder Works Manager.

The Queen's speech read as follows:

> Today, as power from Calder Hall begins to flow into the national grid, all of us here know that we are present at the making of history.
>
> For many years now, we have been aware that atomic scientists, by a series of brilliant discoveries have brought us to the threshold of a new age. We have also known that on that threshold mankind has reached a point of crisis. Today we are in a sense seeing a solution of that crisis, as this new power which has proved itself to be such a terrifying weapon of destruction, is harnessed for the first time for the common good of our community.
>
> In this turbulent century, we have seen one technical revolution succeed another with astonishing speed. Within the span of a few generations, our way of life has been transformed beyond anything our forefathers could have imagined. The age of steam was succeeded by an age of such startling achievement that

we who are close to it can hardly realise that so short a period encompassed the invention of the motor car, the wireless set, the aeroplane, and much else besides which we now take for granted. So quickly have we learned to accept the pace of modern development that we have been in danger of losing our sense of wonder. That sense has been dramatically restored by advent of the atomic age.

For centuries past, visionary ideals and practical methods, which have gone from our shores, have opened up new ways of thought and modes of life for people in all parts of the world. It may well prove to have been among the greatest of our contributions to human welfare that we led the way in demonstrating the peaceful uses of this new source of power.

I congratulate all those who have shared in this fine project. Both those who conceived and planned the industrial application of atomic energy in this way and those who have worked to see their plans fulfilled. And I hope this occasion will be an inspiration and encouragement to all who will continue this exciting enterprise here and elsewhere. It is with pride that I now open Calder Hall, Britain's first atomic power station.[18]

---

1 TNA: PRO AB 6/2563. Calder Hall book; source material.

2 TNA: PRO AB 38/297. Production of electrical power from a plutonium-producing pile: report by Parolle Electrical Plant Co. Also TNA: PRO AB 38/298. Production of electrical power from a plutonium-producing pile: illustrations.

3 TNA: PRO AB 6/2563. Calder Hall book; source material. 'History of the PIPPA Project.' BL Goodlet, 12 December 1952.

4 TNA: PRO AB 15/2042. Engineering problems of natural uranium reactors for the production of power. BL Goodlet and RV Moore. AERE Harwell, September 1951. See also TNA: PRO AB 15/2983. Natural uranium power reactor. (Project PIPPA). 1951–1952 design study: summary report, 1st edition; and TNA: PRO AB 15/5236. Natural uranium power reactor (Project "PIPPA") 1951–1952 design study: summary report. BL Goodlet and RV Moore.

5 TNA: PRO AB 15/3698. Canning for first thermal power reactor (PIPPA). LM Wyatt and VL Fontaine. August 1953.

6 TNA: PRO CAB 134/33. Atomic Energy (Review of Production) Committee: Meeting 1; Papers 1–2. December 1948.

7 *Ibid.*

8 TNA: PRO AB 16/2008. Windscale reactor PIPPA: Calder Hall construction (extract from AB 16/2007).

9 Much of what follows is taken from a paper presented to the 1953 Harwell Power Conference: TNA: PRO AB 15/3457. 'PIPPA — The First British Nuclear Power Project.' RV Moore and BL Goodlet.

10 TNA: PRO AB 6/1092. PIPPA reactors, including Calder Hall. BL Goodlet to Director.

11 TNA: PRO AB 7/2379. An assessment of the 'Pippa' project. E Anderson, Parolle Electrical Plant Company Ltd, 10 February 1953.

12 TNA: PRO AB 6/1092. PIPPA reactors, including Calder Hall. 'Pippa Economics — Re-assessment.' BL Goodlet, 22 July 1953.

13 TNA: PRO AB 6/1023. Feasibility study by the British Electricity Authority for PIPPA.

14 TNA: PRO AB 16/2700. HG Davey: History of Windscale.

15 TNA: PRO AB 17/52. Calder Hall: The Opening of Britain's First Atomic Power Station by Her Majesty The Queen.

16 TNA: PRO AB 16/1616. Opening of Calder Hall by HM The Queen, October 1956. Sir Edwin Plowden to Lt. Col. Right Hon. Sir Michael Adeare, 29 September 1956.

17 TNA: PRO AB 8/678. Public relations: opening of Calder Hall by HM The Queen.

18 'October 17 1956. Her Majesty the Queen Opens Calder Hall', *Hexham Courant*, 19 October 2006.

Chapter 9

CTR and ZETA

The search for controlled thermonuclear fusion might well be seen as the holy grail of nuclear research for the past 60 years, and despite the time and money that has been spent on it, the goal seems almost as remote now as it did when the quest first began.

Nuclear fusion is the process that powers the sun and the stars, although the process by which it occurs is rather complex. At the enormously high pressures and temperatures at the centre of stars, four protons are converted into a helium nucleus, with other particles being produced in the process. In the more massive stars, the fusion process can go on to produce more and more massive nuclei — indeed, the nuclei of the atoms of which we are all made were created in the centre of a now dead star.

Rather than using ordinary hydrogen, deuterium or tritium provides an easier pathway to fusion in various reactions:

$$^{2}\mathrm{H} + {}^{2}\mathrm{H} \rightarrow {}^{3}_{2}\mathrm{He} + {}^{1}_{0}\mathrm{n} + 3.26\,\mathrm{MeV}$$

$$^{2}\mathrm{H} + {}^{2}\mathrm{H} \rightarrow {}^{3}_{1}\mathrm{H} + {}^{1}_{1}\mathrm{p} + 4.03\,\mathrm{MeV}$$

$$^{2}\mathrm{H} + {}^{3}\mathrm{H} \rightarrow {}^{4}_{2}\mathrm{He} + {}^{1}_{0}\mathrm{n} + 17.6\,\mathrm{MeV}.$$

Thus almost all fusion experiments use deuterium gas at very high temperature. All of these reactions produce neutrons, and one way to discover whether fusion is taking place is to try to detect the neutrons being emitted. Further reaction can take place between the tritium and deuterium producing helium plus another neutron.

The two nuclei have to be very close before they can fuse together. Since they carry the same electric charge, they will repel each other, and hence need to be travelling at very high speed, so that when they collide they have sufficient kinetic energy to overcome these forces of repulsion. This means the gas needs to be extremely hot and at the temperatures necessary, the deuterium atoms will have become ionised. The resultant mixture of ions and electrons is called a plasma.

One of the major problems is that the hot gas will tend to lose heat and cool down very rapidly. Break-even of the reaction is said to take place when the fusion energy produced is greater than the heat being lost; ignition has occurred when the input of energy can be switched off. For this to happen, three conditions are necessary, called the Lawson criteria after the Harwell physicist, John Lawson. These conditions are: firstly, a sufficiently high plasma density, secondly, a sufficiently high temperature, and thirdly, a sufficiently long confinement time. It is this final criterion that has been the most difficult to fulfil.

To stop the plasma losing heat, it has to be kept away from the walls of the container. In the case of a straight tube, there will be heat losses at the ends. One way to solve this problem is to have no ends at all — in other words, bend the tube round to make a ring or, more technically, a torus. If this torus is surrounded by coils carrying an electric current, then there will be a magnetic field running through the torus. This magnetic field can be used to constrict the plasma and confine it to the centre of the torus. At the same time, a magnetic field is set up by the current in the plasma. These two fields combine to confine the plasma within the torus.

Most of the work in the post-war period was carried out at the universities, particularly the Clarendon laboratory in Oxford and Imperial College London. The London group was led by Sir George Thomson (son of JJ Thomson, who had discovered the electron), and the Oxford group by Peter Thonemann, an Australian from Sydney. In the early 1950s some of these groups moved to Harwell and to Aldermaston.

Many of these early experiments used radio frequency waves to heat the gas, but then a new method was devised. This used a transformer in which the torus itself — or, more strictly speaking, the plasma in the torus — was effectively the secondary coil. A large bank of capacitors was charged up and then discharged into the primary coil of the transformer. This created a current in the plasma in the torus, which was confined to the centre of the torus by the magnetic field from the coils which were wrapped around the torus.

The major problem was that the plasma would form a wriggle or 'kink', and this kink very rapidly developed into an instability. The wriggling can be suppressed by applying an additional steady magnetic field parallel to the axis of the tube, but this is difficult to achieve, and suppressing plasma instabilities is still a major difficulty in fusion reactors.

Peter Thonemann, working on fusion at the Clarendon laboratory at Oxford, managed to produce a current of 2,000 A in a plasma contained in a copper torus. His work impressed Cockcroft and Lord Cherwell, who was at that time responsible for atomic energy (Cherwell was once Director of the Clarendon laboratory, appointed in 1919), and as a result he moved to Harwell.[1] The apparent success of some of Thonemann's early experiments then led to the design of a new, very large, apparatus named ZETA, which was built in a hangar at Harwell.

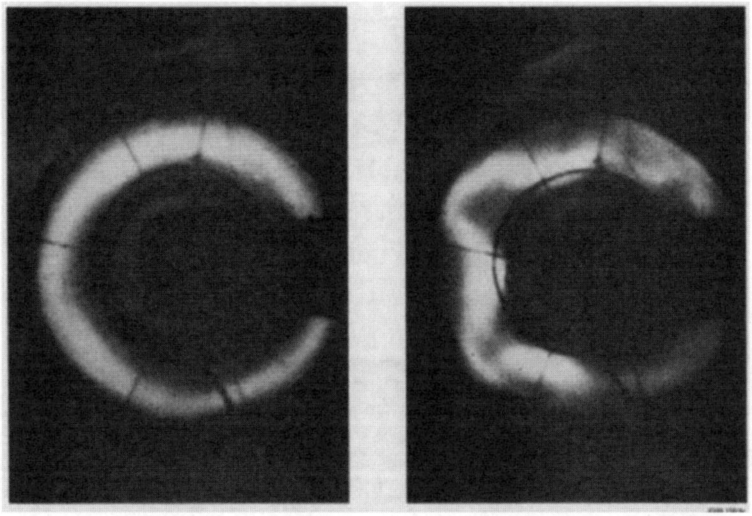

Figure 9.1. Instability forming in a plasma.

In ZETA, the discharge chamber was a ring-shaped tube or torus of one metre bore and three metres diameter, containing deuterium gas at low pressure. The tube was linked to the iron core of a large pulse transformer, then a bank of capacitors capable of storing 500,000 J of energy was discharged into the primary winding of the transformer. This pulse in turn induced a very large pulse of current in the gas. Peak currents up to 200,000 A could be passed through the ionised gas for periods up to 5 ms. The current pulse was repeated every ten seconds, and detectors were fitted to measure the neutrons being produced.

ZETA first became operational in August 1957, heating deuterium gas to a temperature of between two and five million degrees. Neutrons were observed during the heating pulses, leading the scientists running the experiments to believe that fusion was taking place, but there were other possible sources of neutrons such as collisions with the walls of the vessel, or from bombardment of stationary ions by deuterons. On the other hand, it seemed that the number of neutrons produced by each pulse of energy was roughly that which might be expected from a thermonuclear reaction at the measured temperatures.

Harwell did acknowledge that the results were only provisional, and hedged their claims around with a good number of provisos, but many of the statements made by the organisation did appear to give the impression that the experiments had been a success, and that the secret of controlled fusion had been cracked. An example of this comes in a booklet which Harwell produced on ZETA,[2] describing how it worked and which ended with a section entitled ‘Questions and Answers’ in which

Figure 9.2. A view of ZETA. The horizontal torus contains the plasma. The large coil in the centre is used to induce a current in the plasma. (Image courtesy of NDA and copyright NDA.)

some rather unwise statements were made:

> Q What are the next steps in this field of research?
>
> A . . . While experiments continue in ZETA, Harwell will design and build its successor — ZETA II — which will aim at achieving the break-even point. This should take about four years. Stage II will be work leading to the construction of a prototype of a practical and economic thermonuclear power station. Stage IV will be commercial application.
>
> Q If it proves ultimately possible to build fusion reactors which will generate electricity economic, what will be in the long-term significance of this development?
>
> A ZETA's long-term significance is that, if commercial fusion reactors can be built, a virtually inexhaustible source of fuel will be available in atomic development throughout the world.
>
> This makes it possible to contemplate a continued increase in standards of living which would otherwise — 200 or 300 years from now — have to level out or even slip back. It should, however, be borne in mind that practical application for electricity development are not likely to be obtained 10, 20 or even 50 years.

Hubris was to be followed by nemesis, as it turned out that, after all, ZETA was not the success it was thought to have been. There is no doubt that it produced many interesting results, but it did not lead to controlled nuclear fusion. What it did lead to was considerable political embarrassment for the Macmillan government.

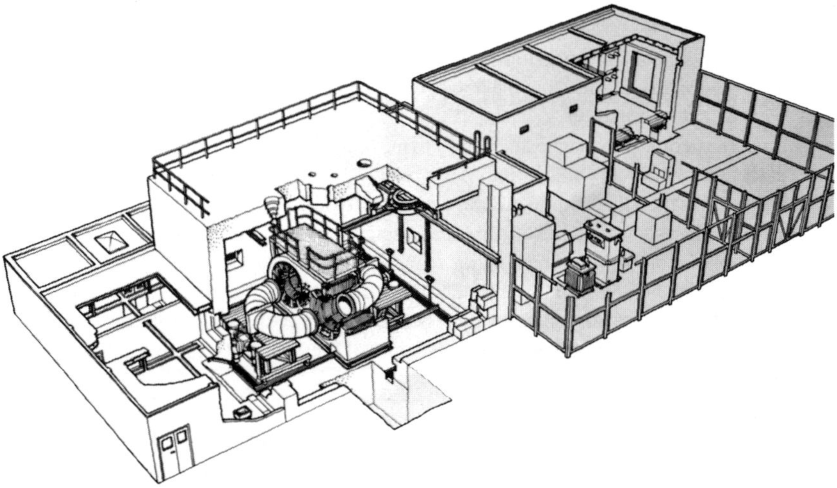

Figure 9.3. ZETA was built at Harwell — this is the layout of building in which ZETA was housed.

Although no official announcement was made, knowledge of the early results of the thermonuclear experiments at Harwell had obviously leaked out and had become fairly general knowledge. The delay in making an announcement aroused suspicions amongst the more chauvinistic. This came to a head with an article in the *New York Herald Tribune* in December 1957 by Anthony Nutting. Nutting had been a Member of Parliament and a junior minister at the Foreign Office before resigning over the Suez affair.[3]

In his article, Nutting hints very strongly that the reason for the delay was to give time for the United States to catch up and to claim credit for the breakthrough for itself:

> A few days ago at Cape Canaveral, occurred one of history's best publicized failures. [The first American attempt to launch a satellite into orbit had failed when the Vanguard rocket exploded on the launch pad.] A few weeks ago at Harwell, England, occurred one of history's best concealed triumphs.
>
> The best publicized failure needs no further emphasis from me. I will only say that far more deplorable than the failure was the publicity that attended it. (No doubt the Soviets had their rockets and satellites that fizzled but they wisely saw to it that the world learned only of their successes.) What is of far greater concern is the concealment of the triumph at Harwell. In the last few weeks British nuclear scientists have, I am reliably informed, achieved a 'controlled hydrogen reaction'...
>
> This is an achievement beside which the Sputnik pales into insignificance. This is a scientific revolution which shrinks the launching of Russia's earth satellites into a display of firecrackers. This is a discovery which can put an end to the needs of the have-not nations. It is as if the rivers and the oceans of this planet had suddenly become filled with oil and gasoline.

> Yet Britain is not allowed to proclaim this miracle of science. Why? Because it is bound by an agreement with the United States which forbids either party to declassify the good information about nuclear development without the agreement of the other party. Harnessing the power of the hydrogen bomb, it seems, is treated as classified information . . .
>
> Some people have suggested darkly to me that the real reason for this American reluctance to have this momentous news released is politics. They point to the loss of prestige which the Administration would suffer if they had to admit that Britain as well as Russia was ahead of America in scientific development. If this were the true explanation, it would be a major scandal.
>
> I prefer to believe that this attitude stems from a slavish and misguided application of security. But, whatever may be the reason, it shows a deplorable misconception in Washington of the true meaning of Western partnership and the real nature of the Soviet threat.

The article and the ensuing fuss meant that Macmillan had to write to Sir Edwin Plowden, Chairman of the UKAEA, asking him to sort matters out:

> Representations have been made to me that some Conservative Members of Parliament are getting restive about the position about controlled thermo-nuclear reaction. I think that this agitation has been fanned by the article by Mr Nutting in the New York Herald Tribune of December 12.
>
> I know that you agreed with the Americans to make no announcement until the end of January. I should, however, be grateful if you would consider with the Foreign Office whether anything at all can be said to damp down this unwise agitation before then. Of course I quite agree that we must not jeopardise the great prize but I should not like there to be a foolish anti-American campaign. This would be in the interests neither of ourselves nor of the United States.[4]

The 'great prize' to which Macmillan refers was the possibility of the resumption of nuclear cooperation between Britain and America, which was to come to fruition with the bilateral agreement of 1958, and which had only become possible as a consequence of the first successful tests of an H bomb at Christmas Island a month previously.

There was a further problem in that it had been intended that the results of the experiments should be presented to a meeting of the Royal Society. This also raised the possibility of further embarrassment, as a letter from Plowden illustrates:

> . . . given the Royal Society's cordial relations with the Russian Academy of Sciences they feel it would be difficult to invite Americans without inviting Russians as well. (You will no doubt recall that Academician Kurchatov gave a lecture about controlled thermonuclear reactions at Harwell in the middle of 1956). Penney tells me that he thinks this is an entirely reasonable attitude for the Royal Society to take, and we must therefore decide whether we encourage the society to go ahead with an 'all British' occasion (which I understand they would be prepared to do) or whether we ask Lewis Strauss [chairman of the Atomic Energy Commission in America] if he would like to send one or two of his people, pointing out that this will involve a similar invitation going from the Royal Society to the Russian Academy of Sciences.

My own feeling on the matter is this. In essence what we want to do is to get due credit for the work at Harwell. We have no particular interest in making this into an international jamboree. Moreover, Strauss' feelings on this whole matter are so easily inflamed that I think we might run into all kinds of trouble by suggesting to him that his people should be confronted with the Russians. If you agree, therefore, what I would propose to do is to send a cable to Lewis Strauss telling him that the Royal Society are arranging a meeting in the week following the announcement to discuss controlled thermonuclear work and to say that we welcome this development as something which will help to put the announcement in its right (i.e. strictly scientific) perspective.[5]

Macmillan scrawled a comment at the bottom of the letter, 'I hardly think the Americans will wish to meet the Russians. It would be wiser to keep the Royal Society to a British show, rather than upset Strauss'. The matter was even raised in Parliament — principally by Roy Mason, Labour MP for Barnsley,[6] in January 1958.

Mr. Mason asked the Prime Minister if he is now able to make a statement on the recent thermo-nuclear experiments which have been conducted on the Zeta reactor at Harwell; what proposals have been made and adopted by the joint United States/United Kingdom declassification committee; and if he will now disclose more details about the work going on in the United States of America and the United Kingdom towards harnessing the power of the hydrogen bomb for peaceful purposes.[7]

Figure 9.4. Another view of ZETA.

He got a reply from RA Butler, the then Home Secretary and Lord Privy Seal:

> On 11th November, 1957, my right Hon. Friend the Paymaster-General informed the House of the general position regarding research on controlled thermonuclear reactions. The United Kingdom and the United States have brought into effect a further measure of declassification, and it is now possible to publish technical details about the experiments which have been taking place in the two countries as part of the full collaboration between them on all research work in this field . . .

This answer did not satisfy one MP:

> Mr. Price: . . . may I ask him to examine the machinery for releasing this information, as I hope he is aware that over the last three months this information has been leaking to the British Press in a rather backstairs manner which suggests that the authorities are trying to hush up a failure, whereas in fact this is one of the greatest triumphs of British science comparable with those of Lord Rutherford, J.J. Thomson and Sir John Cockcroft? Will my right Hon. Friend discuss with the authorities how they can ensure either that there are no leaks in anticipation of statements or that there are earlier statements of such successes?

Butler replied:

> I think it much better that this highly scientific information should be published, as was done on a previous occasion, in a scientific journal. We may then be quite satisfied as to its accuracy and as to those who understand it publishing it.

Mason was not happy with events, and raised the matter again via an Adjournment debate.

> The fly in the ointment, I think, was the Joint United Kingdom-United States Declassification Committee. American influence predominated to stop any announcement. No one knows to what degree Admiral Strauss, Chairman of the American Atomic Energy Commission, was responsible. Hazarding a guess, I would say that he was, in the main, responsible . . .
>
> I have kept a number of cuttings of newspaper comments. A few weeks after the success of Zeta, but many weeks before the Government made the announcement that we had managed to build up that temperature successfully and pointed the way towards harnessing hydrogen power, the News Chronicle, on 10th December, had a headline: 'H-energy gag on British Scientists. Harwell wants to tell all. But Americans won't agree.' The Sunday Express said: 'United States gag 'riles' British H-power scientists.' Again, there was a comment in the Yorkshire Evening Post, which said that the Government 'won't talk about the newest discovery of the nuclear age.' So it went on. Following the comment on 10th December by the News Chronicle, the Observer, in its headline on the front page, said: 'Harnessing H-Bomb; News soon' and said, in the course of its article: 'The Atomic Energy Authority originally planned to make this announcement last October, but it was delayed by pressure from Admiral Lewis Strauss, Chairman of the United States Atomic Energy Commission.' I believe that to be substantially correct.
>
> The Americans were, and still are, behind us in this work. We might well ask ourselves at this stage, because it is relevant: why this should be so? First, they tried to explore too many avenues, none with great success - atomic energy power stations, rockets, nuclear stations, nuclear fusion, and so on. Prior to the Sputnik

shock, America suffered from McCarthyism. There was little interchange between the universities and research establishments. The anti-Red complex curtailed the free exchange of ideas and progress . . .

Of course, we have an urgent need for this new form of power, and this is proving a strong driving force. I should like to praise the Harwell team for their magnificent achievement. It was, of course, of Commonwealth composition, but that is part of our strength. We have the scientists, although perhaps not enough. We certainly have the skill, and, given sufficient finance, we can maintain a lead in applying atomic energy to peaceful and industrial uses. Despite Admiral Strauss's pressure on the Declassification Committee, it was most obvious that American lay opinion was not being fooled either. American newspapers made it plain that the success belonged to the Commonwealth team at Harwell. Admiral Strauss, in this case has made a fool of himself. Indeed, the whole exercise over the past few months has been a foolish one . . .

There are bound to be milestones of progress. Shall we, on these occasions, receive the news immediately? Can we have assurances that the Declassification Committee will not cause any more delays of future announcements? It seems to be a committee with incredible power. Few people are aware of its composition, or when it meets. No one knows to what extent it has been classified and declassified, but is it not proving a very strong barrier between Harwell and the Government? Is this not a publicly-owned industry? Why cannot we have periodic Government statements?

The question was how co-operative the USAEC would be, and it would seem that there might still be some difficulties. Plowden replied to a cable from the British Ambassador in Washington in an exasperated letter which was not at all like his usual tone:

I am extremely disturbed by the news in [your telegram] and think it would be unwise to leave the U.S.A.E.C. with any impression that this is a minor matter from our point of view. I also think that this matter should be dealt with at a high level and I should be grateful if you would see Admiral Strauss about it.

I suggest you should remind Admiral Strauss that only with the greatest difficulty and in the face of such continuing criticism have we preserved the understanding that we should not publish the Zeta results forthwith. The Prime Minister will be put in an intolerable political position if there were now a prior United States announcement. The fact that this dealt only with 'some aspects of unclassified work' would do little or nothing to lessen the gravity of the situation. The important thing from the United Kingdom political view would be that the much criticised silence had been broken unilaterally by the Americans. I am convinced that had I not been able to assure the Prime Minister there would be no American publication before February 1 he would have found it most difficult to agree to joint announcements on that date . . .

I should be grateful if you would also in this connexion give Admiral Strauss a personal message from me. It is that, as he knows, I have exerted all my influence in an endeavour to see the United States and the United Kingdom act jointly in this matter. If I fail I shall be placed in a position of such difficulty vis-a-vis both Ministers and my colleagues and staff that my power to further the cause of collaboration which both Admiral Strauss and I have at heart will be seriously reduced . . .

> Our general policy is that we should do all we can to make sure that it is treated in its right scientific perspective and proportions and to do our best to avoid the sort of sensational presentation which will, in the popular mind, make this seem like another Sputnik race. To achieve this objective the right thing is to have publication of the results centre round the sort of statement of scientific fact that is most appropriately published in a paper in 'Nature'.[8]

Agreement was eventually reached, and a full press release was put out by the UKAEA on 24 January, 1958. There were some agreed guidance notes as part of the release to give further background information.

> In discussing this announcement with the press and others a number of considerations should be borne in mind:
>
> (a) During recent months the Authority have been unable to comment on the progress of this research because it was — until recently — covered by certain security agreements to which Britain and the USA are parties. During this period of silence the press, both at home and abroad, have indulged in a wealth of speculation as to the exact nature of the results obtained and their implications. Most of these speculations have been highly exaggerated. Some are given the impression that power generation from fusion was a practical possibility within one or two years, with some adverse (though temporary) effects on the price of uranium shares.
>
> (b) Although the USA will be making an announcement about their own research in this field on the same day, the results they have obtained are less impressive. In the light of the recent Sputnik incident, American opinion will obviously be sensitive to odious comparisons.
>
> The publicity which the Authority is planning in the United Kingdom is designed to place the results of Harwell's research in their correct perspective as a considerable scientific achievement, but not to exaggerate them beyond this limit. Any success which UK publicity on atomic energy is attained can undoubtedly be ascribed to a determination to avoid claims which outrun the facts. Harwell's achievement should not be played down — it is a considerable feather in the caps of the British and Commonwealth scientists concerned. But it should not be inflated.
>
> Two points are to be particularly borne in mind:
>
> (i) No suggestion should be countenanced that fusion power reactors are just round the corner. Apart from any other considerations, this could militate against the export prospects for British fission reactors.
>
> (ii) in research of this kind, the major atomic powers rarely have more than a short lead over each other at any given moment in their places in the race are constantly re-shuffled — sometimes from month to month.[9]

Even the Cabinet was warned to be circumspect in any speeches they might be intending to make:

> The Home Secretary informed the Cabinet that an announcement would be made on 24th January of the recent achievement of a controlled thermo-nuclear reaction at the Atomic Energy Research Establishment. It was desirable that Ministers, in any public reference to this achievement, should describe it in terms which, while

> in no way diminishing the significance of this further advance by the United Kingdom in the development of nuclear energy, should not excite premature expectations of its commercial application or imply that we had necessarily established a decisive advantage over other countries with whom we sought to co-operate in nuclear research.[10]

Despite the circumlocutions, it is not difficult to guess which 'other country' was being referred to.

A major press conference was held at Harwell on 23 January with not only the British press but also representatives from foreign newspapers and a BBC outside broadcast unit, which was a distinct novelty in those early days of the media. During the conference Cockcroft was asked how confident he was that thermonuclear fusion had been achieved, and after several promptings, made the assertion that he was '90% certain'. This was distinctly unwise, since journalists and editors like clear-cut stories. The publicity was widespread, causing Harwell to issue another statement saying that 'there are good reasons to think that [the neutrons] come from thermonuclear reactions' but that this 'has not yet been definitely established'.[11] The press were not interested in such caveats, and Cockcroft and Harwell would come to regret the wide publicity achieved by ZETA.

FRANCE-SOIR 26-27 JANVIER 1958

SOURCE D'UNE ENERGIE INEPUISABLE : RESERVE POUR UN MILLIARD D'ANNEES

Le soleil artificiel est né dans un cube de béton, sous un vieux hangar d'aviation dans la campagne anglaise

Dans 20 ans – pensent les savants britanniques – des centrales thermo-nucléaires s'élèveront sur les côtes et puiseront leur combustible directement dans la mer

Figure 9.5. The story was not only news in Britain but also abroad. (The caption translates as 'The artificial sun is born in a concrete cube, inside an old aircraft hangar in the English countryside'.)

It is surprising in some ways that Cockcroft was prepared to make such a premature announcement, although no doubt he was under considerable pressure from the press on one side and from the expectations of his colleagues on the other. There was probably a more general hope for good news to bolster Britain's self-confidence which also weighed on Cockcroft, but the fact remained that the origins of neutrons being produced in ZETA were still uncertain, and there were certainly other groups working on thermonuclear fusion, who might well have been brought in to help investigate. Inter-group rivalries prevented this, or possibly a simple lack of communication between them.

A Harwell physicist, Basil Rose, who was not part of the ZETA team but was at the press conference, together with a colleague, AE Taylor, were able to work out a method of discovering the origins of the neutrons being observed. They set up a device which could measure the energy of the neutrons emitted, and discovered that the number of neutrons emitted with a particular energy when the current was flowing in one direction round the torus was different to the number when the current was flowing in the opposite direction. If the neutrons had come from fusion, the two sets of readings should have been the same.[12] ZETA's neutrons were not from fusion after all.

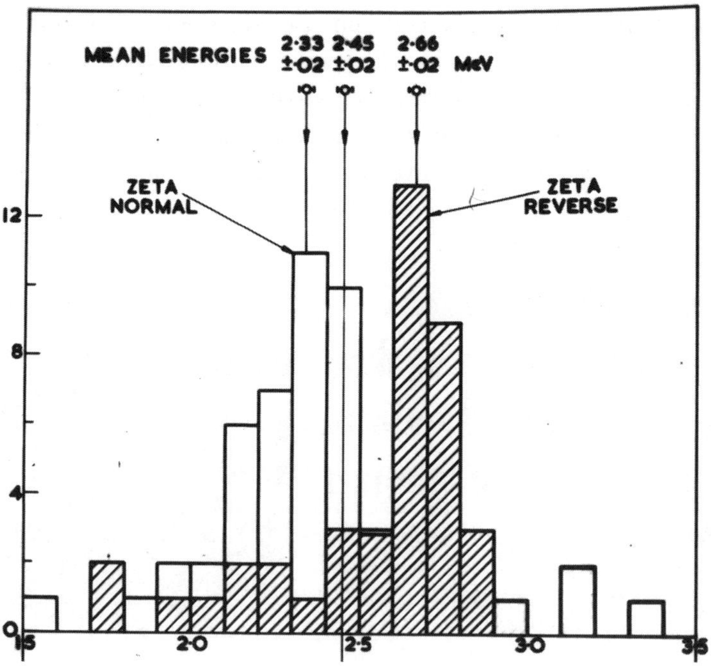

Figure 9.6. Neutrons flowing in opposite direction had different energies. This showed that they could not have been a result of nuclear fusion.

As can be imagined, the news was not received well in the press. ZETA was written off as a failure, which is not quite true. Although the claims for fusion had been misplaced and overhyped, ZETA was still able to provide valuable data on the behaviour of a plasma in magnetic fields.

Despite the setback, there was still considerable interest in controlled thermonuclear research (referred to as CTR in all the internal documents), and the hangar in which ZETA had been built was running out of space. It was proposed that the

CTR work be moved to the new site at Winfrith Heath in Dorset, but there was considerable opposition from the CTR team, who thought the site too remote. Instead, the fusion work moved to an entirely new site at nearby Culham, which had been a Royal Naval station, HMS Hornbill. This was near Abingdon in Oxfordshire, and only about 10 miles from Harwell.[13]

Later work on CTR by the Russians in the 1960s was more successful, with a device called a tokamak. This was very similar to ZETA, but with one important difference.

As the charged particles flow round the torus, they create a magnetic field around it. In ZETA, the magnetic field created by the coils around the torus was less than the field produced by the current. In a tokamak, the reverse is true, making for a much more stable plasma.

Research has continued at Culham ever since, and it is probably the last major nuclear centre left in the UK other than the Atomic Weapons Establishment at Aldermaston. Currently it is home to JET, or the Joint European Torus, which is a large tokamak now being used as a precursor for an even larger international project, ITER, which will be built in France. Construction of the JET began in 1978 and was completed in 1982, with the first experiments beginning in 1983. It is now acting as a test bed for ITER.

---

1 R Carruthers (1988). 'The Beginnings of Fusion at Harwell', *Plasma Physics and Controlled Fusion* 30(14), 1993–2001.

2 TNA: PRO AB 17/180. Facts About ZETA.

3 Israel invaded Egypt in October 1956. Britain and France then intervened amidst allegations of collusion with the Israeli government.

4 TNA: PRO PREM 11/2556. UK and US publicity on results obtained from ZETA, apparatus at Harwell for producing thermo-nuclear reaction. Macmillan to Plowden, 13 December 1957.

5 TNA: PRO PREM 11/2556. UK and US publicity on results obtained from ZETA, apparatus at Harwell for producing thermo-nuclear reaction. Plowden to Macmillan, 2 January 1958.

6 Later to become a Minister of State at the Board of Trade, Minister of Defence (Equipment), Minister of Power, President of the Board of Trade, Secretary of State for Defence, then Secretary of State for Northern Ireland.

7 Controlled Thermo-Nuclear Reactions (Experiments), House of Commons Debate (Fifth series), 21 January 1958, Vol. 580, c. 888.

8 TNA: PRO PREM 11/2556. UK and US publicity on results obtained from ZETA, apparatus at Harwell for producing thermo-nuclear reaction. Plowden to Sir Harold Caccia, 3 January 1958.

9 *Ibid.*

[10] TNA: PRO CAB 128/32. Cabinet conclusions: 1(58)–88(58). Minutes of a Cabinet meeting held on 22 January 1958.

[11] TNA: PRO PREM 11/2556. UK and US publicity on results obtained from ZETA, apparatus at Harwell for producing thermo-nuclear reaction. 'Controlling the Fusion Reaction.' 24 January 1958.

[12] TNA: PRO AB 6/2127. ZETA and Controlled Thermonuclear Reactor Project.

[13] TNA: PRO AB 16/2364. Experimental fusion reactor, ZETA.

Chapter 10

Research Reactors

LIDO and DIDO, HECTOR and HERO, BEPO and GLEEP — not characters from Greek mythology, but research reactors; built not to produce electricity or plutonium, but as sources of neutrons, as test beds for new systems, or for materials testing (to see how different materials withstood neutron bombardment or radiation damage). It was cheaper and easier to test out new technology in a relatively inexpensive research reactor than to have it fail when built as a part of a much bigger system. Fuel rods are a good example: many different materials and configurations of fuel rod were devised then fabricated and put through intensive testing in the materials testing reactors before going into manufacture.

Other than power reactors, the many reactors which were built in Britain can be classified in various different ways. There were the reactors designed to produce plutonium for military purposes — in particular the two Windscale piles. The PIPPA design, which later became the Calder Hall and Chapelcross reactors, was intended to produce both power and plutonium. There were also prototype reactors which were intermediate in size between research reactors and full-scale power reactors. The Windscale AGR was just such a reactor and the two fast reactors at Dounreay were also prototypes, as was the SGHWR at Winfrith. These were built to iron out all the engineering bugs before producing a full-sized commercial design. The commercial AGR design was based on the Windscale AGR, but the fast reactors and the heavy water reactor remained as prototypes and were never put into commercial operation.

Research reactors can be further subdivided into two categories: one being for direct research such as studying physical phenomena and the nuclear characteristics of different materials, and the other being for what might be described as materials testing. The materials testing reactors would have a high neutron flux to allow experiments to be made on reactor components such as fuel elements.

Figure 10.1. BEPO — British Experimental Pile 0. (Image courtesy of NDA and copyright NDA.)

GLEEP and BEPO fell mainly into the first category. GLEEP in particular was used for measuring neutron absorption properties of materials, and BEPO used to produce radioisotopes. The main materials testing reactors included three reactors which were of very similar design: DIDO and PLUTO at Harwell, and the DMTR (Dounreay Materials Testing Reactor) at Dounreay. DIDO and PLUTO were designed to be as versatile as possible, so that a variety of different experiments could be carried out simultaneously.

Other reactors were purpose built for specific tasks. ZEBRA (zero-energy breeder reactor assembly), for example, was built to investigate the neutron physics of fast reactors, which have no moderator.[1] Many were 'zero-energy' reactors, which are systems which operate at a very low power level so that the component parts of the system did not become significantly radioactive. Additionally, shielding and an external cooling system were not required. Alterations in design could be made very easily and the overall nuclear properties of a wide range of systems could be determined quickly and empirically. The nuclear effect of a coolant inside the reactor could be seen by including it in a static form within the zero-energy system. The results could then be scaled up for the design of much larger reactors.

An example of this would be the reactor called VERA, which was commissioned at Aldermaston in February 1961. A description of the reactor states that

> Up to April 1963 the reactor was used for studies of assemblies containing U235 and U238 mixed with various amounts of graphite and polythene. Work with

plutonium cores started in April 1963. The future programme will include studies both uranium and plutonium with detailed spectrum measurements.[2]

Figure 10.2. The DIDO reactor at Harwell, used for test purposes. (Image courtesy of NDA and copyright NDA.)

On the other hand, certain nuclear effects will only be seen when a reactor is operating at a high neutron flux. One of the first of these to be discovered was the so-called xenon poisoning. Xenon 135, which has a half-life of 9.2 hours, is formed from the decay of iodine 135, which is a relatively common fission product with a half-life of 6.6 hours. Hence soon after a reactor is started up, iodine 135 is produced, which then decays into xenon 135. Xenon 135 has an extremely large neutron capture cross-section, so that some of it will decay and some of it will absorb neutrons. This results in a large wastage of neutrons, as they are being absorbed by the xenon rather than contributing to the activity of the pile. After some hours, an equilibrium concentration of iodine and xenon will have built up. The presence of the xenon has to be allowed for when calculating the reactivity of the reactor.

Xenon poisoning is thought to be one of the causes of the explosion of the reactor at Chernobyl. When the reactor was powered down, there were few neutrons available to remove the xenon 135, but it was still being produced from the decay of the iodine 135, and so its concentration increased. When the operators attempted to increase the power of the reactor, the extra neutrons were being absorbed by the xenon. They then removed the control rods further to force the pile into greater activity, which in turn burned away the extra xenon, making the pile very much more active, causing voids of steam to appear in the cooling water, making the pile more active still and driving it out of control.

Although many of the names of the reactors can be seen as acronyms, their derivation was somewhat fanciful. The first heavy water reactor was christened DIDO — heavy water being deuterium oxide, D_2O, or, stretching things, DDO — hence DIDO. Another example was a new heavy water zero-energy reactor being built at Harwell in 1960. A note was sent to the Director:

> I gather that in the past it has been the prerogative of the Director to select a name for large pieces of equipment... we have had some names suggested for the new reactor and they fall into two categories — those formed from abbreviations and those which are symbolic. You may like to choose from this list, or suggest an alternative yourself.[3]

Among the symbolic names suggested were MENTOR and MONITOR, DATUM and ORACLE. Among the abbreviations (more correctly known as acronyms) were LEOPARD, standing for low energy pile for reactor development, and ZEST, for zero-energy support reactor.

A slightly pompous reply was duly received:

> Sir Basil Schonland proposes that your new reactor should be known as DAPHNE, rather than any of the names suggested in your memo of the 1st September.
>
> Although not a water nymph, Daphne was reputed to be the daughter of a river. The letters could also be regarded as standing for "Dido's and Pluto's Handmaiden in Nuclear Engineering".[4]

Unlike the Harwell reactors, the third DIDO reactor at Dounreay went by the rather more mundane name of Dounreay materials test reactor or DMTR. This system of naming seems to have been a tradition confined to Harwell and Winfrith.

A major role for such research reactors was testing fuel elements, which was referred as 'loop' testing. A loop was a hole or channel through the reactor, and the fuel elements to be tested were placed inside the channel. The cooling system would then run through the channel and around the elements. At either end of the channel, usually on a platform built outside the reactor, was a complete replica of all the apparatus necessary to operate the channel, i.e. the pumps for pushing the coolant through, the burst slug detection gear, heat exchangers and so on. in effect, the loop was a miniature reactor with only a single channel instead of many.

In the early 1950s, when demand for such testing arose, facilities were limited, with only BEPO and the Windscale piles being available, although some use was made of the Canadian NRX pile at Chalk River.[5] To supplement these, the DIDO class reactors (three reactors were built in the UK and three were exported) were built specifically to be used for loop testing.

GLEEP and BEPO

GLEEP, which stood for graphite low energy experimental pile, was the first reactor to operate in Western Europe, and went critical for the first time on August 15 1947.[6] It was not the first operational reactor in Europe: the first Soviet nuclear reactor had gone critical on Christmas Day 1946, at 6 p.m. local time at the Kurchatov Institute in Moscow.

Built at Harwell, it was designed to meet two main requirements, which were to run at as high a power as possible without elaborate cooling arrangements, and to measure slow neutron absorption cross-sections of various different elements.

> The pile was built in the form of an octagonal prism of graphite lying on its side. The core, which had 676 fuel channels, was loaded with uranium metal bars 12 inches long and 0.9 inches diameter, which were sprayed with aluminium of 0.003 inch thickness to prevent the escape of fission products. The outer sections of the core were loaded with uranium dioxide, pressed into pellets 1.6 inches in diameter and 2 inches long. These were wrapped in paper containers and inserted in batches of six into aluminium cans. The reactor contained 12 tons of uranium metal and 21 tons of uranium dioxide.[7]

Figure 10.3. GLEEP under construction. (Image courtesy of NDA and copyright NDA.)

The graphite was a mixture of British and Canadian manufacture. As the Canadian contained fewer impurities such as lithium and boron, it was used in the centre of the reactor and the British towards the outside.

> The ventilation system for the pile was capable of moving 5,000 cubic feet per minute. This was intended to remove radioactive argon (a fission product) and to

> provide some cooling of the uranium cartridges. The air is extracted by a suction fan on the top of the pile. This means that the pressure of air inside the pile is always less than atmospheric pressure, which means there will be no leak of radioactive air into the building. The air was vented through a stack, the top of which was 60 feet above ground level. By using the air-cooling system, the pile could be run at a power of 100 kW.

In a lecture on the 20 September 1947, HWB Skinner, Cockcroft's deputy at Harwell, described the build-up to criticality thus:

> About the beginning of July [1947] stacking of the graphite began, and it was completed, well ahead of schedule, in about one month. The uranium was then introduced slowly. As the neutron multiplication factor increased with increasing uranium, so the approach of pile towards criticality could be noted by the readings of a BF_3 [boron trifluoride] chamber recording the flux density of the neutrons in the pile. On August 7th, when the pile obtained several tons of uranium, the counter recorded 17 neutrons per minute. By August 11th the figure was 55 neutrons per minute, by the morning of August 15th, 2400 and by the afternoon 6600. At this point the chamber saturated, the pile being almost divergent. On loading a little more uranium, the pile became divergent and worked at about 0.1 watt, the power increasing exponentially but with a very long time constant. The control rods were then somewhat withdrawn and the time constant decreased so the power rose fairly rapidly to 100 watts, at which point the shut-off rods, which had been set for this figure, operated and shut down the pile.[8]

Figure 10.4. The GLEEP commissioning team.

There were four control rods which moved together to act as a coarse control, with a fifth which was used as a fine control. These were made of cadmium and could be moved up and down using electric motors which were situated outside the pile and operated from the control room. There were also two sets of three rods which were for an emergency shutdown. These were held outside the pile when it was in operation using magnetic clutches, and when the pile power rose above a certain level, the current to the clutches was cut so that the emergency rods fell into the pile under gravity.

In the early days of nuclear research, very little was known about the nuclear properties of various materials and elements. One important property was the neutron cross-section of an atom, which is a measure of the likelihood of an interaction between a neutron and a target nucleus. This cross-section is measured in barns, a barn being 10^{-28} m^2. The neutron may be absorbed by the nucleus or scattered by collision. Knowledge of the neutron cross-section of all the different materials in a reactor is essential if the reactivity of the reactor is to be successfully calculated. One disadvantage of an open air-cooled pile was that changes of atmospheric pressure could affect the power of the reactor, since nitrogen has a relatively high cross-section for thermal neutrons.

Much of the experimental work with GLEEP was done with an apparatus called the oscillator. This took small samples rapidly from the edge of the pile to the centre. The samples were moved in and out of the pile with periodic motion, which produced a periodic modulation in the power level of the pile. From the change in power level, the degree of neutron absorption by the sample could be measured.

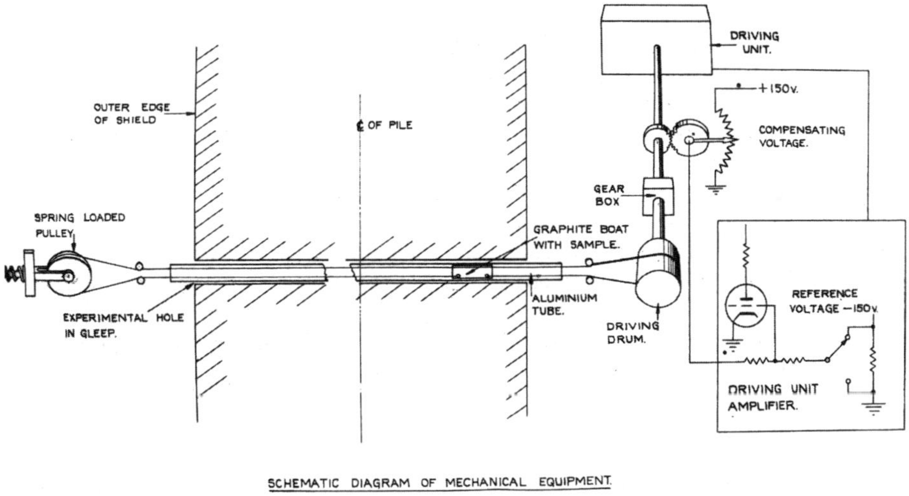

Figure 10.5. The GLEEP oscillator. The sample would be moved in and out of the reactor periodically, and the change in activity in the reactor meant the neutron absorption of the material could be measured.

GLEEP had other functions. In particular it was used for irradiating samples of materials with neutrons, thus producing radioactive isotopes for medical and commercial use.

> Designed to operate at a maximum of 100 kW, the reactor ran at 80 kW for 18 months for the purpose of producing radioactive isotopes until BEPO was commissioned. The reactor then reverted to its planned use which was the nuclear

testing of materials to be used in other reactors. Its maximum operating power was limited to 3 kW to minimise radioactivity of samples produced.[9]

Users would be charged for this service, as the minutes of a meeting at Harwell in 1948 illustrate:

It was decided that as an interim measure the following handling charges be made for standard containers.

Single irradiations	£3 3s 0d
Repeat irradiations	£2 2s 0d

Valuable target material will be supplied by the user, or charged for at commercial rates. Special rates will be quoted for non-standard irradiations.

Transport to London and delivery there (or putting material on board trains) would be charged at a flat rate of £1 0s 0d package.

Mr Jones stated that a reasonable cost for transport elsewhere would be at the rate of one shilling per mile.[10]

Even allowing for inflation, these prices seem extremely good value!

In 1960, GLEEP was overhauled, as the following paper describes:

GLEEP, Europe's first reactor, has received an extensive overhaul after having been in use at the Atomic Energy Research Establishment, Harwell for nearly 13 years. This modernisation will increase the safety and efficiency of the reactor and will enable it to give valuable service for many further years.

GLEEP first went critical on 15th August, 1947 and since that date has operated on the original loading of fuel and without major modifications. It was recently decided the time had come when if the highest degree of safety and efficiency were to be maintained, some modernisation of the reactor and its instrumentation would be necessary. At the beginning of March the reactor was shut down and the 33 tons of fuel in the form of canned uranium oxide and bare uranium bars were unloaded. The latter were some of the first examples of uranium fabrication in this country and had deteriorated with time. To give maximum safety during unloading the mechanism for pushing out the fuel was designed to supply argon as a blanket which would eliminate any possibility of fire, while powerful vacuum cleaners removed particulate matter and thus reduced friction.

The unloading was carried out by workers who entered the space between the reactor core and the five foot thick biological shield of concrete. This is possible as the reactor operates at extremely low power and there is negligible residual radioactivity. The fuel has since been sent by road for reprocessing at Windscale. Each of the five consignments was packed in sealed steel boxes within a large shielded container.

The reactor has been recharged with fuel elements originally intended for the Windscale reactors closed down following the fire which occurred in Pile Number 1 during October, 1957. These fuel elements are formed of natural uranium which, unlike GLEEP's original fuel, is canned in aluminium. Due to the low power at which GLEEP operates (3KW) the build up of Wigner energy is so slow that there is no possibility of an incident similar to that which occurred at Windscale.

During the shut-down of GLEEP the reactor instrumentation was completely removed. The two previous control rooms for the reactor, oscillator and train

> have now been combined in one entirely new control room which commands an extensive view of the reactor and experimental facilities.
>
> Most of the new instrumentation is conventional although the opportunity has been taken of fitting transistorised linear and deviation amplifiers. This is the first use of working transistor units in the U.K.[11]

GLEEP also became a standard for thermal neutron flux for the National Physics Laboratory.

> The reactor is used principally for materials testing, making use of the oscillator. This takes small samples rapidly from the edge of the pile to the centre, and back again. The resultant fluctuation of power level is measured and the slow neutron absorption cross-sections of different materials compared. Samples of every batch of graphite made in this country for use as a moderator in reactors of the Civil Power Programme are tested in GLEEP. So, too, are other specimen components for reactors.[12]

After continuous operation for 43 years, GLEEP was closed in 1990. Until the fuel could be removed, extra control rods were inserted into the core. Stage two decommissioning involved the removal of fuel and control rods, then leaving the reactor in a state of care and maintenance. 11,500 fuel elements rods had to be removed, with workers using rods to push out the elements manually into a retrieval unit. The reactor was finally demolished in 2005.

Figure 10.6. A cutaway view of GLEEP.

BEPO was designed by British scientists who were then working at the Montreal laboratory in Canada during 1945–6. The Department of Atomic Energy at Risley, who were responsible for the engineering design and construction, began work on the project early in 1946, and the Ministry of Works began the actual construction at Harwell in June 1946. Like GLEEP, BEPO was graphite-moderated with horizontal channels for the uranium bars, and cooled with air, but it was intended to operate at much higher power levels than GLEEP — its normal operating power was 6 MW.

The graphite moderator was made of several thousand separate blocks, and stringent precautions had to be taken to ensure clean conditions and keep out dust and other impurities which might have a high neutron capture cross-section and so prevent the pile from working. Construction sites are not noted for their freedom from dust, and so the shield was built as a complete box, the air ducts and all holes through the shield sealed off, the inside of the pile meticulously cleaned and then lightly pressurised with clean air before graphite stacking was started. The entire shield therefore had to be constructed as a unit and one of the problems in the construction of the pile was the extreme accuracy with which the pile shield, made of around 3,000 tons of concrete and 600 tons of steel, had to be assembled so that the continuity and alignment of the 3,800 holes common to both the graphite and shield were preserved.

The moderator was built up from standard blocks each 7.25 inches square and 29 inches long, with all the holes already drilled through them. 850 tons of graphite needed machining into around 25,000 blocks with more than 60 variations on the basic types. The machining tolerance adopted was ± 0.0025 inches on all dimensions, and the accuracy was such that the total height of the 26 foot complete stack was correct to within 0.03 inch.

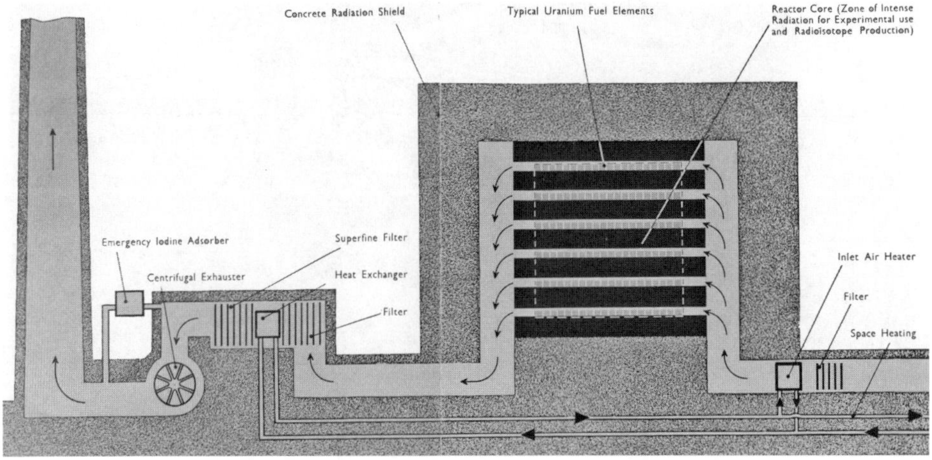

Figure 10.7. Diagrammatic view of BEPO.

BEPO had a critical loading of 28 tons of uranium metal, and a full uranium load of 40 tons. The air-cooling system was designed to limit the maximum surface temperature of the fuel elements to 200°C. Loading to critical size took place on 5 July 1948, the uranium being added channel by channel until the pile became divergent. In the ensuing months the pile was gradually worked up to full power by Christmas 1948.[13]

BEPO was constructed in one of the four large hangars built originally for aircraft when Harwell was an RAF base, although a section of the roof had to be raised by 20 feet to provide additional headroom. Large blowers were needed to draw around 180,000 cubic feet per minute of air (around 85 m^3/s or around 110 kg/s) through the pile, and filters were installed in the air intake to clean the air before it was passed through the pile. Another set of filters were installed between the pile and the blowers to remove any trace of radioactive dust before the cooling air was vented into a stack which was 200 feet tall.

BEPO was a much higher powered reactor than GLEEP, and needed much greater cooling. This was to be done with a flow of air, and the choice was between blowing the air into the pile or extracting it. The advantage of extracting the air was that there would be a negative pressure within the pile which meant that any leakage of air out of the holes through the shield wall would involve fresh air moving inwards, but not activated air or dust moving outwards.

The pile was loaded by pushing in a row of slugs from the charge face of the pile, and unloaded by means of steel pushrods which pushed the irradiated uranium slugs out through the unloaded face into a lead shielded container. The holes through the shield were plugged to prevent the escape of radiation except when an individual channel was being loaded or unloaded.

Since the irradiated uranium cartridges would be radioactive on removal, a concrete storage block was built which could accommodate around five tons of cartridges. Other irradiated material had to be withdrawn direct from the pile into lead flasks and a feature of the pile building was the overhead crane system so that these heavy flasks can be easily moved around.

The design of the Windscale piles had been based on BEPO, and after the discovery of the effects of Wigner energy in the production piles, it was decided that BEPO would also need annealing periodically. This became rather sensitive politically after the 1957 fire; so much so that Plowden felt it circumspect to write to the Prime Minister before the next release.

> The Atomic Energy Authority propose to carry out a release of Wigner energy on the research reactor BEPO at Harwell. The operation is planned to begin in the late afternoon of 14th March and should be over in 24 hours.
>
> This was the operation which led to the Windscale accident. It has, however, been carried out successfully from time to time in the past, and the Fleck

Committee have approved that it should be carried out again when required, subject to certain technical conditions which will be observed.[14]

When it came to the question of a public announcement, Plowden's syntax becomes extremely garbled:

> We have considered whether there should be a prior public announcement of the proposed Wigner release. The Authority's view is that there should not be any such announcement, although if, as is not unlikely, it becomes known and questions are put to us, we should propose to confirm that the operation is to be carried out, stressing that this is with the approval of the Fleck Committee. We regard it as a normal operation, which should not be represented, and is not in fact, so unusual or dangerous as to require a public statement, especially when this might stimulate unjustified public alarm
>
> I would be grateful to know if you agree.

The Prime Minister scribbled a handwritten comment near the bottom of the letter: 'I agree. HM'.

Whether public alarm would be justified is a good question: certainly if the same procedure as before had been proposed then it probably would have been. Instead, a new technique was to be used.

Penney's report on the Windscale fire had blamed the incident on a uranium cartridge catching fire during a Wigner release, so using the same technique on BEPO — nuclear heating — was obviously out of the question. Instead, it was decided to leave the fuel in the reactor and heat the incoming air with electric heaters instead.

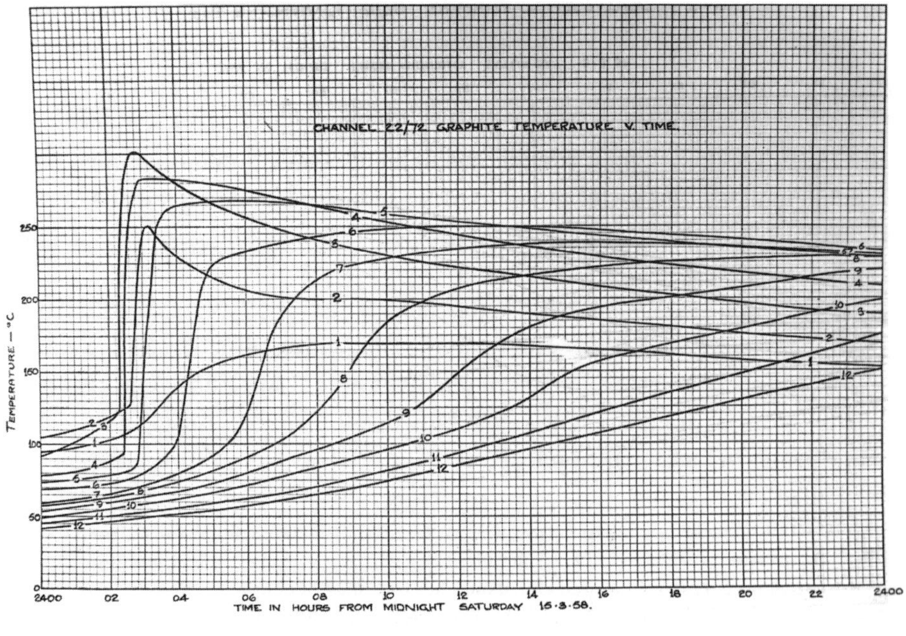

Figure 10.8. Temperature readings from the BEPO annealing.

The graph (Figure 10.8) shows the thermocouple readings from within the reactor.[15] As can be seen, two hours into the heating, the temperatures in most of the channels suddenly rises very rapidly as the release begins. There is obviously little or no release by thermocouple number 12, but the effect on some of the others is very marked. In the event, the Wigner release passed by with very little incident.

BEPO was closed down in 1968, when it was replaced by the materials testing reactors, DIDO and PLUTO, and it was then taken to stage one decommissioning, which involved the removal of the fuel and other items.

Other Research Reactors

This section does not cover the prototype reactors, nor the reactors built to investigate particular designs. Instead, the reactors described below were used for research and general materials testing. They were based at various sites: mainly Harwell and Winfrith, but also Aldermaston, Dounreay and Windscale. They are described in no particular order.

DIMPLE

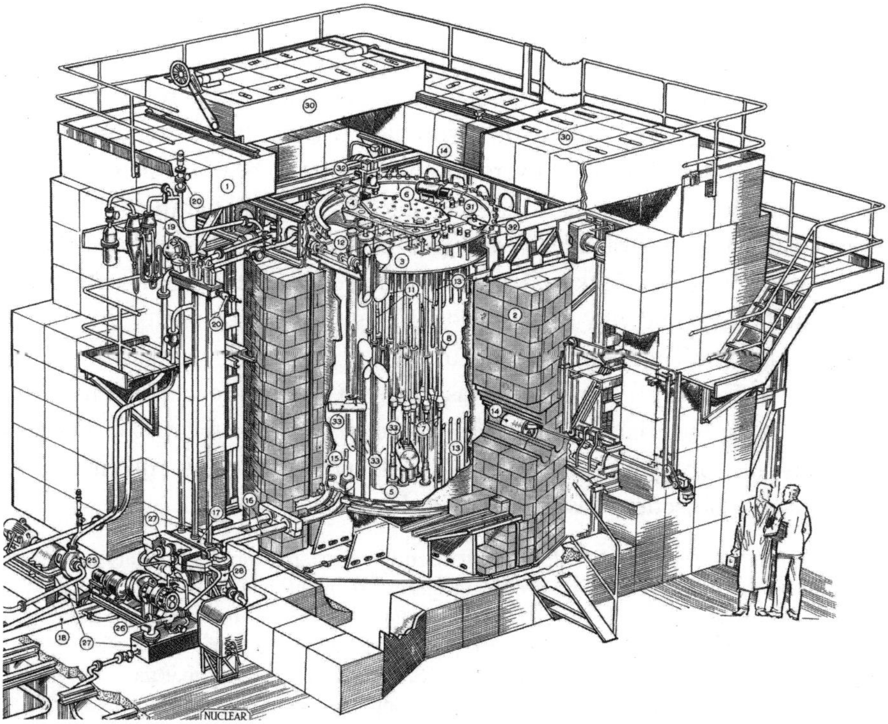

Figure 10.9. DIMPLE — deuterium moderated pile, low energy. (Courtesy of *Nuclear Engineering International.*)

The nickname DIMPLE was an acronym based on deuterium moderated pile, low energy, and was the third reactor to be built at Harwell after GLEEP and BEPO. It first went critical in July 1954 and was the first to use heavy water (deuterium oxide) as a moderator. The heavy water moderator was contained in a tank surrounded by a graphite neutron reflector. Outside this was a concrete radiation shield. The reactor fuel itself was submerged in the heavy water. Both the type of fuel and its arrangement in the tank could be changed quickly so that what is, in effect, a different design of reactor could be built up in a matter of a few days.[16] After the Reactor Group moved to Winfrith, DIMPLE was dismantled and rebuilt at the new site, and used for a wide variety of experiments.

DIDO, PLUTO and DMTR

These reactors were originally proposed to carry out materials research in support of the power reactor programme. An early plan had been to build a heavy water-moderated pile to produce plutonium, nicknamed HIPPO. There were problems with building this reactor at Harwell; in particular the discharge of radioactive effluent. Any liquid effluent discharged at Harwell, which was in the Thames basin, would find its way into the river, and this obviously limited the amount and nature of the discharge possible. There were also doubts about building such a high-powered reactor in such a heavily populated area. Thus HIPPO was abandoned.[17]

Instead, there were proposals to build heavy water-moderated research reactors, and this produced one of the few rows with the Treasury. It is remarkable looking at the files of the AEA how little oversight there seems to be of the money that was spent and in times of government cutbacks the AEA seemed hardly to be affected. However, Treasury approval had to be sought for items costing more than £100,000. In effect, this meant that Cockcroft would write a letter describing the nature of the proposal and explaining why it was needed. This seems to be one of the very few occasions when the Treasury raised any objects.

One of the Treasury's complaints was that the Canadian reactor at Chalk River could be used for materials testing, and it was explained that the reactor in Canada was already fully occupied with American work and was not powerful enough. The Treasury's other objection was summarised thus:

> Willson [representing the AEA] emphasised that these reactors were purely for research purposes. He sought to make the general point that one of Harwell's main jobs is research on reactors and they must have reactors for that purpose if the staff are to be fully employed. The Treasury must of course make the rejoinder that we require stronger reasons for projects than the argument that they will give employment; we cannot be expected to approve schemes which are nothing better than the digging and filling in of holes, even though full employment would thereby be ensured.[18]

Figure 10.10. A cutaway view of the DIDO core.

Willson was not very pleased with this misrepresentation of his remarks:

> . . . a statement so astonishing that I find it hard to believe that he intends it to be taken seriously. If it isn't serious, however, I cannot understand why it is included. He attributes to me an absurd statement I certainly did not make — that the main reason for going ahead quickly was to keep our staff from idleness, and that — to the Treasury mind at least — this was comparable to digging holes and filling them in again.
>
> What I did stress was that a high proportion of our total effort at Harwell, in which considerable capital is invested, is devoted to theoretical, scientific and technological advances leading to new and better reactors. The type of design studies we were discussing represents the spearhead of our attack on reactor improvement, and to hold up this vital stage for relatively small sums of money makes nonsense of the whole planning of reactor work. I added that it would be more logical to slow down the entire programme, but I do not imagine even Beighton would expect to succeed in such [a] move at the present time.
>
> Is there no hope at all of any intelligent effort by the Treasury to understand what are the objectives of our work?[19]

It would not have been the first time that the Treasury objected to the funding of the project simply because they were not capable of understanding the rationale behind it.

Sir John Cockcroft described the need for these new reactors when writing to the Treasury requesting funds for the PLUTO reactor as follows:

> The programme of nuclear power development proposed in the Trend Report [the report on which the 1955 White Paper was based] depends for its achievement on the development of fuel elements for Stage 1 reactors which will withstand an irradiation of the order of 3000 megawatt days per ton. The reactors of later stages of the programme, such as fast reactors and homogeneous reactors, will again depend largely on the development of satisfactory fuel elements or liquid fuels.
>
> In order to carry out the tests in a reasonable time we require reactors giving a high neutron flux and we require much space as is possible.
>
> At the present time we make use of the following facilities:
>
> BEPO, the Chalk River NRX pile, and the Windscale piles.
>
> We are building at Harwell the heavy water research reactor E443 (Dido). This provides extensive facilities for testing of small samples and will also provide for one large-scale "loop" . . .
>
> We consider that in addition to this reactor the Authority requires much more extensive facilities for testing experimental fuel elements for PIPPAs, LEO and fast reactors . . .
>
> We require two types of facilities — the first should provide space for 6 to 8 'loops' in which fuel elements can be operated at their design temperature with the correct coolants but in which the flux should be rather higher than normal operation to shorten the testing period.
>
> For this service we would propose a variant of the E443 reactor designed specifically for testing of large-scale new systems. In most cases each loop will be an integral experiment giving information on a wide variety of the specialised reactor components such as fuel elements, coolants, burst slug detection gear, pumps, heat exchangers.
>
> To provide for this we require two reactors giving 16 loop positions. We recommend that one should be built at Harwell (Pluto) and one at Windscale [this would become the DMTR].
>
> Each reactor requires 10 tons heavy water . . . The cost of these reactors is estimated at £2 million each, inclusive of heavy water.[20]

DIDO and PLUTO were built at Harwell; DMTR stands for Dounreay materials test reactor, and was the first rector to be built at Dounreay. Various experiments could be set up in 'loops' with these reactors.[21] When applying to the Treasury for funds, a 'loop' was described thus:

> The method of testing fuel elements is referred to by our scientists as "loop" testing, which I think requires some explanation. A "loop" is in essence a hole or channel through a pile. Inside it are placed the fuel elements to be tested and through it and around the elements runs the cooling system devised for them. At either end of the channel, probably on a platform erected outside the reactor, is a complete replica of all the apparatus necessary to operate the channel, i.e. the pumps for pushing the coolant through, the Burst Slug Detection Gear, delay tanks, heat exchangers, etc. You will see, therefore, that a loop is a miniature reactor with only a single channel instead of many.[22]

Examples were given of the intended tests:

> We have to provide for the experimental testing of (a) PIPPA fuel elements, (b) LEO fuel elements, (c) homogeneous reactor aqueous liquid fuel, (d) fast reactor solid fuel elements, (e) fast reactor liquid fuel elements.

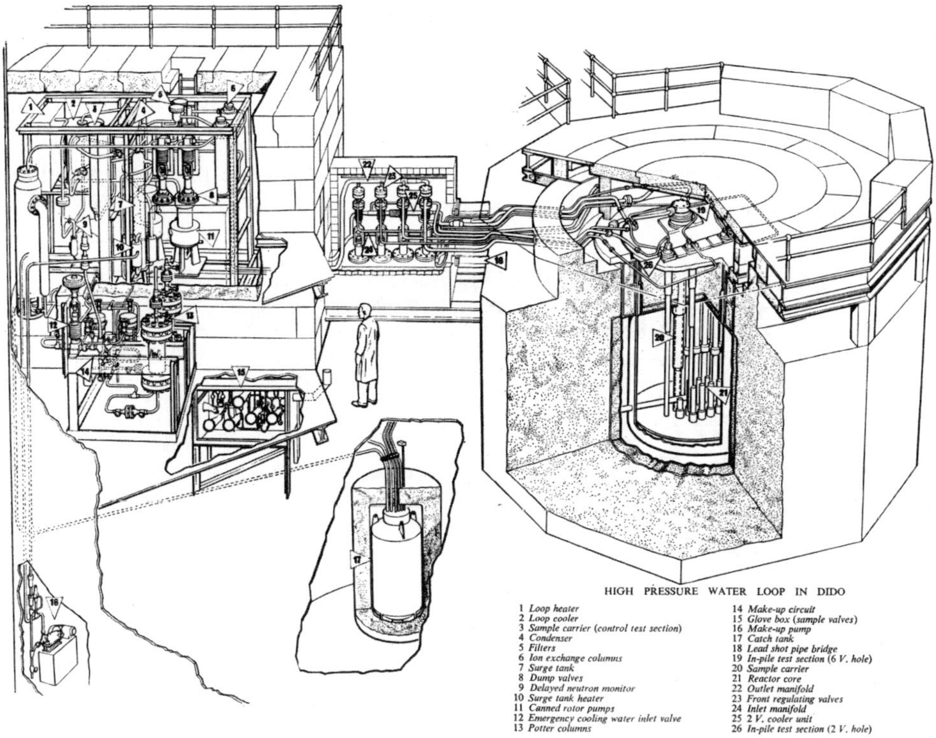

Figure 10.11. An example of a 'loop' in DIDO. This was designed to simulate the conditions in a reactor core for test purposes.

Neither GLEEP nor BEPO were entirely suitable for these sorts of experiments, and they were also limited in the number of experiments that could be carried out at any one time. The new class of reactor was designed so that it could accommodate a wide variety of experiments, and also had a much higher neutron flux than the older reactors. Although they were not identical, they were built to the same general specification and were described as the DIDO class of reactor, after the first to be built.

DIDO was built by the Ministry of Works in conjunction with the firm of Head Wrightson Processes Limited. It first went critical on 7 November 1956, and its official opening was on 21 November. It was nominally of 10 MW power, although it often ran at higher ratings.

The reactor core contained 2.9 kg of highly enriched uranium 235 in the form of 25 box-type elements, and each element contained ten plates of uranium–aluminium alloy sheathed in aluminium. The core was mounted in an aluminium tank of 80 inches diameter, surrounded by a graphite reflector 24 inches thick. This was contained in a steel tank lined with boral sheet which acted as a thermal neutron shield and beyond this was a 4 inch lead gamma shield. Outside the steel-lead shield was the barytes concrete bowl shielding, approximately 5 feet thick, in the shape of an irregular decagon. The whole reactor was 22 feet across by 21 feet high, and built inside an air-conditioned cylindrical steel containment building 70 feet high by 70 feet diameter. Air locks were used to access the working area. Below the reactor was a small shielded room containing the heavy water circulating pumps, heat exchangers, ion exchangers, dump tank, and storage tank, leaving the main reactor floor above completely clear for experimental equipment.

Figure 10.12. The top of the reactor core in PLUTO.

The core tank and some of the sealed sections of the reactor were pressurised to a little above atmospheric pressure with helium, and it was controlled using six single-arm type control rods and a fine control rod. Two safety rods were also provided. There was a complex system of guidelines and interlocks (which were integrated with the experimental equipment control circuits) to prevent malfunction of the reactor.[23]

There were 58 experimental holes in all, and as well as these built-in facilities, hollow fuel elements had been developed to enable damage experiments be carried out inside the elements where there is a very fast flux.

PLUTO was similar to DIDO except that it was intended more for major engineering loop testing, and had only a third of the number of holes as DIDO, but these were bigger and capable of taking much more complex items.

Three DIDO class reactors were also sold abroad — one to Australia, one to Germany, and one to Denmark.[24] The Australian reactor was known as HIFAR, an acronym for high flux Australian reactor, and first went critical in January 1958.[25] HIFAR was shut down in January 2007.

The German reactor was built at the Forschungszentrum Jülich GmbH (Jülich Research Centre) near Cologne and known as the FRJ-2. It was finally shut down in May 2006 after almost 44 years of operation.

Denmark had three nuclear research reactors at the Risø National Laboratory north of Roskilde on the island of Zeeland. DR-3 was based on the DIDO design and operated until 2000.

The AEA produced a book (*The Nuclear Energy Industry in the United Kingdom*, first published in September 1958[26]), which was intended as a sales pitch for British reactors, and the staffing requirements for DIDO were described thus:

> The reactor requires about 18 professional, 20 ancillary and 50 industrial operating staff. (It is assumed that a professional scientist or engineer has a university degree or equivalent, and ancillary worker has a lower professional qualification, and an industrial worker is trained on the job.) These figures relate to the people required in the reactor area for operation, maintenance, health and hygiene, chemical control, physics services, and housekeeping and exclude stores, workshops and specialist personnel, and make no allowance for scientific effort associated with the experiments in the reactor.
>
> The capital cost of construction is estimated at £2 million, with running costs in the region of £600,000.

LIDO

Another general purpose reactor was LIDO, which was designed initially for use by the Admiralty (see the section on nuclear submarines in Chapter 16) for testing materials to be used for shielding reactors.[27] Whilst land-based reactors could be surrounded by heavy biological shields, this was obviously not the case in a submarine, and so research into alternatives was needed. LIDO could also be used as a general purpose neutron source and that became its main function once the Admiralty had finished with it.

It could run at powers of up to 100 kW, and used the same type of fuel elements as the materials reactors. These were submerged in a tank of water 28 feet by 8 feet by 24 feet deep. The water acted both as coolant by natural convection and as moderator.[28] LIDO was closed down in 1972, and has since been fully decommissioned with the site being returned to greenfield.

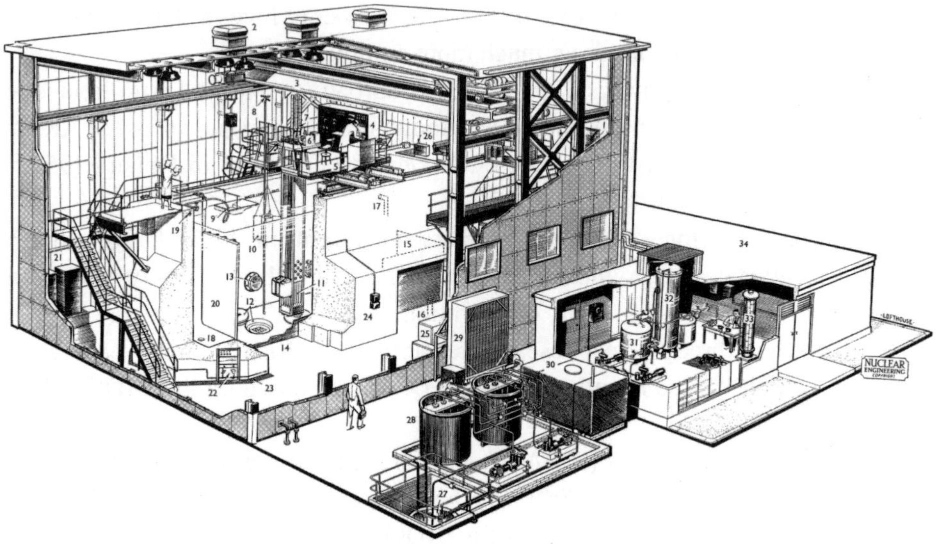

Figure 10.13. LIDO. This was a 'swimming pool' type reactor, built originally for the Admiralty to conduct experiments in shielding the radiation from reactors. The pool and core are labelled '10' in the drawing. (Image courtesy of *Nuclear Engineering International.*)

NESTOR

NESTOR, built at Winfrith, was based upon the JASON type of reactor (an American design) and constructed by the Hawker Siddeley Nuclear Power Company. It acted as a source of neutrons for the experimental assemblies of nuclear fuels and moderators used to obtain data for the design of reactor systems. JASON was modified to be capable of continuous operation at a power of up to 10 kW and its layout altered so that it could drive up to five experimental assemblies simultaneously. Natural water was used both as coolant and moderator.[29]

The name NESTOR (neutron source thermal reactor) was chosen because in Greek mythology Nestor was one of the Argonauts led by Jason in the quest for the Golden Fleece.

HERALD

The research reactor HERALD (highly enriched reactor Aldermaston) had been built at Aldermaston for military purposes but, around the time it was completed, the embargo on the supply of US warhead information was lifted and, as a result, the military experimental development programme was reduced. It thus became available for civilian and general purpose use. Part of its initial rationale was described thus:[30]

> It is, for example, of the greatest value to determine the transmission properties of neutrons of a particular energy through fissile material. There are laborious theoretical processes which can give part of this answer, but the time and calculating effort involved is enormous. A second example is in the estimation of performance of test weapons. "Tracer" elements can be incorporated in the weapon, the distribution of which after the explosion leads to quantitative assessments of the effects of individual processes leading to design of an efficient weapon. To ensure that the "tracer" elements are not masked by other radiochemical effects of the explosion, a systematic study the elements included in the weapon components and a neutron bombardment of the correct flux is essential. By this means, the best "tracers" can be determined.

A HERALD type reactor was sold to Chile by Fairey Engineering Ltd of Stockport, Cheshire.[31] Construction began in October 1970, with the reactor becoming critical in October 1974. It was built for the Comision Chilena De Energia Nuclear at a cost of £8 million and is still operational today.

HECTOR

Heated experimental carbon thermal oscillator reactor. This was built at Winfrith and became operational in March 1963. Like the oscillator in GLEEP, this was intended to study the neutron absorbing properties of materials.[32]

JASON

JASON was an Argonaut-type reactor, originally designed by the Argonne National Laboratory in America (In Greek mythology, Jason was the leader of the original Argonauts). It was built by the Hawker Siddeley Nuclear Power Corporation at Langley in Slough, Berkshire. Construction began in February 1959 and the reactor reached criticality on 30 September 1959.

Soon after the Hawker Siddeley Nuclear Power Co. Ltd suspended activities at their nuclear power division in June, 1961, the Admiralty expressed an interest in buying it, since it was unlikely that a new JASON type reactor would be built in the UK. The Navy chose to rebuild the reactor at its college at Greenwich — just over three miles as the crow flies from Tower Bridge in London.[33] The Royal

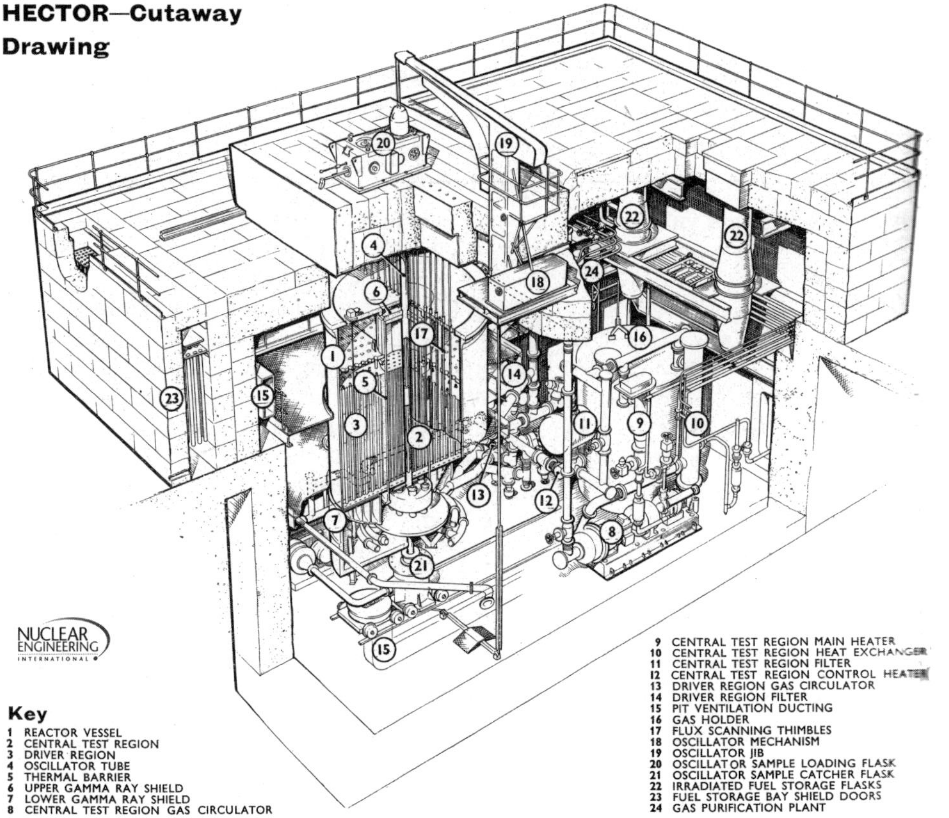

Figure 10.14. HECTOR. The crane for lowering the test sample into the reactor can be seen at the top (19 and 20). (Image courtesy of *Nuclear Engineering International.*)

Naval College building was the former Greenwich Hospital, built between 1696 and 1712 by Christopher Wren, where the reactor was located within the King William Building. It was operational at the site from 1962 to 1996 and used for training potential nuclear submarine captains.

---

1 TNA: PRO AB 6/2306. Zero energy reactor ZEBRA.

2 TNA: PRO AB 17/302. AEA publication: 'Reactors UK'.

3 TNA: PRO AB 6/2489. Zero Energy Reactor DAPHNE. WF Wood to Director AERE, 1 September 1960.

4 TNA: PRO AB 6/2489. Zero Energy Reactor DAPHNE. RE Lockett to Mr WF Wood, 22 September 1960.

5 TNA: PRO AB 16/1440. Fuel element testing reactor: PLUTO. TB Le Cren to JDK Beighton, Treasury Chambers, 4 January 1955.

6 TNA: PRO AB 6/2174. GLEEP; (graphite low energy experimental pile).

7 TNA: PRO AB 17/191. GLEEP. Graphite low energy experimental pile.

8 Sir John Cockcroft's deputy at Harwell until becoming Professor of Physics at Liverpool University in 1949.

9 TNA: PRO AB 17/191. GLEEP. Graphite low energy experimental pile,

10 TNA: PRO AB 6/328. Irradiation of material in GLEEP and BEPO.

11 TNA: PRO AB 6/2174. GLEEP; (graphite low energy experimental pile).

12 *Ibid.*

13 TNA: PRO AB 17/108. Harwell. The British Atomic Energy Research Establishment 1946–1951. (Re-issue of 1952 edition.)

14 TNA: PRO PREM 11/2557. Proposed release of Wigner energy on research reactor BEPO at Harwell. Sir Edwin Plowden to Prime Minister.

15 TNA: PRO AB 6/2015. Wigner energy release in BEPO.

16 TNA: PRO AB 16/908. Reactor programme: policy pre Authority.

17 TNA: PRO AB 6/1243. Heavy water research reactor (DIDO): E443 project, CP5 type: construction and operation. 'The Harwell Reactor Programme.' JD Cockcroft, 29 July 1953.

18 TNA: PRO AB 16/908. Reactor programme: policy pre Authority. 'Harwell reactor programme.' 16 October 1953.

19 TNA: PRO AB 16/908. Reactor programme: policy pre Authority. 'Harwell reactor programme.' 4 November 1953.

20 TNA: PRO AB 16/1440. Fuel element testing reactor: PLUTO.

21 TNA: PRO AB 6/2229. Research reactor study. 'Experiences of Loops.' RF Jackson, presented at European Atomic Energy Society Symposium on 'Experiences in the Use of Research Reactors.'

22 *Ibid.*

23 TNA: PRO AB 17/298. The Nuclear Energy Industry of the United Kingdom. This was published by the AEA in 1958, and was obviously intended as something of a sales brochure for overseas customers.

24 TNA: PRO AB 16/1840. DIDO reactor for Cologne.

25 TNA: PRO AB 16/3177. Australia; nuclear projects, HIFAR.

26 TNA: PRO AB 17/298. The Nuclear Energy Industry of the United Kingdom.

27 TNA: PRO AB 16/1642. Collaboration with the Admiralty.

28 TNA: PRO AB 17/202. LIDO. Shielding Reactor.

29 TNA: PRO AB 16/2961. Neutron Source Thermal Reactor NESTOR. See also TNA: PRO AB 17/102. NESTOR, Neutron Source Thermal Reactor. TNA: PRO AB 6/2312. Atomic Energy Establishment, Winfrith: NESTOR (JASON type) neutron source reactor. TNA: PRO AB 17/302. Reactors UK.

30 TNA: PRO AB 16/1420. AWRE Aldermaston: experimental pile R61, HERALD. See also TNA: PRO ES 4/1311. Description of the research reactor HERALD.

31 (1969). *ATOM* 148, February 1969.

[32] TNA: PRO AB 6/2305. Zero energy reactor HECTOR. See also TNA: PRO AB 17/100. HECTOR. Hot Enriched Carbon-moderated Thermal Oscillator Reactor.

[33] TNA: PRO POWE 74/83. Rebuilding of Jason at Royal Naval College, Greenwich: fire near Hawker Siddeley reactor building, Langley, 22 May 1961; safe operation of critical assemblies and research reactors.

Chapter 11

The Magnox Stations

Calder Hall had been designed to produce plutonium with electricity generation a secondary consideration. Indeed, the two reactors of Calder Hall A were to be followed by a further two at Calder Hall B, then four more at Chapelcross in Scotland. These were capable of generating 60 MW of power each, and Chapelcross was formally opened in May 1959. Since these stations were required for military purposes, responsibility for them stayed with the AEA, whereas later power stations would be owned and operated by the CEGB.

Whilst Calder Hall and Chapelcross produced electricity successfully for more than 40 years, there was one incident which was to put a reactor at Chapelcross out of action for some time.[1] In 1967, reactor 2 was being brought up to full power after refuelling, when one of the precipitators used to detect radiation inside the pile gave warning that there had been a major leak from one or more fuel elements. Within 30 seconds, the reactor was shut down. This was due to the melting of fuel elements within one of the channels, and the hot magnesium and uranium reacting with the carbon dioxide.

Investigation and clearing out of the channel was not at all straightforward, since all operations had to be done by remote control. To make things more awkward, the channel in question was not directly below the opening in the pressure vessel biological shield. Specially made tools had to be used to grind out the debris in the channel and remove it. Eventually it proved necessary to bore out the entire channel to increase its diameter by 0.5 inches.

Whilst the exact cause was never established, two small pieces of graphite sleeve, of a type different from that in the channel, had probably been lodged in the channel entry. This would have restricted the gas flow through the channel, and the fuel element would have become hot enough to melt the magnesium cladding. Even when the channel had been cleared, decontaminating the reactor took a very considerable time, so that it was not until June 1969, just over two years later, that the reactor was restored to full power.

The magnox stations were intended as an improved version of the PIPPA or Calder Hall reactors, but whereas Calder Hall was optimised to produce plutonium, these new reactors would be optimised to produce electricity. To produce weapons grade plutonium, the fuel needed a relatively low irradiation before being removed from the reactor for reprocessing, but in power station reactors, it was desirable to be able to leave the fuel in the reactor for as long as possible.

Needless to say, even before work had begun on what would become Calder Hall, a PIPPA Mark II was being considered.[2] Some obvious improvements could be made, such as increasing the heat output and improving the efficiency for steam production. The Mark II study was for a power station to produce 100 MW (E), and among the changes were:

> Improved design of fuel element extended surfaces for heat transfer from fuel element to coolant;
>
> Maximum fuel element surface temperature raised from 400°C to 420°C. Actually this value will tend to be reduced as optimum design of the extended surfaces has not yet been reached;
>
> Increased velocity of coolant through the reactor channels;
>
> Increased pressure of the CO_2 cooled — 100 psi to 150 PSI;
>
> A 17½ per cent increase in core diameter from 36 foot to 42'6".

Nearly two years before Calder Hall was completed, the government was already considering a civil nuclear power programme. The supply of coal could not meet demand and nuclear power stations were seen as filling the gap, as well as being the way forward. A committee was convened in 1954 under the chairmanship of a senior Treasury official, Burke Trend (later Cabinet Secretary, 1963–1973). It took as its starting point the availability of nuclear power from 1960 onwards, and attempted to look ten years into the future.

While forecasting is necessary for long-term planning — and nuclear power stations were certainly long-term projects — the forecasts both of energy demand and of fuel supplies made by successive committees over the next 30 years were to prove embarrassingly wrong. Thus a subsequent White Paper of 1960 stated that:

> Since 1957 coal has become plentiful and oil supply prospects have also improved. The need on fuel supply grounds for an immediate and sharp acceleration in the rate of ordering nuclear capacity has therefore passed.[3]

Similar prognostications have littered the nuclear landscape ever since. In 1979, the then Secretary of State for Energy, David Howell, stated that 'the electricity supply industry has advised that even on cautious assumptions it would need to order at least one new nuclear power station a year in the decade from 1982'.[4] In reality, no further reactors were ever ordered, let alone one a year.

The Trend Report was published in a slightly modified form (information about plutonium was removed) as a White Paper in February 1955.

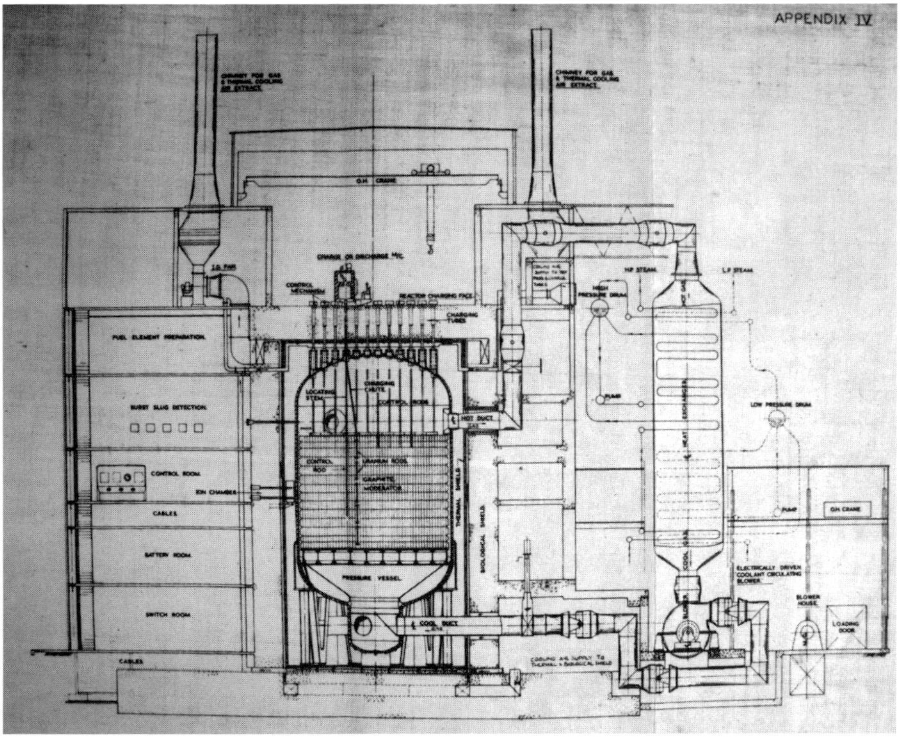

Figure 11.1. Nuclear power station as envisaged in the Trend Report of 1954.

> The provisional programme for the construction of nuclear power stations is as follows:
>
> (i) the construction of two gas-cooled graphite-moderator stations (each with two reactors) would be started about mid-1957. The stations should come into operation in 1960–1961.
>
> (ii) the construction of two further stations would be started about 18 months later, i.e. in 1958–1959. These would also have two reactors each would be similar type to the early two stations but should show an improved performance, particularly in heat rating. Each of the eight reactors in these early stations would have a net output of electricity of 50 to 100 megawatts so that the total output from these four stations, which should all be in operation by 1963, would be somewhere between 400 and 800 MW.
>
> (iii) the construction of four more stations starting in 1960, and then a further four 18 months later, say, 1961–1962. These might come into operation in 1963–1964 and 1965. It is difficult to specify what type of station these would be, but it is possible that each station would consist of only one reactor which would be much more highly rated them the reactors in the first four stations . . . [5]

A total construction of about 2,000 MW was envisaged over a ten-year period. As to who should build the stations,

Figure 11.2. Berkeley power station under construction. The River Severn is in the background.

> The stations will be designed and built by private industry for the Electrical Authorities, who will own and operate them. The Atomic Energy Authority, as the only body with the necessary experience, will be responsible for giving technical advice on the nuclear plant. British industry and consulting engineers have as yet no comprehensive experience of nuclear technology. They will be faced with a major task in training staff, in creating the necessary organisation and in designing the stations. This work has already begun. Owing to its complexity and diversity teams drawn from several firms may have to be formed. The preparatory work will call for greater efforts from all concerned, and even so it will not be practicable to start building any commercial stations before 1957.

This programme was soon to be expanded. At a Cabinet meeting in February 1957, the Minister of Power, Lord Mills, said:

> ... If we were to keep pace with a demand for electricity which was increasing at a rate of 7 per cent per annum, the total electricity output capacity installed by 1970 would need to be of the order of 51,000,000 MW. There was no prospect that supplies of coal would match an acceleration of demand at this rate, and since it would clearly be unwise, from every point of view, to rely too heavily on oil burning plant, a considerable expansion of the existing nuclear programme was indicated.[6]

The new target was for a capacity of 5,000–6,000 MW, which would cost about £770 million. This would, apparently, save 18 million tons of coal a year by 1965. The comment about oil-burning stations related to the recent Suez crisis, when the Suez Canal had been closed, resulting in petrol rationing.

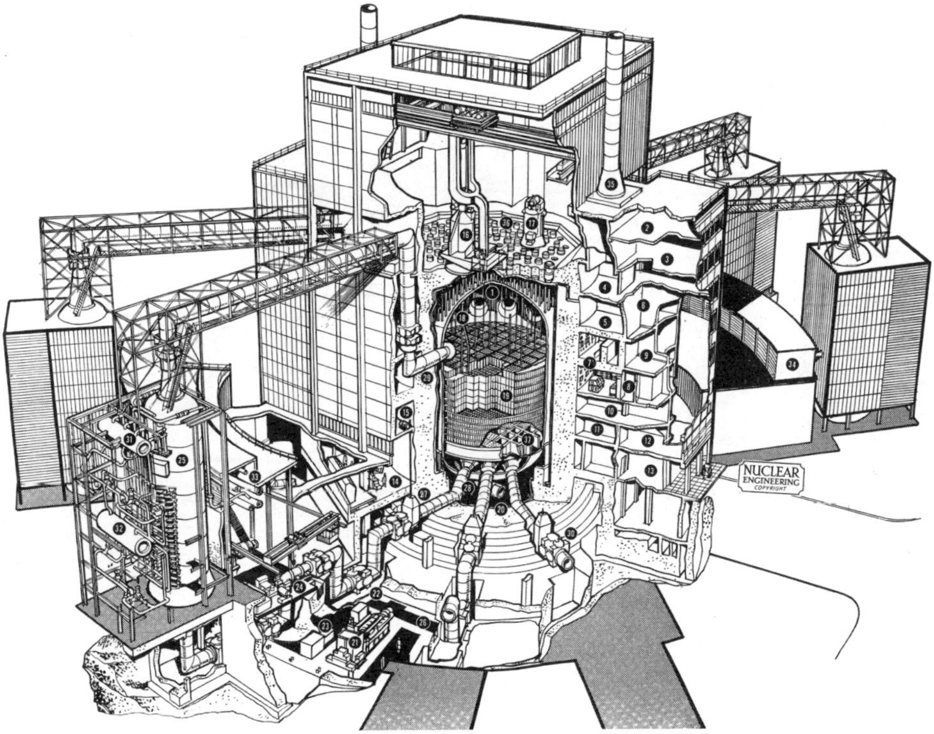

Figure 11.3. A cutaway view of Berkeley. (Image courtesy of Nuclear Engineering International.)

Although the new stations would be based on the PIPPA concept, there was no such thing as a 'standard' magnox power station. They were intended as commercial propositions from the outset, and designed and built by consortia from industry, entirely separately from Harwell and Risley. The consortia were groups of companies, each with their own specialities, who between them could design and build a power station from scratch. At the outset, these were:

- the Atomic Power Construction Ltd, jointly owned by Richardsons, Westgarth and Co, International Combustion (Holdings) Ltd and Crompton Parkinson Ltd;
- the Atomic Power Group with English Electric, Babcock and Wilcox and Taylor Woodrow;
- the GEC/Simon Carves Group;

- the Nuclear Power Plant Co. Ltd, with CA Parsons, A Reyrolle, Head, Wrightson and Sir Robert McAlpine and Sons.

Repeated amalgamations meant that the life of any one particular consortium was relatively short.

Figure 11.4. Bradwell power station under construction.

Initially, these four consortia, which briefly became five in number, would each produce a design for a complete power station, including the reactor, steam generators and electrical generation plant. The design would then be costed before the final tender was submitted to the CEGB. Producing a bid could be extremely expensive, and as a result, not every consortium entered a tender for every site. If a particular consortium had its hands full with building one station, it saw little point in bidding for another one. In the same way, a consortium might be reluctant to put in a bid if it felt that it was not its turn to get a contract. Although in theory each bid should have been treated entirely on its own merits, contracts were sometimes issued to a particular consortium simply to keep it in business. Thus, the point of having several consortia was that, in theory, competition would keep prices down, but in practice, this was not always the case, for the reasons outlined above.

These contracts were for what might be described as 'turnkey' stations — in other words, the consortia would build the power station and hand it over to the CEGB as a working operation. This was a policy that the CEGB would come to regret, although the relationship was complicated by the CEGB being a nationalised industry dealing with private companies.

One of the most essential elements of any nuclear power station is the design of the fuel rods. Each individual consortium would come up with its own particular variation on the fuel rod, as can be seen in Figure 11.5. The essentials of the design of a magnox fuel rod had been laid down by the AEA factory at Springfields. The fuel rods in the Calder Hall stations were designed for a relatively short life. The situation was very different in a commercial power station, where the fuel rods would be irradiated for as long as possible before refuelling became necessary. This imposed a much greater strain on the can.

Figure 11.5. A Wylfa fuel element in a graphite block. There were 49,200 fuel elements in a complete reactor load.

The maximum fuel element temperature was set by the magnesium alloy which was used to can the uranium. Magnox AL80, which is a magnesium alloy containing approximately 0.8% aluminium and 0.04% beryllium, begins to oxidise in carbon dioxide at about 520–550°C and melts at 650°C. The maximum operating temperature for the fuel can and all load-bearing fittings in this material was around 485°C. This set an upper limit on the design.

The conditions of temperature and stress were near to the limit of structural strength for the materials, and advances in design could only be demonstrated by the direct testing of full-size fuel elements in accurately reproduced testing environments. Prolonged endurance testing both in and out of reactors was an expensive but necessary feature of fuel development, since it was anticipated that fuel rods might be in the reactor for as long as five years. In the case of the Bradwell fuel element, for example, the key decisions on the basic design and heat transfer service had to be made by the Nuclear Power Plant Company (as it then was) and the AEA before direct experimental confirmation of the design became available from endurance and irradiation trials mounted in the AEA reactors.

The power programme also meant the construction of a completely new manufacturing plant at Springfields capable of producing around 2,500 tonnes of fuel a year. To be competitive with fossil fuels, the cost of electricity needed to be kept down to about 0.2 d per unit (kilowatt-hour) sent out or about £15,000 per tonne of uranium. The economics of magnox stations would become a matter of considerable debate, but at the time it was acknowledged that whereas the capital costs would be much higher than conventional stations, the fuel and running costs would be much lower.

The Consortia

Industrial firms had been working with the Department of Atomic Energy, as it then was, since the 1940s. They began to play a more active role as the design of PIPPA evolved. Harwell and Risley might have been expert at designing reactors, but they had no particular expertise in the design of steam turbines or electrical generators. They therefore turned to the specialist firms for help and advice. The Parolle Electrical Plant Company Limited of Newcastle upon Tyne had produced the long report entitled 'An Assessment of the "PIPPA" Project' mentioned earlier, and many private firms were involved in the final construction of Calder Hall. These firms included CA Parsons, Babcock and Wilcox, and Whessoe, who produced pressure vessels. At Calder Hall and Chapelcross these firms were acting as subcontractors to the AEA, but when it came to commercial construction of power stations, the arrangement was altered, and not even the Authority themselves were quite sure how the system had evolved.

> It will be seen that the cardinal event was a suggestion made in March, 1954 by the (emerging) Authority that, for the purpose of acquiring knowledge of developments in reactor design, British Industry should make up teams. It was visualised that the best course would be to place a design study with the resulting consortia on condition they would put up adequate technical staff on the project, they would be prepared to undertake adequate research, and that they would do so at their own expense. The authority would undertake to provide technical guidance.
>
> There seems to be no explicit record of the Authority's reasons for making this suggestion; but it can be explained in the light of the circumstances prevailing at the time.[7]

Talking of the earliest successes in the atomic energy field, such as Windscale, Capenhurst and Dounreay, the memo goes on to say:

> Every one of these projects reflected major advances in technology, and was pursued against a tight schedule. Such of the technology had to be developed while construction was in progress; and the successes achieved were due in no small measure to the system of appointing a project leader with overall powers of control and co-ordination. It was natural — and probably necessary — for Industry to approach the construction of the first large nuclear power stations by exercising overall project control on a similar basis. Teams of firms comprising all the main skills were an obvious corollary.

An obvious question was how many consortia there should be, and initial plans were to have four. The formation of these four consortia followed informal discussions with industry in and before 1954. Indeed, a loose association of English Electric, Babcock and Wilcox and Taylor Woodrow, which still constituted one of the initial consortia, had already been formed to fulfil a contract with Harwell for the design of a light water reactor (LEO).

> The (then) British Electrical Authority agreed that they would at first only be likely to place orders for nuclear reactors with GEC, AEI, Parsons and English Electric; and, following Executive approval Sir Edwin Plowden wrote to the chairman of these four heavy electrical firms. He said that the Authority had been considering the best way of imparting knowledge of developments in reactor design to British industry and had concluded that the best course would be to make up teams from industry. It was suggested that the heavy electrical plant manufacturers would each be expected to associate with a suitable firm of boilermakers who would be likely to make a useful contribution to the heat exchange problem.

Other firms then expressed interest and a fifth consortium was formed. Indeed:

> In 1957, the Authority were approached by Hawker Siddeley and John Brown who wished to form a sixth Consortium. The formation of this Consortium was discouraged by the Authority and subsequently abandoned.

The AEA was explicitly ruled out from building power stations:

> … why was the task of designing and building civil nuclear power stations given to industry and not to the Atomic Energy Authority or the electricity authorities or some other national organisation? In general, the discussion about this would rehearse the familiar arguments about nationalised and private industry. But it might be worth adding that electrical power industry was already organised on the basis of private industry for the provision of plant and equipment, the nationalised industry for its operation. There was no reason in principle why the advent of nuclear power should change this. Indeed, there was an explicit assurance in the House of Commons that the Authority would not act in competition with the BEA as a major supplier of electricity.

There was one problem with this. The AEA was the only organisation in the country with the knowledge and expertise of designing nuclear reactors. The CEGB were to build some laboratories at Berkeley, and the various consortia would also have their design facilities, but in the end, the AEA's word was final. For the consortia, this meant that their designs had to be approved not only by the CEGB but by the AEA, since the size of the nuclear industry coupled with the number of companies involved meant that individual companies could not afford to set up any large-scale R&D facilities. In addition, the AEA, through its subsidiary BNFL, supplied all the fuel, removing another possible source of income from the commercial firms. Hence the power programme effectively became a three-way process between the customer, the CEGB, the construction industry in the form of the consortia, and the nuclear experts in the form of the AEA. This is summarised in a diagram (Figure 11.6) of the early 1970s illustrating the structure of the industry.

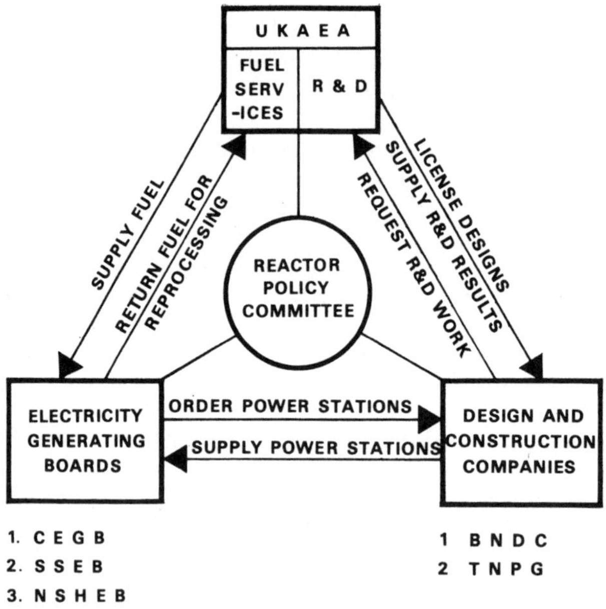

Figure 11.6. The industry structure in the early 1970s. The number of consortia has now been reduced to two.

The consortia were to amalgamate further and further as time went by. Table 11.1 gives some rough indication of which consortium built which power station.

As can be seen, almost all the British magnox stations were built by different consortia. By the time of the advent of the AGR, the number of consortia had effectively shrunk to two.

One of the problems was that research work at Harwell or Risley might throw up new problems during the construction of a station. This is certainly true of the earliest stations, Bradwell and Berkeley, where the graphite core was redesigned

Table 11.1. The consortia and their power stations.

Berkeley	AEI–John Thompson	Amalgamated with NPPC in 1960 to form The Nuclear Power Group (TNPG).
Bradwell	NPPC	Nuclear Power Plant Company.
Hunterston	GEC/Simon Carves	Managed by UPC 1962–1964 (UPC was formed from GEC/Simon Carves and Atomic Power Constructions).
Latina	NPPC	See above.
Hinkley Point	English Electric etc.	Became Nuclear Design and Construction (NDC) in 1965 then British Nuclear Design and Construction (BNDC) in 1969.
Trawsfynydd	APC	Atomic Power Constructions formed as fifth consortium in 1957.
Tokai Mura	GEC/Simon Carves	Managed by UPC 1962–1964.
Dungeness	TNPG	Formed from AEI-John Thompson and the NPPC.
Sizewell	NDC	
Oldbury	TNPG	
Wylfa	BNDC	
Dungeness B*	APC then NDC	APC went into administration in 1969.
Hinkley Point B*	TNPG	
Hunterston B*	TNPG	
Hartlepool*	NDC	NDC became the BNDC in 1969 (see above)
Heysham 1*	BNDC	
Torness*	NNC	Staff from BNDC and TNPG formed the core of the National Nuclear Corporation (NCC)
Heysham 2*	NNC	

*AGR stations.

after the Windscale incident. It was agreed that the cost for this would fall on the customer (the CEGB or the SSEB) rather than the consortium.

Each consortium had an engineering team, which might simply co-ordinate the work between the various companies. This approach proved to be less successful, since a design change in one area might impinge on other areas. Furthermore, the design decisions of one part of the work might not always be compatible with other parts. The lesson from this was that the central engineering team needed to draw up the design as a whole before dealing with the individual companies.

The first power programme was for 5,000 MW of nuclear power, but as the size of the stations increased, fewer of them were needed, and thus there was less work for the consortia. This began the start of the amalgamations. The problems became worse with the gap between the last of the magnox stations and the start of AGRs, when the consortia were left with little to do, meaning that keeping teams together became increasingly difficult. With the demise of APC after the Dungeness fiasco, there were only two consortia left, which in turn merged for the last of the AGRs at Torness and Heysham.

Figure 11.7. Oldbury under construction. This was the first station to use pre-stressed concrete for the pressure vessel rather than steel.

The consortia were also known as the 'design and construction' companies, and as part of a report into the nuclear industry in 1970–1971 (the Thermal Reactor Working Party) it was noted that these companies 'are, on their own admission, the weakest part of the nuclear industry'. They had no stake in the nuclear fuel business, which was handled entirely by BNFL, itself a wholly owned subsidiary of the AEA. It was also noted that they lacked

> any responsibility for the applied R&D on which their designs depend, and exist by selling these designs and supervising the construction of nuclear power stations. In this way they bear most of the responsibility without earning the benefits enjoyed either by the fuel company or by their own shareholders in the heavy electrical and heavy engineering industries. Unless one of these shareholders or some other business interest steps in to give them a new cohesion, it is reasonable to doubt whether they will be strong enough to fulfil their function, which ever reactor type is chosen.[8]

It was not only the nuclear industry which was having problems — there were also considerable delays during the construction of conventional power stations in the 1970s, and the heavy engineering firms also suffered from the same type of dislocation from delays in ordering conventional power plants.

The Stations

Table 11.2. Evolution of the stations.

	Operational	Construction time/ months*	Power MW(E)	Tonnes uranium	Coolant outlet/ °C	Specific power kW/kg
Calder Hall	1956–2003	39	45	127	340	1.35
Chapelcross	1956–2003	41	45	127	340	1.35
Berkeley	1962–1989	66	138	231	345	2.40
Bradwell	1962–2002	67	150	241	390	2.20
Hunterston	1964–1990	77	150	251	395	2.13
Hinkley Point	1965–1999	89	250	376	378	2.55
Trawsfynydd	1965–1991	69	250	280	392	3.11
Dungeness	1965–2006	63	275	300	410	2.78
Sizewell	1965–2006	59	290	321	410	2.96
Oldbury	1968–2012	66	280	293	412	2.85
Wylfa	1971–2014?	98	590	595	414	3.16

*Time from start of construction to first commercial operation.[9]

Table 11.2 shows how the design of the stations evolved very rapidly. It is perhaps slightly unfair to include Calder Hall and Chapelcross in the table, since they were optimised for plutonium rather than power production. The most interesting figure is the specific power — in other words, the number of kW produced per kg of reactor weight. As can be seen, this rises steadily, showing how each design becomes successively more efficient.

There was a problem with the early stations arising from the Windscale incident, which had had its origins in stored Wigner energy. There was still much that was unknown about Wigner energy and its release, so it was decided that the graphite cores on civil stations should work at higher temperatures than those for which they had been designed. Sleeves were fitted inside the fuel channels to insulate the bulk graphite moderator from the coolant gas. This was a very serious modification which affected Chapelcross (reactors 2, 3 and 4 — reactor 1 had been completed before the incident),[10] Bradwell, Berkeley, Hinkley Point and Latina. It required modifications of the machining of all the graphite, and subsequent reassessment of performance, as well as a redesign of the fuel handling equipment. At Hunterston, this modification was unnecessary as the design of the reactor already incorporated sleeves in channels as an integral part of the fuel element. As more graphite irradiation data became available, it was realised that the sleeving of channels was, in fact, unnecessary. Latina and the British stations had been modified with changes as near as possible to the original designs, with appreciable interference to the manufacture and construction programmes.[11]

Bradwell and Berkeley

The first magnox stations were to be built at Bradwell on the Essex coast and Berkeley on the eastern side of the Severn estuary. The bids from the consortia were submitted to the AEA for evaluation. The successful bid for Bradwell was made by the Nuclear Power Plant Company. The AEA's remarks were:

> The Nuclear Power Plant Company has submitted proposals which, although not lowest in capital cost per unit of electrical capacity, nor in cost per unit sent out, are yet very competitive.
>
> The Company displays considerable strengths and a high general standard of competence. They have a high standard of preparedness and are considered to have established their claim to favourable consideration in their own right, and in no way merely by comparison.
>
> Their scheme is judged to be immediately acceptable providing that certain points of detail are cleared up satisfactorily and classification is obtained in cases when it appears that difficulties have been encountered.[12]

The successful tender for Berkeley came from the Associated Electrical Industries–John Thompson Consortium. The AEA commented that:

> The group has displayed considerable technical insight and the quality of the engineering design is sound. There is no doubt however, that certain points of the design require revision.
>
> We consider that the reservations made here and elsewhere do not detract from the way in which the group has firmly established its claim to favourable consideration for an early start.
>
> The method and sequence of construction proposed will in our view lead to congestion, disorganisation and considerable loss of time. It should be reviewed very carefully with a view to completely revising it.

Sir Claude Gibb, Chairman of the consortium which would be building the Bradwell station, wrote to Hinton inviting him to the ground breaking ceremony:

> The Chairman of the Central Electricity Authority, the Right Honourable Lord Citrine PC, KBE, has very kindly consented to perform the cutting of the first sod ceremony for the Bradwell Nuclear Power Station. The ceremony will be at 11:15 on Friday 18th January, 1957.[13]

On 5 April 1963, Prince Philip, piloting his own helicopter, flew in to Berkeley, Gloucestershire, for the opening ceremony. At Bradwell, the Lord Lieutenant of Essex performed a similar ceremony simultaneously on Prince Philip's behalf. Welcoming the achievement of nuclear power, Prince Philip said that whilst there had been many problems,

> ... nothing can alter the fact that these two stations represent a triumph of research and engineering ... It is plain that nuclear power is going to play an increasingly important part in the British energy programme of the future.[14]

These two had been the first stations to be ordered as a result of the 1955 White Paper, and contracts were placed late in 1956. Construction had started when, in October 1957, the Windscale accident occurred. One of the consequences of the accident was that the AEA then undertook a major programme of research into the effects of irradiation on graphite. This had a major impact on the design of the cores of the reactors, the first being whether the fuel elements should be based in graphite sleeves. This led to considerable controversy. The other problem arose in light of new data on the dimensional changes that took place within the graphite, leading to a further redesign of the core. Despite this, the stations were completed with relatively little delay.[15]

Hunterston

Hunterston was the third power station to be built, and was ordered by the South of Scotland Electricity Board (SSEB). The bid was won by the GEC–Simon Carves consortium, based on its Bradwell design, and the SSEB wrote to them accepting their tender in December 1956. The price for a complete turnkey station was £37.5 million, but this was based on site conditions at Bradwell. The final cost would almost certainly change since the civil engineering work at the Scottish site would be very different, and there would also be modifications to the original design required by the SSEB and the AEA to accord with safety criteria, modifications introduced during the course of the work and a standard cost variation clause.

Transferring the design from Bradwell clay to Hunterston rock added to the cost. Other changes were required after the tender was evaluated by the AEA, so that price for the civil work done at Hunterston was nearly £6 million more than for Bradwell.

The management at Hunterston was also weak. They were slow in getting onto the site, and lack of managerial decisions at all stages added to the complexity and exaggerated the cost of modifications. A further problem was that although both SSEB and GEC must have realised the development nature of the project, due to the looseness of the agreement both assumed that the other would pay for any changes. A memo written for the new Minister of Science, Lord Hailsham, who had taken over responsibility for the AEA from the Prime Minister, describes the situation thus:

> As far as the Authority understands the position, work began on the strength of a letter of intent from the SSEB to the GEC dated 12th December, 1956. The letter, while referring to the fact that the tender design required modification, did not define the scope of these modifications. Nor was there, at that time, any re-quotation by the G.E.C. of the price of the job. The GEC interpretation of the letter of intent seems to have been that this represented cover for all modifications that might have to be carried out. The SSEB, on the other hand, have expressed the view on several occasions, at the official level, that it meant they would meet the cost of modifications for the changed site, and for modifications which might be subsequently found to be necessary to meet changes in technology, but that

> modifications identified before work started were the responsibility of the GEC as they have not adjusted their tender price.[16]

All the nuclear sites have suffered the measure of labour problems, but Hunterston's were on a different scale, and the management seemed incapable of coping with the spate of unofficial strikes and after a series of warnings by both the pressure vessel contractor and GEC, the site was closed down completely for four months. This was, in effect, another admission of managerial failure. In the end, the consortium was merged with the APC into the United Power Company.

The AEA also insisted on modifications to the design. The first was to the charge/discharge machine, which unusually was situated beneath the reactor. The redesign meant a very considerable delay — perhaps of 18 months or so. The boilers had to be raised at the AEA's insistence, which meant modifying other parts of the design. As the journal *Nuclear Engineering International* put it:

> The AEA who as SSEB consultants and the UK authority responsible for safety work were of course looking for the ultimate, and it was not easy for the contractor or customer to distinguish between recommendations of fundamental nature and those which should be balanced against cost. Regrettably when the contractors did dig their toes in, it was not necessarily at the right time . . . The contractors had always tended to look for ingenious solutions to problems rather than just workable ones; the board were woefully short of staff for a project of this magnitude; the AEA was seeking perfection.[17]

And as the brief to Hailsham put it:

> The contract for Hunterston is with the GEC, who are the main contractors and all the other participants are subcontractors to the GEC. Before the advent of UPC this placed a heavy responsibility on the GEC engineer in charge of the project. He not only need[s] to manage the job itself, from the point of view of design and construction, but he had responsibility for controlling the contracts with the several hundred subcontractors involved. As the final cost to the GEC will depend to a large extent on what they have to pay to the subcontractors, it is clear that this engineer needed to be backed by a very strong services organisation dealing with planning, contracts, estimating and costing. Such an organisation, sufficient for the job, was never built up in the Erith works, was clearly revealed when UPC took over the management of the job.[18]

As mentioned in the memorandum, another consortium, the UPC, took over the job and completed the station without too many further problems.

Hinkley point

Although Hinkley Point was the CEGB's third reactor, it too suffered from a redesign of the core following the Windscale incident, delaying the project by around a year or so. Also as a consequence of the incident, the CEGB decided that reactor number 2 should be fitted with a great deal more instrumentation than would be necessary simply for operational purposes. It was intended that extensive studies would be made of the changes in the pressure vessel shape over its life, movements of the graphite core and so on, and around 60% of the total instrumentation on reactor number 2 was for research purposes.[19]

However, Hinkley Point was to suffer another problem, which was rather unusual. Unstable gas flow at the intakes to the carbon dioxide blowers had set up high-frequency oscillations, which resulted in fatigue cracking in both the blowers and some of the internal fittings of the duct work. Large pieces of the outer shell of the blower fractured off and pass through the circulator itself or fell into the main casing. This meant a redesign of the blower, with consequential delays before they were replaced.[20]

Figure 11.8. Instabilities in the pressurised carbon dioxide gas flow set up oscillations which caused the disintegrations of the blower.

Trawsfynydd

Trawsfynydd was built in the Snowdonia National Park, in North Wales and the site is the country's only inland nuclear power station (the rest of the UK's nuclear power stations are located in coastal positions for easy access to cooling water and effluent discharge purposes). It was the first (and only) magnox station to be built by the fifth consortium, the Atomic Power Company (APC).

Dungeness

Slightly unusually, the proposal for Dungeness was discussed in Cabinet in June 1959.[21]

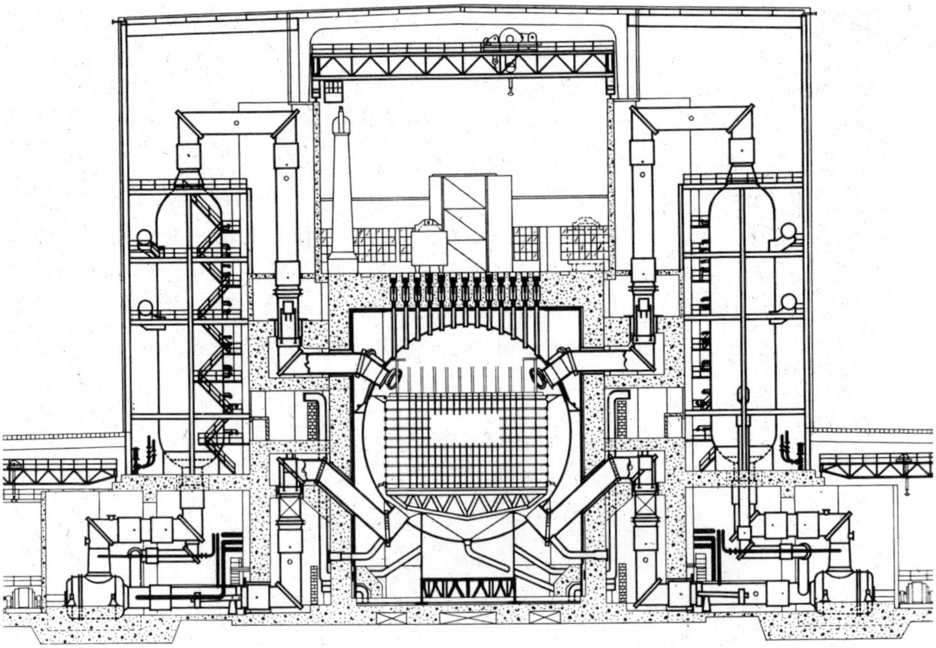

Figure 11.9. Hinkley Point. The circular pressure vessel is in the centre of the picture. The hot gas flows into the heat exchangers shown either side to generate steam.

> The Minister of Power said that a public enquiry had been held into this project and the inspectors who had held it recommended that consent should be given for the erection of a power station of 500 MW. capacity on this site. A decision to proceed with this project would be criticised, both by those interested in amenities and nature conservancy, and by others who wished the nuclear power programme to be curtailed in the interests of the coal-mining industry . . .
>
> The Minister of Housing and Local Government said that when the report of the public enquiry was published, it would reveal that the application by the Generating Board was partly based on the assumption that coal production would not be able to keep pace with the increasing demand for power. This assumption was likely to be challenged, in view of the present difficulties of the coal industry and the large surplus of coal . . .
>
> The Prime Minister said that, from the long-term point of view of our economy and our national prestige, it was desirable that we should proceed steadily with the nuclear power programme on which we had embarked.

The arguments in favour of proceeding were

> . . . [although] there would be advantages in postponing the construction of further nuclear power stations until a more advanced and economical design could be produced, these were outweighed by the importance of maintaining in being the scientific and industrial staffs now engaged on these projects.

Sizewell

Sizewell was designed with the two reactors in one building, which greatly simplified the layout and services. Design and construction was by British Nuclear Design and Construction Ltd (BNDC), a consortium of English Electric, Babcock International Group and Taylor Woodrow Construction. It was completed almost on schedule and almost to budget. The original estimate was for £56 million; inflation meant that the final cost was £65 million.

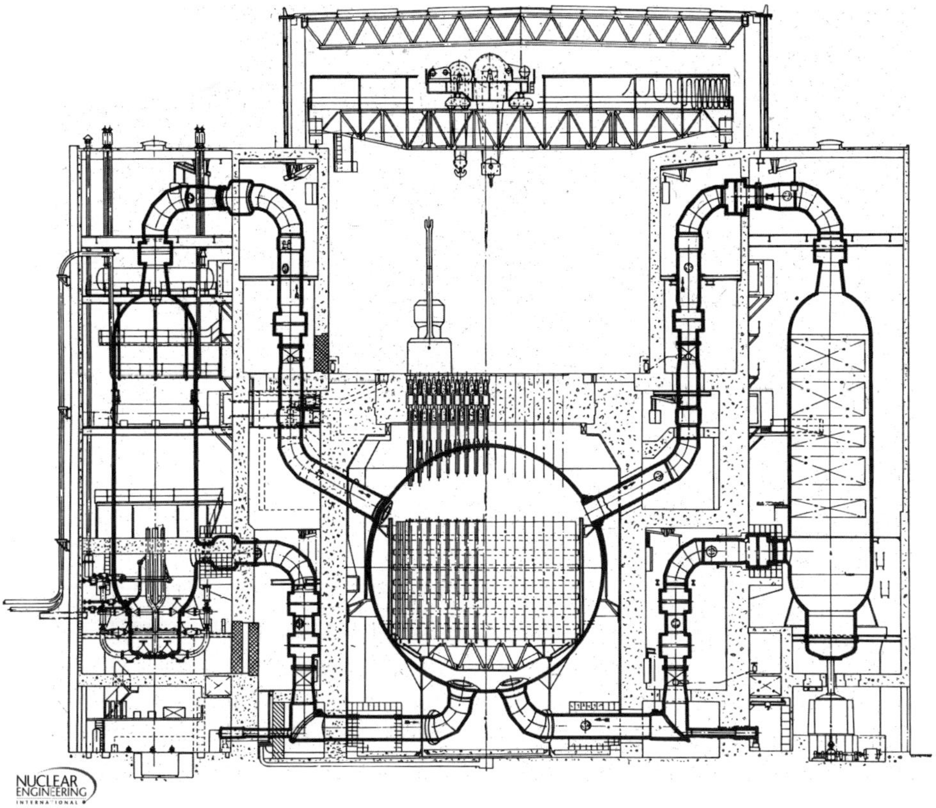

Figure 11.10. Sizewell. No two magnox stations were the same, although there are obvious similarities.

Oldbury

Oldbury introduced a new concept into the gas-cooled stations. Instead of a steel pressure vessel, pre-stressed concrete would be used instead. This was cheaper, simpler, quicker to build, and, as much as anything, safer. Steel pressure vessels can fail catastrophically, but a reinforced concrete dome will not.

Wylfa

Wylfa was the last of the magnox stations to be built, and its construction — or, at the least, the tender for its construction — would cause considerable controversy, highlighting the contradictions in government policy. Indeed, it could be said that it highlighted the lack of any government policy.

By 1963, the consortia had been reduced to three in number. One of these was the UPC. The consortia in general were not happy with the government's policy, feeling that it was too short term. They had suffered as the nuclear programme had first been expanded in 1957, and then cut back later. A further problem was that Wylfa would be the last of the magnox stations, and it was not clear what was going to happen after Wylfa. Thus they faced a distinctly uncertain future.

The consortia had not been formed by the demands of industry but by the demands of the government, or by the demands of the government at one remove — that is, the CEGB, who, apart from the SSEB, was the sole customer. There had been five consortia, and forcing them to amalgamate at government behest did not make for a stable or progressive industry. The UPC had been formed from just such a merger, and it had been expected that it would be offered the Oldbury contract as a reward, but this went elsewhere. By now there was only the Wylfa contract left. The UPC therefore faced a very uncertain future.

The CEGB's solution was to split the Wylfa site in two, giving one part to English Electric and the other to the UPC. This would have kept them in business, but made the Wylfa contract very much more expensive than it might otherwise have been. The UPC quoted a price of around £120 per kilowatt for the relatively small (400–500 MW) reactor asked for by the CEGB, but said that the price for a larger reactor (600–800 MW) would be a good deal less — £103 per kilowatt. If it were to build the complete station — that is, both reactors — the cost came down to £89 per kilowatt.

Despite this, the CEGB went ahead with the split site, and the UPC submitted its design for assessment. Negotiations went on for 17 months, including 151 meetings between the engineers of the UPC and the engineers of the CEGB. All outstanding technical differences appeared to have been resolved, when, abruptly, the tender was rejected. This would mean the demise of the UPC with considerable repercussions for the constituent firms.

Hinton was the Chairman of the CEGB at the time, and the decision was undoubtedly his, one motive being to reduce the number of consortia down from three to two. Unfortunately for Hinton, the Deputy Chairman of the UPC was Lord Coleraine, a member of the House of Lords. As well as Deputy Chairman of the UPC, he was also Chairman of APC, and a member of the board of the GEC (a member of the UPC consortium). The row received lengthy coverage in the press including a full page article in the *Financial Times*.[22]

Figure 11.11. Two views of Wylfa charge face. The refuelling machine has to extract the spent and highly radioactive fuel elements from the core and store them safely before inserting the new elements.

Since Coleraine was a peer, he was able to put down a motion in the House of Lords deploring the CEGB's actions. Quintin Hogg (Lord Hailsham) was leader of the House of Lords, and so had to deal with the matter. He wrote to the Minister of Power, Richard Wood:

> What on earth is Hinton thinking about? Whatever his commercial responsibilities may be and whatever the commercial and technical merits, he cannot just call off a contract for the construction of a nuclear power station at the present state of play without creating first-class political and economic chaos. This is now about to descend on our heads, and so far I have not been consulted or informed nor, so far as I know, has anyone assessed the consequences of his action. Quite apart from the unemployment situation in the North East which is important enough, I fancy that the proposed cancellation of the letter of intent in respect of Wylfa may quite possibly bring UPC crashing down. What will be the effects of this on Trawsfynydd, Hunterston (only just extricated from the shambles into which the doctrine of commercial responsibility brought it) and Tokai Mura?
>
> Apart from telegrams from Chetwynd, letters from Richardson, Westgarth and frenzied phone calls from Kerans [MP for The Hartlepools, whose constituency would have hard hit by the cancellation] demanding interviews, which I have been subjected to in the past 48 hours, Dick Coleraine came in to see me yesterday about the motion he has put down on the Order Paper of the House of Lords, for which I shall have to find time before the Recess. I suppose I shall have to answer this myself, partly because of my responsibilities for atomic energy and partly because of Coleraine's eminence. I told him to write his troubles down on a piece of paper and send them to me, and also to go and see you.[23]

Opening the debate in the Lords, Coleraine spoke for nearly 70 minutes with hardly a note, and spoke eloquently. His speech was made the more eloquent by his obvious sense of injustice. He did have considerable advantages such as parliamentary immunity — in other words, he could say what he liked within the House without fear of libel action. It also gave him an excellent platform for his views, since they were being brought to the attention of ministers and would be widely reported in the press. He did not mince his words.

> I think that Parliament must consider very seriously the powers which are vested, almost accidentally, in the hands of some of these nationalised Boards and in the hands, in particular, of the Chairman if he has a forceful personality. The Central Electricity Generating Board are, I think, far and away the largest electricity supply organisation in the world, and therefore exert tremendous influence as a customer. I do not know to what extent your Lordships are familiar with the electricity supply industry, but perhaps I may put it this way. The private sector of the electricity supply industry is dealing, in effect, in single articles costing millions of pounds. The cost of a large generating set might be anything between £10 and £50 million. For that article there is only one customer in England. There is another, a much smaller one, in Scotland. At any rate, there is, effectively, only one customer. If that customer is offended, even the most powerful firms in this country are at his mercy. I do not believe that that is a healthy situation. I do not believe that any man should have that power. If he must have it, then he must, too, have very special qualities: he must be known to be of absolutely balanced judgment; he must be

> known to be absolutely fair-minded and impartial; he must be known to be able to listen courteously and reasonably to the arguments that are put to him. Above all, he must be known to be free of any trace of vindictiveness.
>
> Sir Christopher Hinton has many outstanding virtues. He is a brilliant engineer. I daresay that he is the most brilliant engineer that we have in this country. He is a man of dominating personality. He is a man who thoroughly and completely knows his own mind, until he changes it. But I do not think that Sir Christopher Hinton's warmest admirers would attribute to him those particular qualities which I have ascribed to the ideal chairman of a nationalised Board with these immense powers in his hands. It is not unfair to say that even the biggest firms are cowed by the powers which are exercised by the Chairman and the Central Electricity Generating Board.[24]

Later in his speech, Coleraine made some important points about the relationship between private industry, the CEGB, the AEA, and government ministers. First of all, the CEGB and AEA were almost completely autonomous organisations. There was very little ministerial oversight. Coleraine described the forced amalgamations of the consortia thus:

> This is done by a single man, or, if you like, by the Board, who have no responsibility to anyone, except for that narrow shadowy responsibility which is owed to, or at any rate exacted by, my right honourable friend the Minister of Power.
>
> Of course Sir Christopher Hinton would deny that he exercises this dictatorship; and in a sense he would be right. His method is more subtle, but not so much more subtle. What he says is: "It is not for me to dictate to your company what it should do. That is your responsibility, not mine. All I tell you is that unless this suggestion is adopted, your company is extremely unlikely to get an order from the Board." He has said that to me. My Lords, I believe that that is an abuse of power.

In the same way, the AEA was also remarkably free from governmental oversight. In one sense, this was less important, since there were few large industrial contracts involved. On the other hand, relations between the AEA and the CEGB were poor, and there was no one in government who could use their influence to sort matters out — or to put it in a more vernacular style, to bang heads together. At the time Coleraine was speaking, the AEA were pushing hard for the AGR to be adopted for the next generation of power stations, but Hinton and the CEGB were far less convinced and obviously preferred some form of light water reactor. After its brief flirtation in the mid-1950s, the AEA had lost all interest in light water reactors. The real failure in government was that there was no one with the authority to sort the problem out. Coleraine put his finger on the problem when he noted that Hinton had 'no responsibility to anyone'. Meanwhile, industry found itself as 'piggy in the middle'.

Hinton was soon to retire from the CEGB, but whilst later chairmen may not have been quite as forceful as Hinton, the problem still remained, and would lead to a great deal of policy muddle in the 1970s.

Exports

The AEA had great hopes of being able to export reactors. At this time, Britain had more nuclear power installed than all the countries in the rest of the world put together. In the event, there was no great rush of orders. A single reactor station was built at Latina in Italy, with construction starting in January 1959 and full power being reached by March 1963. Another station was built at Tokai Mora in Japan, which again was a single reactor station. Construction began in October 1960 and the station was running at full power by May 1965.

Figure 11.12. Tokai Mora in Japan. (Image courtesy of NDA and copyright NDA.)

The reactor unit at Latina was based on that of Bradwell, but as a result of improvements in design, it was possible to increase the output from 150 MW to 200 MW. Another important advantage in using the same basic design was that all the experience gained as a result of development work on Bradwell would be directly applicable to Latina, and the construction could therefore follow closely behind Bradwell without risk of possible delays which might have arisen in building an entirely new design overseas.

The station was built on the coast 70 km south of Rome, as a joint venture between The Nuclear Power Plant Company Ltd and Agip Nucleare. At the time, it was the first reactor in Europe with an output of 200 MW, and from 1963 until the last shut down in 1986 the average availability factor of the plant was 73%. In 1983, Latina had a higher availability factor than any other European nuclear station at 96%. There was an outage of 207 days in 1969 when the inner structure of the reactor and the steam generators had to be checked for the oxidation on mild steel components caused by the hot carbon dioxide, as with all the other magnox stations. It was then decided to lower the outlet gas temperatures from 390°C to 360°C, with an output loss of 50 MW from 210 MW to 160 MW. It was supplied with fuel from Springfields, and over the course of its operational life used 1,170 tons of fuel.

In 1986 the station was shut down for a planned overhaul, pending a national referendum on nuclear power, which was called in the aftermath of the Chernobyl accident. The referendum took place in November 1987, and as a consequence the plant was closed permanently in December.

Although there were considerable efforts to sell other reactors abroad, the later confusion in Britain's own nuclear power policy did not help matters, and these two were the only reactors exported by the UK.

The government's own view, expressed in a note by the Lord President of the Council in May 1956, was that:

> the greatest benefit to the United Kingdom balance of payments over the next decade was likely to come from savings on imported coal due to the nuclear power programme in the United Kingdom rather than from exports of nuclear power stations.[25]

The AEA's own view was that:

> The nuclear reactors now being developed for the United Kingdom power programme are of the gas-cooled, graphite-moderated kind. Although more advanced nuclear stations are being studied is gas-cooled, graphite-moderated sets (PIPPA's) are expected to be the only nuclear power stations in full-scale commercial operation in the United Kingdom until 1965. The capital costs of the PIPPA's will be high and there is a certain size — round about 50 MW — below which capital costs per unit of output begin to rise very sharply; for these reasons PIPPA-type nuclear power stations are likely to be economic only where they can be operated at high load factor (i.e. run almost continuously) and where there is already a large electricity load. If these conditions occur when the price of fossil fuels is high, the PIPPA's are expected to be competitive with conventional power stations, as they should produce electricity at between ½d and 1d a unit.
>
> The time-scale for the development of a nuclear reactor is long: natural development and prototype operation of the reactor system known to be feasible takes 5–7 years; the length of time that must elapse before a promising idea can become a nuclear reactor in commercial operation overseas is probably well over 10 years.[26]

Figure 11.13. Latina in Italy. Both this and Tokai Mora were relatively early magnox designs with only one reactor. They were the only power reactors exported by the UK. (Image courtesy of NDA and copyright NDA.)

There were two other magnox designs built abroad — at Yongbyong in North Korea. They were apparently based on the Calder Hall design. A 5 MW design became operational in 1985 and has been used to produce plutonium for the North Korean atomic weapons tests of 2006 and 2009. A larger 50 MW design was started but has been left unfinished, as has a 200 MW reactor at nearby Taechon.

The Corrosion Problem

In the late 1960s, the magnox reactors suffered from severe corrosion, not in the pipes or the pressure vessel as had been assumed, but literally in the nuts and bolts. It had been first discovered in Bradwell in September 1968, when the fuelling machine grab failed to pick up a fuel element during a refuelling operation. The reactor had been shut down and investigation with a TV camera had revealed a 0.5 inch nut together with the bolt shank lodged in the top fuel element lifting cone. Subsequent investigation showed that the debris had come from a steel sample basket. These particular nuts and bolts had been installed to stiffen the basket structure following vibration which had occurred during commissioning tests.[27]

The problem was that when the washers and the nuts corroded, the corrosion products pushed the nut away from the bolt, and if the corrosion was sufficiently severe, the nut could separate from the bolt.

This was potentially catastrophic. The reactor vessel held thousands of nuts and bolts. Many of the components could be changed during routine shut downs, but it would have been impossible to replace them all. There was one solution, which was to reduce the gas temperatures and hence the rate of corrosion, but this, of course, meant a reduction in the power output of the reactors. The reduction in all the magnox reactors amounted to around 500 MW out of a total generating capacity of about 2,300 MW.

The Minister of Technology, Anthony Wedgwood Benn, tried to underplay the problem by pointing out that the reduction in generating power amounted to only 1% of the total generating power of the CEGB. The investigative journalist, Chapman Pincher, accused him of a cover-up, and pointed out that 500 MW represented a considerable portion of the nuclear power capability.

Professor Morrison of Bristol University was brought in as an independent expert. Among his recommendations was that extra foolproof shutdown devices should be installed in the reactors — recommendations that were accepted.

1970 brought a change of government, and a new prime minister in the person of Edward Heath. When he was informed of the problems with the magnox stations, he questioned whether it was worth keeping them in commission, and whether it might not be better to plan a closing down and replacement programme. Professor Alan Cottrell was then Deputy Chief Scientific Adviser and, as a metallurgist, had been involved in the investigation from the beginning. His recommendation to the Prime Minister was that:

> The loss of output is reckoned by the Central Electricity Generating Board to be about 15 per cent of the total power ratings of these reactors. The remaining 85 per cent can thus be had for the expenditure of operating costs only, which, as in all nuclear power stations, are very small compared with capital costs; and so it will pay considerably to continue to use these reactors, providing this can be done safely, rather than to replace them with new nuclear or conventional stations.[28]

Rather than being closed, some of the magnox stations were to soldier on for nearly another half a century under reduced power.

The loss of more than 1,000 MW represented 21% of the original design output as can be seen in Table 11.3.[29]

Table 11.3. Outputs of magnox stations.

Station	Design Output (MWe)	Derated output (MWe)	Loss (MWe)
Bradwell	300	250	50
Berkeley	276	276	0
Hunterston*	300	285	15
Hinkley	500	460	40
Sizewell	580	420	160
Trawsfynydd	500	390	110
Dungeness	550	410	140
Oldbury	600	400	200
Wylfa	1180	886	294
Total	4786	3777	1009

*Hunterston was operated by the SSEB; all the other stations by the CEGB.

Was Magnox Economic?

There was no point in building nuclear power stations merely because it was possible — the more important question was whether it was economic to do so. Nuclear power had certain advantages in that it did not rely on fossil fuel, some of which had to be imported, and the cost and availability of fossil fuel could vary quite sharply.

The capital cost of any nuclear power station was inevitably going to be higher than that of any conventional station. Both used steam to generate electricity, and in that sense the two types of station were equivalent, but building a nuclear reactor was a good deal more costly than a furnace in which coal or oil would be burned. Some calculations as to relative costs were carried out before the first magnox stations were built, and are given in Table 11.4.

These were the costs in pounds per kilowatt, which is the way costings for power stations were usually compared. The nuclear costings were for a magnox station with a pile of diameter 35 feet and a fuel element temperature of 400°C. Cooling towers were a very considerable expense (£15.92 per kW in this case), but it was only the Calder Hall and Chapelcross stations that used cooling towers, and later magnox stations dispensed with them. Another reason why the nuclear station was more expensive was that the limit on the can temperature meant a relatively low steam temperature and so the turbine units had to be of special design to suit the larger mass flow. The need for a 'cooling' pond for the used elements and heavy shielding around the reactor also pushed up costs for the nuclear station.[30]

Table 11.4. Cost comparison of nuclear power and coal power.

Capital costs in £/kW:	Nuclear	Coal
Complete generating plant and auxiliaries	18.13	14.5
Steam raising plant	25.48	25.0
Switchgear	8.0	8.0
Buildings, cooling towers and civil engineering	37.15	22.5
Pressure shell and associated equipment	19.8	—
Graphite	12.35	—
Carbon dioxide and blower system	16.4	—
Administration and services	12.5	—
Temporary	3.3	—
Development	1.09	—
Contingency	15.4	—
	169.6	70.0

Figure 11.14. Aerial view of Berkeley.

Running costs — and particularly fuel costs — were much lower in the nuclear case. The long-term economics depended on various factors. One was the current interest rate. If the nuclear station were more capital intensive, then the CEGB would have to borrow more money, and pay interest on those borrowings. Another was the life of the station — if that extra capital cost were spread over 40 years rather than 20, it made the nuclear case much more worthwhile. In practice, any attempt to calculate the economics of a magnox station is fruitless, given the many changes in interest rates and inflation between 1960 and 2010, not to mention changes in the economics of conventional power stations against which it would be compared.

The other problem with trying to do any long-term costings was that the price of fossil fuel was volatile, as was the supply. There appeared to be great shortages of coal in 1950s, a situation that was reversed in the 1960s. The design of coal-fired stations improved considerably, so that they became much more efficient, leading to cheaper power production. North Sea oil and gas was to become available in the 1970s. Later magnox stations were more efficient but still limited by the fuel can temperature. The only solution to this was to change the design completely, and the AGR used uranium dioxide as the fuel, enabling it to run at a much higher temperatures. All this meant that economic comparisons varied almost from year to year, as did government energy policy. The vacillations of the 1970s were to hit the AGR and other designs, rather than the magnox stations which had all been completed by then.

Table 11.5. Comparison of station load factors.

Station	Load factor (%)	AGR load factor (%)
Bradwell	66	—
Berkeley	58	—
Hunterston	82	70
Hinkley	72	76
Sizewell	75	—
Trawsfynydd	80	—
Dungeness	74	41
Oldbury	76	—
Wylfa	71	—
Hartlepool A1	—	67
Heysham A1	—	70
Heysham B1	—	76
Torness	—	70
Sizewell B (PWR)	83	—

Note: These are for reactor number 1 only. The AGR figures are for comparison. Sizewell B is a PWR station. Data from IAEA Power Reactor Information System (PRIS).

It is also interesting to look at the load factors, which are shown in Table 11.5. Bradwell and Berkeley can perhaps be excused on the grounds that they were 'first offs', but other than that, the figures are quite respectable. Apart from Dungeness, the AGRs turn in a respectable performance, although not, overall, as good as the magnox stations. The best performance comes from Sizewell B — a PWR built to American design.

There is one other expense which has not been allowed for: the cost of processing the fuel and decommissioning the power station. In the early days, it was thought that the spent fuel would be an asset since it contained plutonium which could then be reprocessed and burned in fast breeder reactors. In fact, the plutonium has had to be stored and has since become something of an embarrassment. There is also of course the unresolved issue of the storage of the fission products.

As to the cost of decommissioning: the Wylfa 2 reactor had an output of around 500 MW and was operational for more than 40 years. In that time, it generated more than 108 TW.h of electricity — approximately 10^{11} units. If the cost of decommissioning the reactor amounts to a billion pounds, this amounts to 10^{11} p — or 1 p per unit of electricity.

---

1 TNA: PRO AB 38/592. Chapelcross Reactor 2 Incident (11 May).

2 TNA: PRO AB 15/4099. A 200 MW nuclear power station of the PIPPA type. RV Moore, RJ Haslam, G Duffett and G Packman.

3 (1961). *The Nuclear Power Programme* [White Paper]. London: HMSO (Cmnd 1083).

4 Nuclear Power, House of Commons Debate (Fifth series), 18 December 1979, vol. 976 cc. 288–289.

5 (1955). *A Programme of Nuclear Power* [White Paper]. London: HMSO (Cmnd 9389).

6 TNA: PRO CAB 128/31. Cabinet conclusions: 1(57)–86(57).

7 TNA: PRO AB 38/453. Structure of the UK nuclear industry: Sanders Committee.

8 TNA: PRO EG 12/72. Thermal Reactor Working Party: report, 16 December 1971.

9 Data from IAEA Power Reactor Information System (http://www.iaea.org/PRIS).

10 TNA: PRO AB 16/2362. Windscale incident. Proposals for Extending the life of the Calder and Chapelcross Reactors by Reducing the Rate of Storage of Wigner Energy.

11 TNA: PRO EG 1/355. UK nuclear power programme.

12 TNA: PRO AB 7/11496. Assessment of tenders for nuclear power stations: Berkeley and Bradwell; general report on proposals received. November 1956.

13 TNA: PRO AB 19/29. Industrial Collaboration — Pippa firms. Sir Claude Gibb to Sir Christopher Hinton, 7 January 1957.

14 Central Electricity Generating Board (1990). *The CEGB Story*, London: CEGB.
15 (1963). 'Problems Faced During Construction', *Nuclear Engineering International,* 8(74), 157.
16 TNA: PRO EG 1/355. UK nuclear programme. 'Hunterston', undated.
17 Editorial (1962). *Nuclear Engineering International*, 7(74), 255–256.
18 TNA: PRO EG 1/355. UK nuclear programme. 'Hunterston', undated.
19 (1961). 'From Hinkley to Sizewell', *Nuclear Engineering International*, 6(64) 364–365.
20 (1963). 'Hinkley Point Shows New Problem on Blowers', *Nuclear Engineering International*, 8(80) 381.
21 TNA: PRO CAB 128/33. Cabinet conclusions: 1(59)–64(59).
22 M Shanks (1963). 'Lord Coleraine's Resignation: Background to the Row', *Financial Times*, 25 June 1963.
23 TNA: PRO POWE 25/422. Nuclear power technology: Magnox reactors. Lord Hailsham to Richard Wood, Minister of Power, 25 June 1963.
24 The Nuclear Energy Industry and the CEGB, House of Lords Debate (Fifth series), 10 July 1963, Vol. 251 c. 1389.
25 TNA: PRO CAB 134/1197. Ministerial Committee on Atomic Energy: Meeting 1 (1955); Papers 1–3 (1955); Papers 1–2 (1956) (see CAB 134/745).
26 *Ibid.*
27 TNA: PRO CAB 168/13. Corrosion in Magnox reactors.
28 TNA: PRO PREM 15/134. Corrosion in Magnox reactors: Prime Minister enquired position.
29 TNA: PRO AB 38/950. Magnox reactors: correspondence between UKAEA/TNPG/BNFL.
30 TNA: PRO AB 7/3183 Further Development of the graphite moderated gas cooled thermal reactor for power generation. RJ Haslam, 20 May 1954.

Chapter 12

The Second Power Programme: The Alternatives

The route to the magnox reactors used for the first power programme is easy to trace: the air-cooled Windscale piles lead to the idea of closed-circuit gas-cooling, which in turn lead to the PIPPA design and Calder Hall. Calder Hall can be considered as a prototype for the magnox stations, and the commercial versions took the design to its limit.

The first power programme was for the total of 5,000 MW of electricity to be generated by nuclear means. The magnox stations had been taken as far as was feasible. The question then was what should follow the magnox stations. There was a vast range of possibilities, some of which would be more practicable than others.

The possibilities proliferated to such an extent that a committee was set up under the chairmanship of William Strath, who was at the time a member of the AEA, responsible for external relations and commercial policy. The committee effectively weeded out the less viable proposals.

These included what was described as the homogeneous reactor, where the fissile material would be dissolved in water, the water acting as the moderator. Initial ideas involved

> using a solution of uranyl sulphate in heavy water, operating at 250°C–300°C, at a pressure of 1500 lbs per sq. inch, with a blanket of fertile material in the form of a heavy water slurry of thorium dioxide.[1]

The major drawback to this was that the fission products would contaminate the water, and filtering out fission products from the solution would not have been easy. On the other hand, there were no fuel elements to worry about, and fuel elements were almost always the most difficult part of any reactor design.

Two commercial firms, ICI and Hawker Siddeley also became involved in the work, and some experimental work was carried out with some zero-energy assemblies, ZETR-1 and ZETR-2. ZETR-2 was also known as HAZEL (homogeneous assembly zero-energy laboratory).[2] The liquid in HAZEL was contained in a stainless steel tank seven feet by two feet, surrounded by a layer of graphite to reflect neutrons back into the tank. The tank contained uranyl fluoride dissolved in heavy water (although *The Times* and *The Telegraph* both rendered this as 'curanyl fluoride', implying a typing error in the press release). The experiment cannot have been a great success, since it was started in March 1958 and dismantled by September.[3]

Another idea which was to receive a good deal of attention was the idea of using an organic liquid as a coolant. Finding an organic coolant which did not decompose into tarlike substances under heat and intense radiation was not easy. One such reactor was built in Canada, at the Whiteshell Nuclear Research Establishment in Manitoba. It was heavy water-moderated and cooled by a mixture of terphenyls. The idea never got beyond the theoretical stage in the UK, although it did emerge at one stage as a strong contender for a marine reactor.[4]

A further proposal was for a liquid metal fuelled reactor, as illustrated in Figure 12.1. This came in various configurations, but the basic principle was that the uranium metal would be alloyed with bismuth, and the resultant alloy could be pumped into the graphite moderator, where fission would occur, then pumped out to a heat exchanger. The version illustrated was also designed to exploit the thorium cycle.[5]

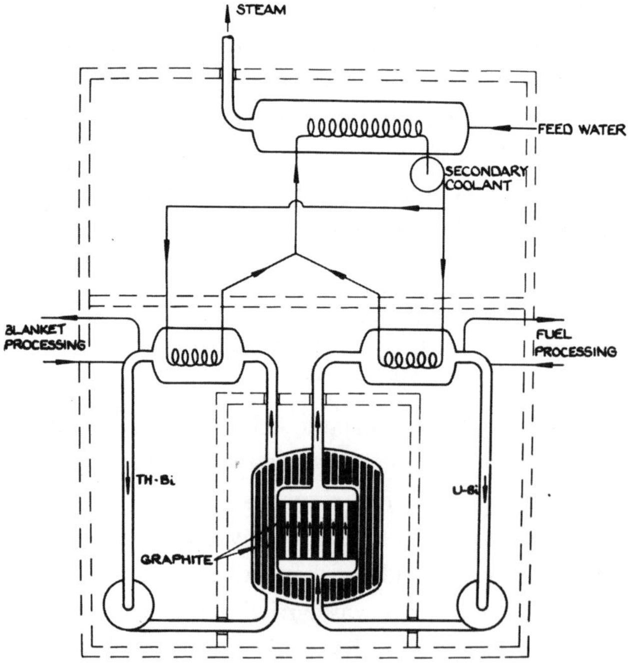

L.M.F.R.

CIRCULATING FUEL MODERATED SINGLE PASS SYSTEM.

Figure 12.1. Liquid metal fuelled reactor — one of several different proposals.

There was, of course, the fast reactor, but a commercial design was unlikely to be ready in time for operation in the mid-1960s. The fast reactor was cooled by liquid sodium, and this gave rise to another idea: a graphite-moderated sodium-cooled reactor. The submarine USS Seawolf also used a sodium-cooled reactor, and although there were no major problems with the design, it was soon replaced with the light water reactor that would become standard in US Navy submarines.

The Sodium-Graphite Reactor

The idea of a sodium-graphite reactor was not new: an experimental design had been built in California. Its construction began in 1954 and it was operational by 1957. It suffered a major accident in 1959, and was eventually closed down in 1964.

As a report on the British design put it:

> Towards the end of 1955 a Research Committee was formed to define and investigate the main problems of the Sodium Graphite Reactor. The Chairman of the Committee was Sir John Cockcroft and members were drawn from the staffs of the Research Group and the Industrial Group. At the end of the Research Study (October, 1956) the Committee issued an Interim Technical Assessment which recommended that the work should continue as a Design Study.[6]

The ensuing design committee comprised almost all the senior members of Risley and Harwell, from Hinton and Cockroft down. The design study was under the direction of RV Moore, who would be involved in the design of almost all the reactors built in the UK. The terms of reference for the study were:

> (1) To assess the possibilities of the Sodium-Graphite Reactor as a power producing Reactor suitable for Stage II of the Nuclear Power Programme. Construction should be possible on large units for operation by 1965. Therefore the development problems must be solved before that date.
> (2) To decide on the minimum size of an Experimental Reactor that would enable the problems of a full scale power reactor to be solved in the time available, and with a minimum of research and development. The Experimental Reactor should be divergent by about the end of 1960.
> (3) To make an accurate assessment of the cost of the Reactor Experiment so as to be able to apply for financial sanction by the end of June, 1957.

The objective was to produce a reactor of high efficiency and of low capital cost, and, on the surface, the sodium-graphite reactor seemed a strong contender. Whilst there were many features in its favour, there were considerable engineering difficulties. The graphite moderator had to be encased in zirconium. If the pipework containing the liquid sodium sprang a leak, then there was the possibility that the liquid sodium would escape into the graphite core. Graphite is slightly porous, and so there was a further possibility that the sodium would soak into the graphite. It would be almost impossible to remove the graphite core once the

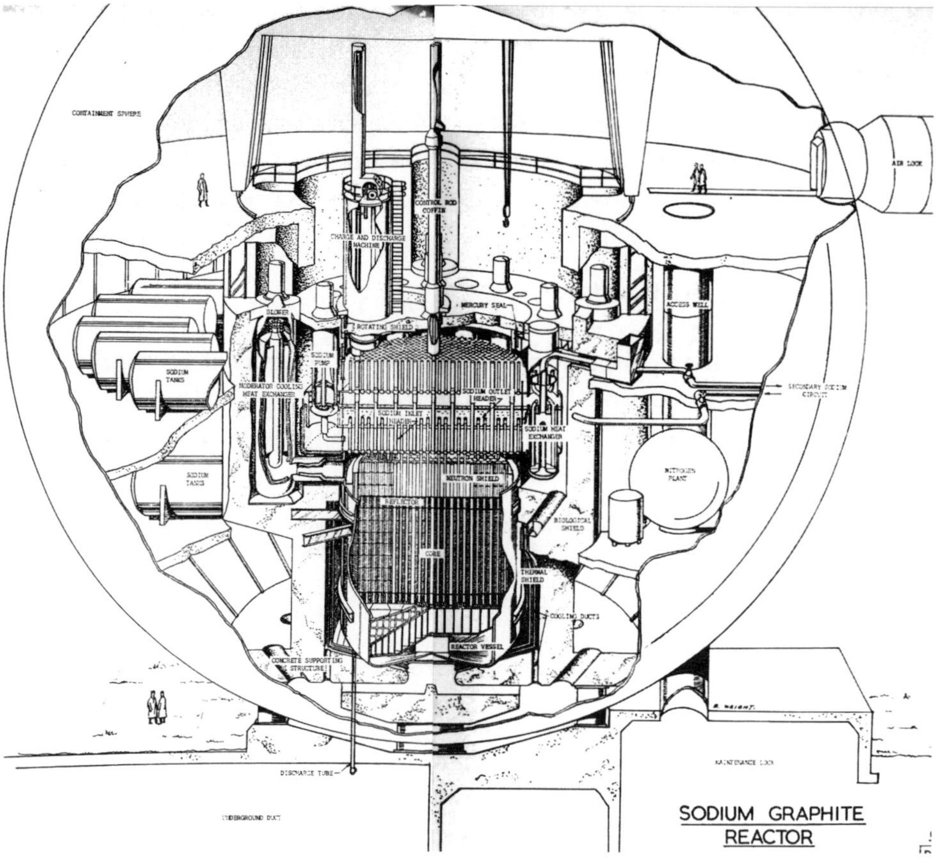

Figure 12.2. The sodium-graphite reactor within a containment dome.

reactor had been constructed, and being able to guarantee the pipework as being leak free over the lifetime of the reactor was extremely difficult. There was one advantage of the system, which was that the coolant circuit did not have to be pressurised.

Closer examination of the economics of the reactor showed that it was not as good an option as originally thought. The capital costs appeared high, as did the generating costs. By March 1957, the future of the reactor seemed in doubt: 'It is almost certain that this reactor will now be dropped — apart from the poor neutron economy, they have run into unexpected corrosion problems with sodium'.[7] At a later meeting to discuss the reactor, Hinton is quoted as saying 'the report on the reactor was better than the reactor itself'.[8] Hinton went on to ask for estimates 'of the cost of power from (a) sodium-graphite reactor (b) heavy water gas-cooled reactor (c) advanced Calder Hall reactor'. Given the date of the meeting (July 1957), it seems likely that Hinton is referring to a possible AGR rather than an improved magnox.

Compared with designs for a more advanced gas-cooled reactor, the sodium-graphite reactor appeared to offer serious technical problems combined with poor economics, which meant that it was soon dropped from the programme.

Water-Moderated Reactors

Power stations, whether conventional or nuclear, are designed to turn water into steam at as a high temperature and pressure as possible, as cheaply as possible, then to use the steam to generate electricity. Power reactors generate heat, and this heat has then to be transferred to the water in order to turn it into steam. Most British reactors used carbon dioxide or liquid sodium as the heat transfer medium. There are, however, other possibilities.

One is to produce the steam inside the reactor itself — a boiling water reactor (BWR). A second is to use water under pressure as the coolant and then transfer the heat to water in a secondary circuit, which will then become steam and drive the turbines. This is a pressurised water reactor (PWR). The cooling water does not boil, even though it will be in temperatures much above 100°C (typically as much as 315°C), as it is kept under very high pressure. These are not the only possibilities for light water reactors: various design studies were even made at Harwell for steam-cooled reactors.[9]

One of the problems of ordinary water, or light water, as a coolant is that it absorbs neutrons. This means that this type of reactor needs to use enriched uranium as a fuel, with obvious cost implications. There is a second hazard, which is that if the system suffers a sudden loss in pressurisation, then the hot water will immediately turn into steam. The steam, which is much less dense, will absorb fewer neutrons and so the reactor will become more active at a time when it should become less active. This was a factor in the Chernobyl accident.

Safety concerns over the PWR, and particularly as to the safety of the pressure vessel, became a source of running battles throughout the UK nuclear power programme in the 1970s and 1980s. The AEA had opposed any move to the PWR from the time it was first suggested in the early 1960s, and remained resolute in its opposition. On the other hand, what is less well known is that the teams at Risley and Harwell pursued design studies and experimental work for an indigenous light water reactor for some years in the mid-1950s. This design was named LEO, standing for low enrichment ordinary water reactor.

Design studies for LEO started around 1953, which was the time when construction of the first PIPPA reactor at Calder Hall had just begun. The preliminary investigations began at AERE with the examination of possible small scale experimental systems, and this was subsequently extended to a survey of a variety of schemes for power stations of around 100 MW(E) in size. Early in 1954 it was decided to proceed to the next stage of the detailed design study of LEO. The EEC together with Babcock and Wilson had requested that they might become involved in a nuclear power design study (this being prior to the commercial programme which began after the 1955 White Paper), and so it was decided that they should take part in the proposed light water study.[10]

A light water reactor involved entirely new engineering problems for Harwell. The major design issue centred, as usual, around the fuel elements.[11] These could use either zirconium or stainless steel as the canning material — aluminium or magnesium would corrode extremely rapidly in hot water. It was known that the Americans were using zirconium in similar reactors, but there was a great deal of experimental work to be done before Harwell could draw up a design for either the fuel elements or the reactor core.

A number of loops were built in research reactors to study the corrosion of carbon steels and stainless steels under the conditions likely to be experienced. One of these loops was installed in the NRX Canadian reactor, another in BEPO, and a third was installed in DIDO. The problem with these types of experiment is that at least 18 months could elapse between devising the experiment, building it, leaving in the reactor for months at a time, then removing it and examining the results.[12]

Another problem was that to keep neutron wastage as low as possible, the core should be as compact as possible, which meant that there would be no space to spare for control rods. Instead, the proposal was that certain fuel rods could be withdrawn from the reactor to shut it down.

The terms of reference for the design group had been to arrive at a likely general design for a large near-natural (in other words, only slightly enriched) uranium power reactor moderated and cooled with light water and generating electric power, and by the end of 1956, an interim report on LEO was produced.[13] The design was still very fluid, although many of the studies had been very detailed. There were still a large number of uncertainties, although some drawings of a power plant had been made (see Figure 12.3).

One point should be noted about the design: the steam from the reactor would not be suitable for generating electricity since it would not be hot enough. This meant adding oil-fired superheaters, which made the plant less efficient. Some early American light water reactors did exactly this, but from the engineering point of view, this was a definite disadvantage.

At the same time, the power programme as laid down in the 1955 White Paper was well underway, with gas-cooled reactors being chosen. There seemed little future in pursuing the light water reactor, given the success of the magnox stations, even though the Admiralty were working quite intensively on a light water reactor of their

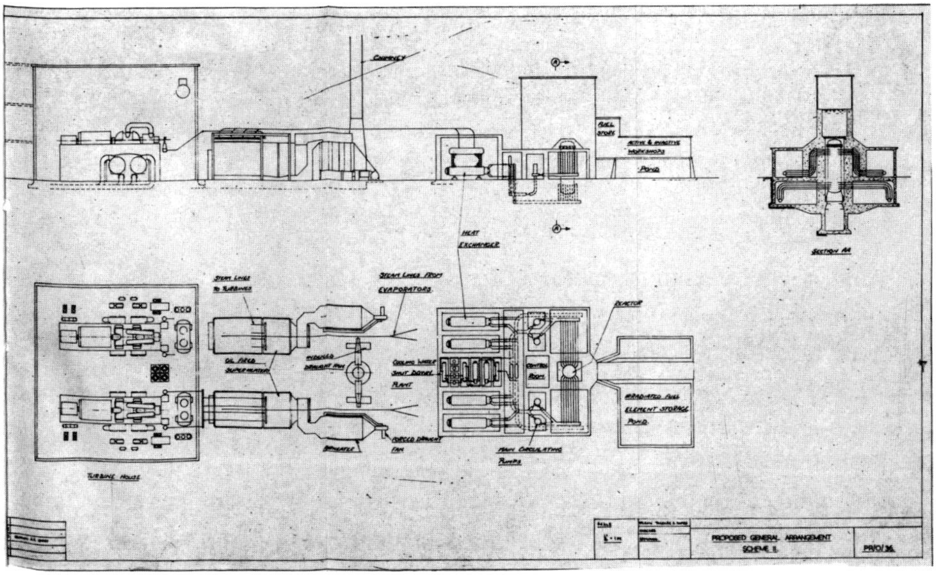

Figure 12.3. A power station based on the PWR design, LEO.

own for a submarine. Work on LEO was wound up in November 1955, with some of the work being transferred to the Naval project.[14] The report of the reactor group for 1958 describes the decision to abandon the programme thus:

> On present designs it cannot compete, at UK fuel prices, even with the first civil power stations. Prospects for the development of the design are limited. Nevertheless, for small outputs, and particularly if cheap fuel were available (i.e. enriched uranium at US prices, or cheap civil plutonium) the reactor has certain advantages because of its compactness both for ship propulsion and as a small plutonium burner to meet peak loads. This may make it suitable for development in this country at a later date. The boiling water version of the reactor does not have the same problems of extremely high pressure and large output versions with consequent low capital cost may be possible.
>
> The work being done by Harwell staff on the submarine pressurised water reactor forms part of their work on basic studies of water systems generally. The studies, together with our experience with the submarine reactor and information available to us from the US will enable us to keep a careful watch on these systems. We can thus continue to assess their place in the UK program and can, if thought desirable at a later date, develop the system ourselves.[15]

Although the light water programme is dutifully mentioned in each of the annual reports of the AEA, there is very little mention of it elsewhere in policy documents. There was certainly no great enthusiasm for the system, and it seems to have had little support from the hierarchy at Harwell or Risley. There is an interesting memo from Hans Kronberger (Director of Research and Development at Risley) after the

Windscale fire, when he is objecting to the wording of a press release:

> I suggest we strongly object to the release to go out in its present form. Technically it is approximately correct but it shows complete lack of judgement in the phrasing. For example, he says that Wigner Energy is potential energy and then gives as an example for potential energy a *stick of dynamite*.
>
> I cannot believe this is an oversight. There is an obvious intent somewhere: possibly to promote the sales of pressurised water reactors![16]

Kronberger was quite right about the wording of the press release, and whilst his comment about pressurised water reactors might have been something of a jest, it is quite revealing that this interpretation should have occurred to him.

Certainly, the AEA were well aware of the American programme, as an undated report comparing Calder Hall with the PWR at Shippingport, which concluded that the generating costs from each type was almost the same.[17]

Although LEO had been dropped from the programme, work on various forms of water reactor did not stop. A variety of studies were continued into various other esoteric forms of water-cooled reactor, for example, the steam cooled heavy water reactor (SCHWR) or the steam generating heavy water reactor (SGHWR). Meanwhile, the Canadians continued to build on their wartime work on heavy water, and had produced a design for a reactor using natural uranium and heavy water. This design was known as the CANDU (Canada deuterium uranium) reactor.

It was the CANDU design which would act as the trigger for a major row concerning the choice of reactor for the second nuclear programme. The first programme had been for a total nuclear generation of 5,000 MW, and this had been accomplished using the magnox design. It was generally accepted that, for any future programme, a more advanced reactor would be a better choice. There was also the point that any decision needed to be made fairly rapidly, otherwise there would be a large gap between the completion of the first programme and the starting of the second, during which the industrial firms would be sitting idle.

Hinton had written an article in the journal the *Three Banks Review* in which he expressed an interest in the CANDU system with the possibility of the CEGB ordering a reactor. Given that the AEA was in the process of developing the new AGR and had the prototype under construction, this seemed to show a lack of confidence in the new design. The article also brought to light the poor relationship between the CEGB and the AEA.

The responsibility for the AEA had been transferred from the Prime Minister to the Minister of Science, Lord Hailsham, who was a member of the Cabinet with the general title of Lord President of the Council. (The Council in question is the Privy Council, and the post is often given to ministers whose responsibilities cover several areas.) Hailsham involved himself with the affairs of the AEA much more than any of his predecessors.

Hinton had left the AEA just before the decision to go ahead with the AGR, and was obviously not convinced of the merits of the system. There had been problems, principally with the canning, where beryllium had to be abandoned in favour of stainless steel, which meant using fuel of a higher enrichment. As a memo to Hailsham put it:

> The CEGB is a public corporation with a statutory monopoly on the generation of electricity for sale and it has been enjoined by the present government to operate on commercial principles. The AEA is a public corporation supported, however, by Exchequer funds which gives it a virtual monopoly of long-term research and development of new reactor systems.
>
> Even if someone rather than Sir Christopher Hinton were the chairman of the CEGB, the latter would always be likely to resent being compelled to buy only reactors of an AEA type in the development of which they had had no say and to pay whatever royalty the AEA might demand. In considering the construction of the Canadian CANDU, Sir Christopher Hinton is in effect giving notice that under these circumstances he is not willing to be solely dependent on the AEA and that he is looking for a competitive source of supply.
>
> Had the AEA been willing to pursue its development policy on the AGR in conjunction with the CEGB as its major customer, the present impasse might not have arisen. The CEGB would have been party to the main decisions on the specification and development of the AGR and could not have refused to build at least one station of the new type. Co-operation on the development of a reactor system may be difficult between two big public corporations each jealous of its independence... The new reactor system is presumably developed to meet the needs of the major potential customer; and it is difficult to uphold the doctrine that the customer should not have some say in what he might be compelled to buy. Since the AEA relies on public funds, it can afford to ignore the customers view in asserting its independence; CEGB for its part says that as a quasi-commercial organisation it must buy in the best market.[18]

The memo went on to claim that ‘It is common knowledge in the nuclear engineering industry that the AEA and the CEGB are scarcely on speaking terms’. Handwritten below was the comment that:

> The Public Accounts Committee has shown surprise that CEGB has so little say in what is developed allegedly in their interest...
>
> But the difficulties are very considerable. There is first the fact that the CEGB feel that they were pushed into a big nuclear programme against their own judgement and have been proved right. There is the translation... of Sir C Hinton from the AEA. It is probably justifiable if the AEA feel that cooperation is not possible...

Hailsham was distinctly disturbed by these comments. He scribbled across the top of the memo:

> This is very serious. It is damaging to the public service if two public bodies cannot cooperate. Cooperation is the right pattern. You had better come and talk to me about this and what I ought to do... You must tell me also what is really behind this.

Another memo suggested a possible way out.

> I suggest that less acrimony might be aroused if a Working Party of Officials, possibly under the chairmanship of the Treasury, could be brought into being by the agreement of those concerned to consider the financial and economic aspects of the rival proposals before any paper is submitted to ministers for decision.[19]

Whether or not this suggestion was acted on directly, a working party was set up under the chairmanship of Sir Richard Powell, then the permanent secretary at the Board of Trade, resulting in a further White Paper[20] published in April 1964. Curiously, the minutes refer to the 'Cabinet Committee on Nuclear Power', a slightly unusual title since the committee contained no cabinet members, but instead consisted entirely of officials. Its terms of reference were:

> To consider and report on the scale of production of nuclear power for civil purposes needed in the five to seven years after 1968 and on the type or types of reactor to be used in that programme,

It began work in 1962.

A timetable was laid out which recognised that the existing nuclear power programme of the magnox stations would be completed by the end of 1968. Building for the new programme would have to start in mid-1965 for a station to be commissioned in 1969, and so invitations to tender for the contracts would have to be sent out early in 1964. If the station was to be of a new type, the CEGB would require about nine months to prepare specifications for tender; thus work would have to start by mid-1963. A decision was therefore required within about 12 months as to the type of reactor to be built.[21]

The committee considered four possible options: improved magnox stations, the AGR, the Canadian CANDU heavy water design, and the American BWR. Hinton showed an obvious preference for the BWR (CANDU now seemed to be out of the running). He appeared to be sceptical about graphite-moderated reactors, particularly ones running at such high temperatures as the AGR. Hinton had never had a high opinion of the gas-cooled reactors and it also seems from his comments that the Windscale incident had affected his thinking.

There was also the point that the BWR seemed to be the cheapest option, and as Chairman of the CEGB, Hinton's sole concern should have been the economics of the system. Hinton's preference cannot have been taken well by the AEA, since adopting the BWR would be a repudiation of all the work that had been done over the previous 10 years. The Windscale AGR was being commissioned at the time, and Hinton wanted to see the outcome before committing himself to the design.

The resulting White Paper was relatively brief. It recommended a programme of around 5,000 MW of new nuclear power, and as to the type of station, it had this

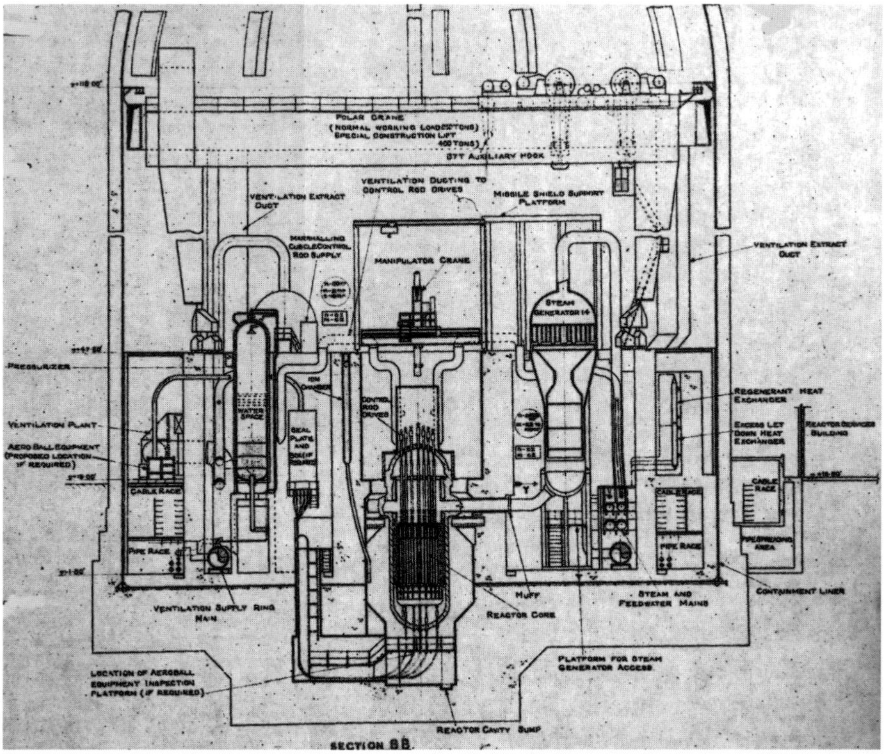

Figure 12.4. The English Electric PWR proposal for Dungeness B. This was rejected in a somewhat controversial decision in favour of the AGR.

to say:

> The Central Electricity Generating Board will issue an enquiry for tenders for a[n] Advanced Gas-Cooled Reactor station. They will also be ready to consider tenders from British industry for water-moderated reactor systems of proved design, providing that full supporting evidence is submitted with the tenders and that requirements of safety and performance comparable with those of the A.G.R. are met. They will ensure that these tenders are judged on a comparable basis.[22]

The first station of the new power programme would be built at Dungeness, and tenders were invited. Four of the bids presented were based on American water reactor designs, and three were based on the AGR. The water designs were thought to be strong contenders, and were presented in some detail, as the accompanying drawings show. However, amid some controversy, the AGR was chosen.

The implications for the AEA of the PWR being chosen by the CEGB were stark: a letter to Dr JM Hill, who was then the Managing Director of the Production Group at Risley, from his assistant notes that:

> I think that if the arguments involved in the choice between AGR and PWR were purely economic, then it would probably be right to take the BWR. The same

> arguments would, however, lead to the halving of the size of the Authority and to the abolition of two out of the three Consortia, and the savings to be made by a movement in the direction of these latter steps appear greater than the real differences between the choice of a first AGR or BWR, (though this is not true if the first inevitably leads to the adoption of the system for the UK programme.) . . . The adoption of the BWR would, it seemed to me, lead to a public enquiry on the size of the investment already made in the AGR and to a general holocaust in the Authority and the nuclear industry generally. I do not see, therefore, how it is possible for the Authority or for Members of the Authority in that capacity to advocate the adoption of the BWR.[23]

The comment about safety in the White Paper was part of an on-going debate which would last for nearly 20 years. There had been considerable concerns as to the safety of the BWR, and these objections were raised every time the BWR came into consideration. Sir Alan Cottrell, who would become Chief Scientific Adviser to the government in 1971, was a particular opponent of the PWR on safety grounds, but proving a particular system to be 'safe' was extremely subjective and almost impossible to pin down with any precision. As a result, the BWR and PWR were effectively excluded from the running until the 1980s. In the end though, the last power station to be built in the UK was Sizewell B — a PWR single reactor station of American design generating 1,300 MW.

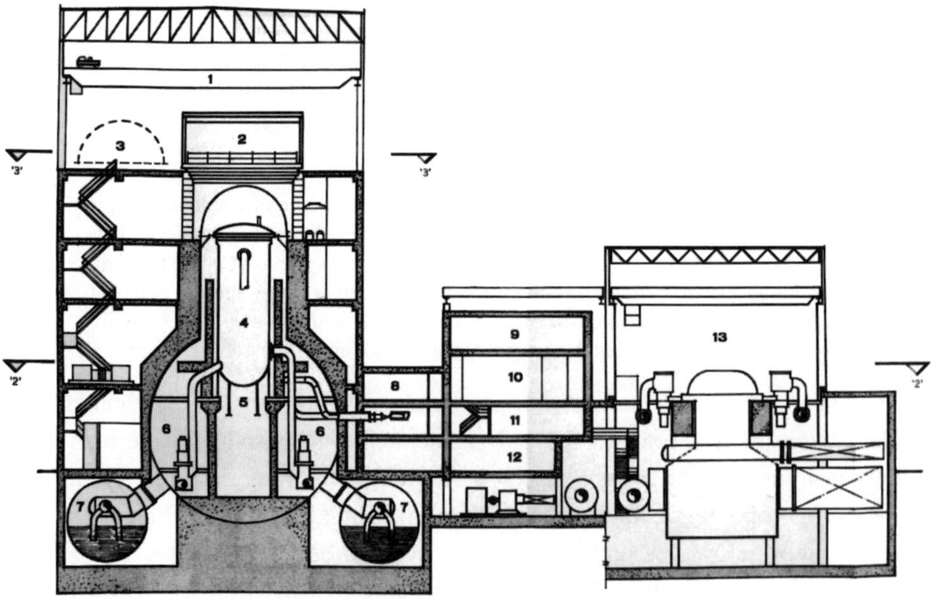

Figure 12.5. A Boiling Water Reactor (BWR) design tender for Dungeness B.

[1] TNA: PRO EG 1/226. The reactor research programme. 'Description Of The New Stage III Systems.'

[2] TNA: PRO AB 16/1249. New reactor (HAZEL) at Harwell.

[3] TNA: PRO AB 16/2561. UK nuclear power programme.

[4] TNA: PRO AB 16/2219. Nuclear propulsion of shipping: correspondence, conferences.

[5] TNA: PRO AB 15/5390. The liquid metal fuelled reactor system. J Smith.

[6] TNA: PRO AB 7/4718. Report on the sodium graphite reactor design study.

[7] TNA: PRO AB 16/2599. Sodium graphite reactor.

[8] TNA: PRO AB 6/1660. Sodium graphite reactor. Note to Sir John Cockroft: 'Sodium-Graphite Meeting — Friday, 12th July'. 12 July 1957.

[9] For example, TNA: PRO AB 15/6235. Progress with S.C.H.W. reactor systems. RV Moore and S Fawcett.

[10] TNA: PRO AB 16/1441. Pressurised light water cooled and moderated reactor (LEO): design study. Atomic Energy Executive Committee: 'Co-operation with Industry.' Sir John Cockcroft, 29 January 1954.

[11] TNA: PRO AB 15/4746. Fuel elements for water-cooled power reactors, SF Pugh, Canada/UK Conference, 1955.

[12] *Ibid.*

[13] TNA: PRO AB 12/195. Light Water Reactor Feasibility Study Committee, Committee 'A': agenda and minutes: includes LEO 'B' Plant Design Sub-Committee agenda and minutes: papers; Volume 3. See also TNA: PRO AB 15/4103. LEO: a plant producing power from a light water cooled and moderated reactor. HW Bowker.

[14] TNA: PRO AB 16/1379. Marine propulsion: naval reactor for Admiralty submarine. John Cockcroft to Edwin Plowden, 22 November 1955.

[15] TNA: PRO AB 41/693. Committee on the Authority's Reactor Programme: Papers 1–35.

[16] TNA: PRO AB 38/51. Windscale incident, 10 October 1957.

[17] TNA: PRO AB 38/300. Comparison of Calder Hall and US Pressurized Water Reactor (PWR).

[18] TNA: PRO EG 1/355. UK nuclear power programme. 'The future of the Nuclear Power Programme.' MI Michaels, 22 January 1962.

[19] TNA: PRO EG 1/355. UK nuclear power programme. 'Note on the A.E.A. paper.' MI Michaels, 9 January 1962.

[20] TNA: PRO CAB 134/2268. Committee on Nuclear Power: Meetings 1–3; Papers 1–13.

[21] TNA: PRO CAB 134/2269. Committee on Nuclear Power: Meetings 1–4; Papers 1–13.

[22] Ministry of Power (April 1964). *The Second Nuclear Programme* [White Paper] London: HMSO (Cmnd 2335).

[23] TNA: PRO AB 38/242. Fuel elements AGR. Letter from NL Franklin (Assistant Managing Director, Production Group, Risley) to Dr JM Hill, Managing Director, Production Group, 26 March 1964.

Chapter 13

The Advanced Gas-Cooled Reactor

The limiting factor to the magnox design was the maximum temperature to which the fuel rods could be heated — in practice, not much more than 400°C. At higher temperatures, it was impossible to find a metal which could contain the uranium metal without alloying or reacting with it or with the carbon dioxide coolant. Another problem was that uranium exists in several different physical forms, and as it heated up and cooled down it would undergo phase changes which meant it would expand and contract, making problems for the canning material. The transition temperature from the alpha phase to the beta was 668°C, a temperature would be easily reached in the centre of the fuel rod if heated much further. The solution was not to use uranium metal, but uranium dioxide in the form of ceramic pellets.

This too had its drawbacks: the oxide was a good deal less dense than the metal and so took up more space, but a bigger issue was that the oxide was not nearly as good a conductor of heat as the metal. This meant that the fuel rods had to be very much thinner in order for the heat to able to escape.

Beryllium had been proposed as the canning material for the fuel rods, since it had the great advantage that it was an extremely good moderator. Unfortunately, it also reacted with fast neutrons producing helium gas, which would form pockets within the metal. There were also problems with its mechanical properties as well as its toxicity. However, the main reason for abandoning it was rather more mundane:

> The development programme was stopped before beryllium elements were made which could be safely irradiated in large numbers. It should be clear that this was not because there was an insuperable technical problem, but at the low U235 prices now ruling the economics of a beryllium canned A.G.R. did not seem so much more attractive than one based on stainless steel as to justify further expenditure on development.[1]

Other sources differ: 'Beryllium Hits Snag in British Reactor' was the headline of an article in *American Metal Market*. The article went on to say: 'The new and unexpected problem is corrosion of beryllium in the carbon dioxide coolant of the reactor at its high designed operating temperature . . . '[2]

Any canning metal had to be compatible not only with the uranium oxide fuel but with carbon dioxide. A form of stainless steel[3] (containing 20% chromium and 25% nickel together with niobium) was found to be satisfactory at temperatures up to about 850°C. It had a melting point of almost 1,500°C. The maximum can surface temperature selected was 650°C (this meant the system could produce steam at the same temperature as conventional power stations), which allowed for local hot spots. One drawback to stainless steel was that it had a relatively high cross-section area for thermal neutrons, which meant using enriched fuel, of the order of 2.5% enrichment.

The other problem with raising the temperature of the coolant was the reaction between carbon dioxide and graphite. Under the operating conditions of magnox reactors, the rate of graphite removal was not great enough to threaten the integrity of the moderator throughout the life of the reactor, but in the AGR the higher temperatures as well as the greater intensity of radiation energy in the core, largely due to the higher fuel ratings, led to a higher reaction rate, which had to be reduced to keep the removal of graphite from the moderator down to an acceptable limit.

The only way to see whether the solutions would work was to test them experimentally in the materials testing reactors at Harwell and Dounreay and the results showed that the addition to the coolant of small amounts of hydrocarbon gases such as methane were very effective in reducing the erosion of the graphite. The methane reacted with the carbon monoxide produced to give carbon and water. This still left one final problem: migration of the carbon might occur — that is, the carbon would be removed from one part of the moderator, a hotter region, and deposited again somewhere else which might be cooler.

There was another way of keeping the graphite moderator relatively cool, which involved a fairly complicated path for the coolant — the gas coming back from the heat exchangers was sent down open channels in the graphite, keeping it relatively cool, and then back up through the fuel channels, being heated along the way, and as a result only the graphite in the fuel channels was subjected to the higher temperatures.

There was no doubt that the AGR represented a considerable step up from the magnox design, not only in efficiency but in complexity. The next step was to test various design features in research reactors built specially for the purpose. These included the HERO (heated experimental reactor zero (0) energy) and NERO II reactors.[4] Built at Windscale at a cost of about £1.25 million, and housed in one of the old blower houses of the now derelict Pile 1, HERO had a core which was similar to that of the proposed prototype Windscale AGR, but was capable of being dismantled and rebuilt if necessary.[5] Circulation of heated carbon dioxide through the core meant that experiments could be carried out over a wide range of temperatures, and since the heating was from an external source (the gas was electrically heated by two 450 kW heaters), measurements could be taken at AGR temperatures whilst

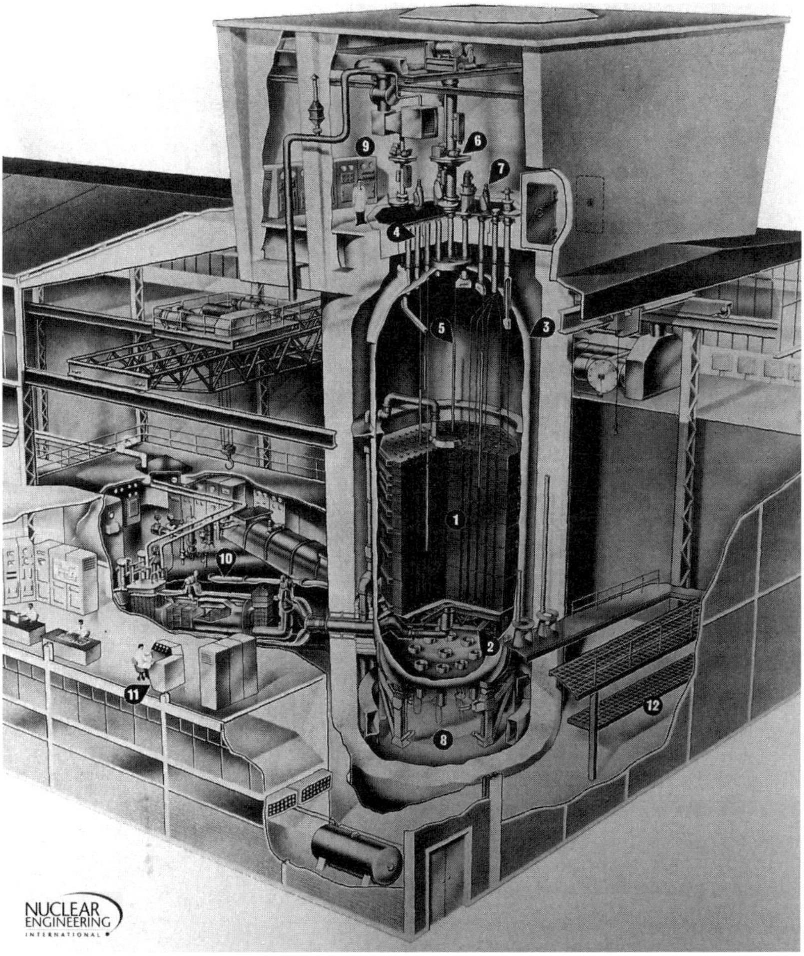

Figure 13.1. HERO — a zero-energy experimental prototype, built in one of the disused blower houses of pile 1.

still operating the reactor at zero energy and so eliminate problems of radiation and fission product build up.[6]

Design and development work on the prototype AGR started in August 1957, and in January 1958, the decision was taken to go ahead with construction at Windscale. Preliminary work began in August, and the excavation for the concrete raft in November. Like the DFR, the prototype would also be housed in a pressure dome. Installation of the graphite core began in January 1961 and was completed by March. There would be a total of 253 channels in the reactor, of which about 200 would be fuel. This contrasts with the magnox stations — the Wylfa station had over 7,000 channels (Wylfa generated around 600 MW compared with the prototype AGR at around 40 MW, but even so, the reduction in the number of channels was considerable).[7]

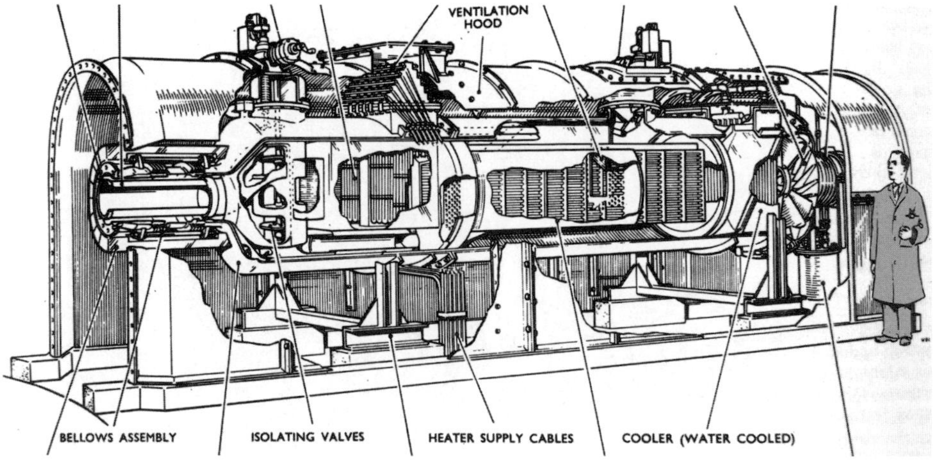

Figure 13.2. One of the 450 kW electrical heaters for HERO.

The fuel elements in the AGR were very different from those in the magnox station: each fuel element consisted of a thin walled stainless steel can 20 inches long and 0.4 inches in internal diameter and contained 46 cylindrical pellets of enriched uranium dioxide. Twenty one fuel elements were grouped together to form a cluster and two such clusters, contained in a graphite sleeve, formed a fuel element assembly; four assemblies were linked together in the fuel element building to form a fuel stringer 14 feet long. The fuel plug stringers were loaded into about 200 reactor channels producing a total charge of some 33,000 fuel elements and over 1.5 million individual pieces of fuel, each of which would stay in the reactor for an average of three years. The other reactor channels (roughly 50) contained control, trimming and shutdown rods, the four irradiation test loops, and graphite samples under test.

Since the Windscale AGR was still an experimental design, the reactor and heat exchangers were enclosed inside a steel containment building 134 feet high and 135 feet wide. This was a gigantic steel sphere, which would become one of the more famous Windscale landmarks and was designed to contain the entire contents of the reactor coolant circuit and one heat exchanger if the pressure circuit was breached. Any discharges from the containment building were passed through fission product filters and absorption beds before being vented 150 feet above ground through the ventilation chimney.

Loading of the first fuel stringers started at the beginning of August until, on 9 August 1962, four years after the start of construction, criticality was achieved with a loading of 46 fuel stringers. This critical size was very close to predictions based on the results from the HERO and APEX research reactors. Full power of 100 MW(H) was reached on 18 January 1963. The turbo-alternator was synchronised

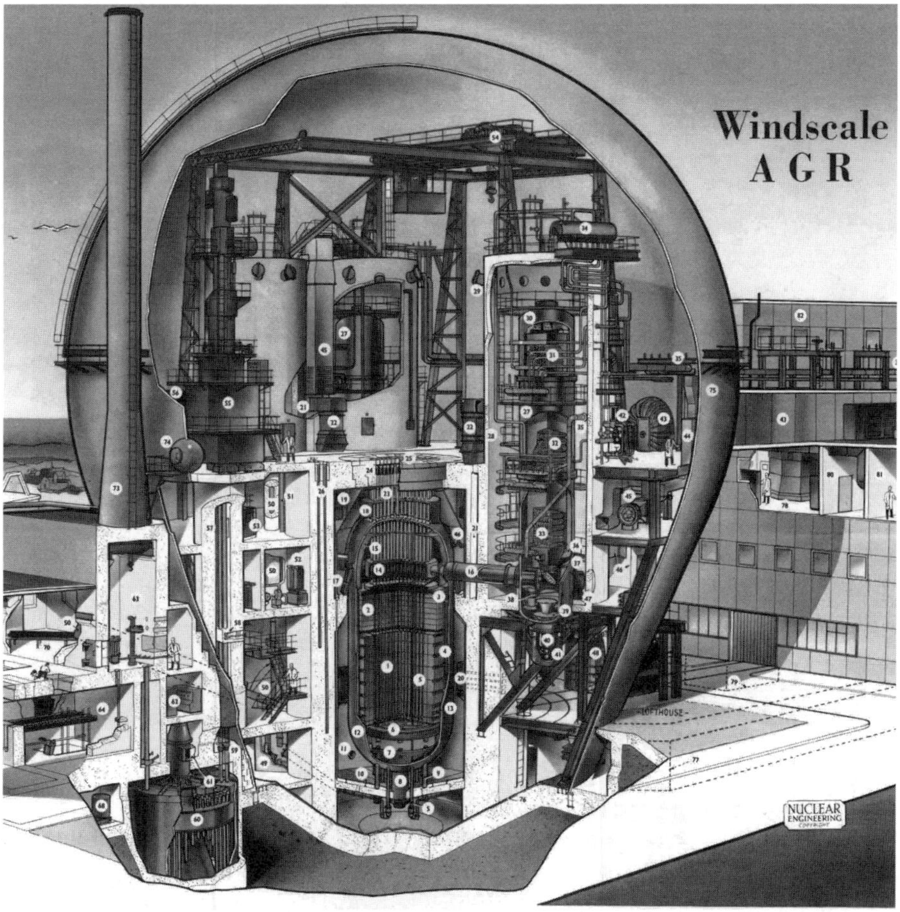

Figure 13.3. Cutaway view of the Windscale AGR.

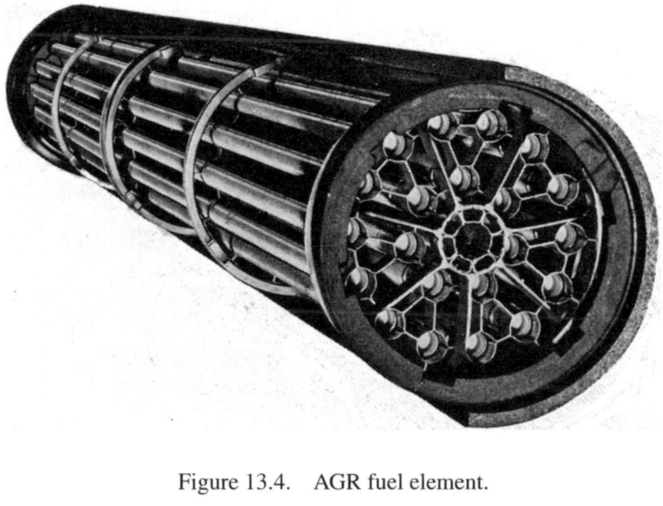

Figure 13.4. AGR fuel element.

Figure 13.5. The Windscale AGR.

to the national electricity grid on 18 February 1963 and subsequently ran up to full design power of 33 MW(E) with export of 28 MW(E). After optimisation of the core conditions it was found possible to increase the thermal power of the reactor to 112 MW and the turbine was re-bladed in 1964 to permit a gross electrical output of 41 MW(E) with export of 31 MW(E).[8]

The Windscale AGR was closed in April 1983, and is currently being decommissioned with the intention of returning the site to greenfield status.

Meanwhile, events elsewhere were casting doubt on the usefulness of the AGR as a commercial power generator. The saga of the controversy as to whether the CEGB should build a water-cooled reactor to an American design or an AGR has already been described. In the event, the CEGB decided to accept a tender for an AGR to be built at Dungeness. Contemporary papers produced by the AEA and CEGB were designed to show how much of an improvement the AGR would be compared with the magnox stations. Many of these points had considerable validity:

> A higher fuel rating permits a more compact core than with Magnox reactors and higher temperatures permit a more compact heat exchanger, hence the nuclear boiler is cheaper.

Simplified on-load refuelling should ensure high availability by enabling maintenance shutdowns to be planned for the most advantageous time and by giving the flexibility to adjust the fuel cycle according to the electrical load requirements.[9]

Figure 13.6. The Windscale AGR charge face.

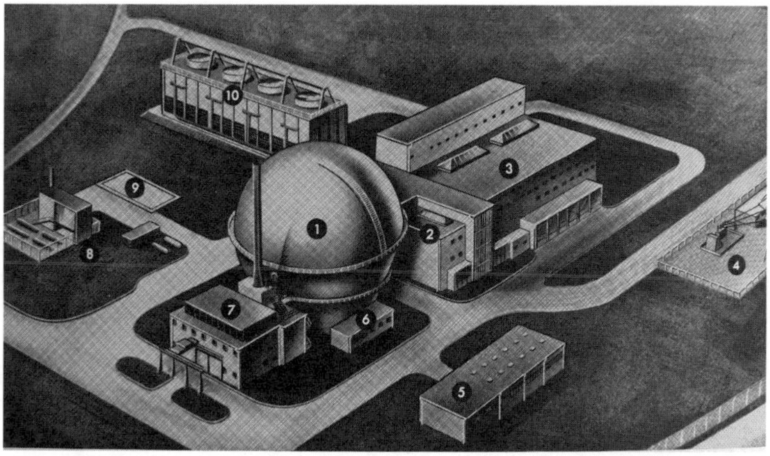

THE A.G.R. SITE

1 *Reactor Containment Building*
2 *Control and Administration Building*
3 *Turbine Hall*
4 *Electricity Output to National Grid*
5 *Test Loop Electrical Plant Building*
6 *Ventilation and Air Conditioning Plant*
7 *Fuel Element Building*
8 *Gas Storage Plant*
9 *Gas Discharge Treatment Plant*
10 *Cooling Towers*

Figure 13.7. The AGR site at Windscale.

On-load fuelling turned out to be rather more difficult than anticipated, and must be regarded as one of those areas where the AGR design was less than effective.

The paper went on to make comparisons between the last and most efficient of the magnox stations, Wylfa, and the AGR design:

Table 13.1. Comparison of Wylfa and AGR.

	Wylfa	AGR
Efficiency*	31.5%	42%
Coolant pressure	27 kg/cm^2	42 kg/cm^2
Channel inlet temperature	247°C	300°C
Channel outlet temperature	413°C	675°C
Steam pressure	45 kg/cm^2	160 kg/cm^2
Steam temperature	393°C	565°C
Core diameter	18.6 m	12 m
Core height m	9.5 m	8.5 m
Total number of channels	7030	<400
Blower power per reactor	56 MW	14 MW

*This is the thermodynamic efficiency — in other words, how much of the heat energy is converted to electrical energy.

These data certainly show the technical advantages of the AGR, and if building an AGR were as straightforward as building a magnox station, then the AGR would have had a great advantage over the magnox.

Technical advantage was, however, not necessarily what the CEGB were looking for: they were more interested in generating electricity more cheaply — and the question should have been not whether the AGR was technically superior, but what the unit cost of electricity would be. Unfortunately, working out the economic performance of a nuclear power station was very much like taking a stab in the dark. There was a further point which would emerge soon after construction began: a more sophisticated design might well mean greater engineering difficulties. Certainly, building the AGR stations would prove a considerable challenge, and the difficulties encountered at Dungeness would sully the reputation of the gas/graphite reactor permanently, although how much of the blame lay with the AGR design and how much lay with the incompetence of consortium building is another matter.

The Saga of Dungeness B

Dungeness B was the first station to be ordered as a result of the 1964 White Paper; it was to be the first of the AGRs which would replace the magnox stations, and it was to be the source of great controversy.

Dungeness B came to personify all that was wrong with the British atomic power programme. It dealt a blow to the reputation of the AGR which discredited the system to such a degree that it is still held up by many as a failure, although once the

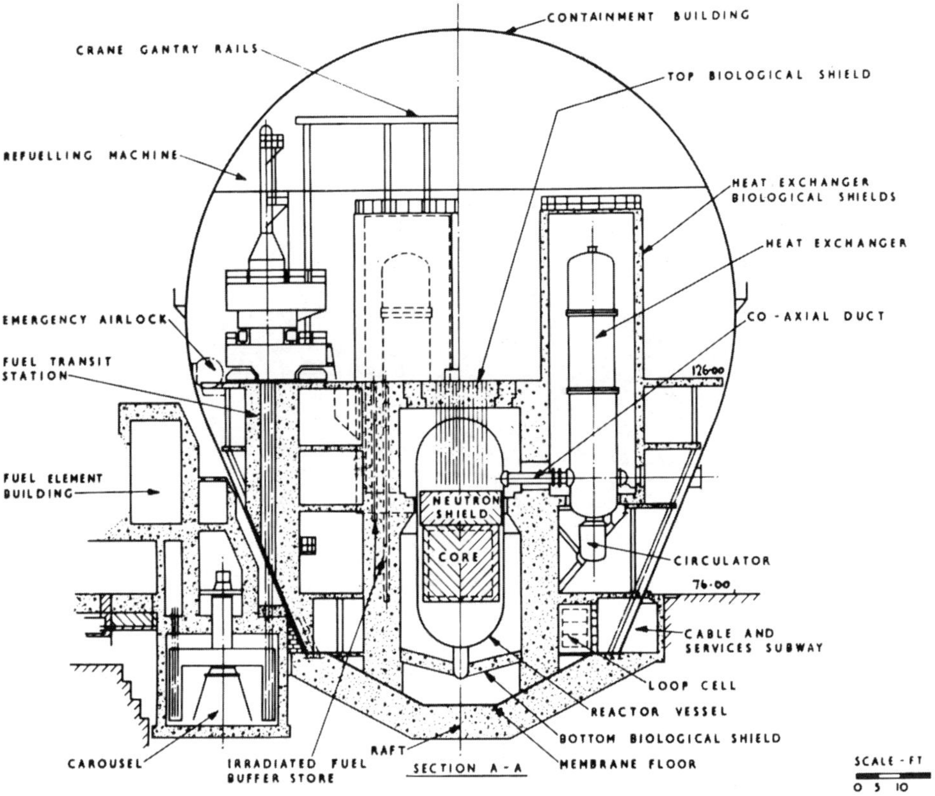

Figure 13.8. Sectional view of the Windscale AGR.

problems of Dungeness and the other AGRs had been sorted out, they would prove to be reasonably successful, even though their load factors were not impressive. Whether they have been economically successful compared with the rival designs available at the time is another question. Unfortunately, the protracted saga of the Dungeness construction programme gave rise to years of negative publicity.

Indeed, the controversy had begun long before the construction. The CEGB, who were the customer, had shown an obvious preference for the American light water reactor system. The decision to order an AGR caused considerable surprise, as shown by an article in the American publication *Nucleonics Week* of 22 April 1965 in which the comment is made that 'Rumors to the effect that "UPC's AGR has done it"... have been met with some disbelief by U.S. water reactor interests in Britain and even by some AGR protagonists.'[10] These sentiments were echoed in an article in *The Economist* magazine. It begins:

> Because of the bitter controversy, the accusations of bad faith, sharp practice and so on that followed the CEGB's decision to give a £85 million contract for Dungeness B to the apparently moribund Atomic Power Construction consortium,

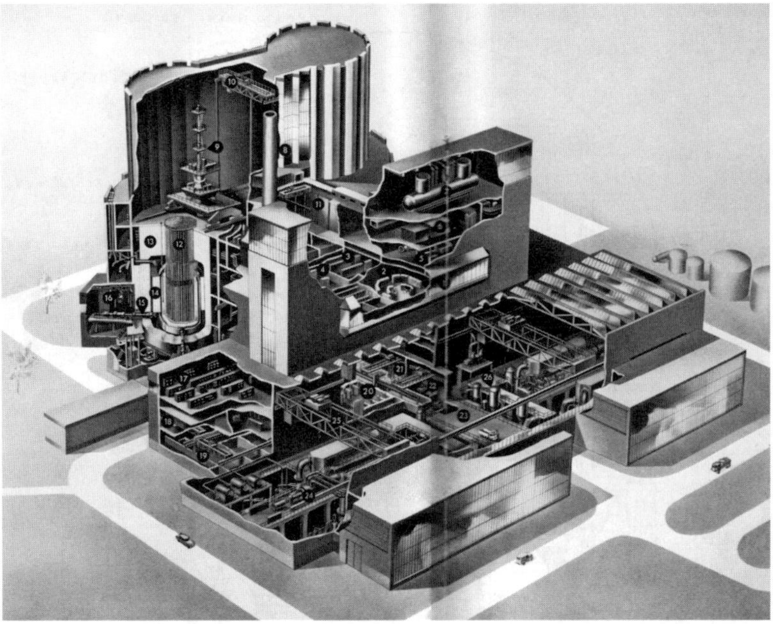

Figure 13.9. Artist's impression of Dungeness B AGR.

Figure 13.10. Dungeness B under construction.

> CEGB has broken its own precedent and published details of both APC's and of the closest of several unsuccessful tenders. The figures ought to provide clues to the two biggest mysteries of the bid; they do not, entirely. These mysteries are:
>
> (a) why did the prices for American-designed reactors [the PWR] come out so high, and apparently so much above the cost of building them in America? and
>
> (b) why was APC apparently the only British consortium to get its price for this particular advanced gas cooled type of reactor down to competitive levels?[11]

These were remarkably good questions which never got a satisfactory answer, including the question of how APC was able to produce such a remarkably low tender.

Indeed, it was not only *The Economist* and the Americans who were surprised by the success of the AGR tender; a letter written in an obvious tone of surprise came from across the channel. The letter was written by M Gaussens of the Commissariat a L'Energy Atomique (Atomic Energy Commission), who asked:

> As a matter of fact, I don't quite understand, neither do several people around me, why the price of the BWR bid is:
>
> £ 60 million ($168 millions) or $168/kWe
>
> whereas the G.E. pricelist is for a capacity of the same range and only one reactor on the site: $126/kWe.
>
> How do you explain that difference?... I would be very interested by your answers and thank you again.[12]

Various points were mentioned in the reply. One was that the General Electric pricelist was based on the expectation that several repeat orders would be received within a fairly short period. It was also claimed that the CEGB issued a more detailed specification and required higher standards of finish and amenity than US utility companies would be likely to do. Finally:

> I would not pretend, however, that these factors would in themselves fully explain the difference between the two prices. Some part of the difference does appear to be due to differences between the organisation of the US and UK industries.[13]

This reply does not seem to be altogether convincing.

The tenders for the PWR and BWR designs had evaluated by the AEA, and there is an interesting document headed 'Authority Tactics Over Dungeness B'.[14] Paragraph two begins: 'Cartwright's note offers the hope that the T.N.P.G. B.W.R. will come out about £20/kW higher than the I.G.E. price list would imply'. Harry Cartwright was the Director of water reactors at Risley, and, as such, evaluated the water reactor tenders. This does not imply that the figures were manipulated in any way, but it does show the attitude that the AEA was showing towards the idea of water-cooled reactors.

There were three AGR tenders; of the TNPG tender, the AEA commented that 'Although capital costs have not yet been seen, it appears that this design of AGR will be hopelessly uneconomic compared with the BWR'. As for the APC bid,

> It is emphasised that the total price quoted, which includes only estimates for the civil work, represents a genuine ceiling price which would not be exceeded if the CEGB decided to proceed with negotiation for a contract for the whole station.[15]

That was a statement which was tempting fate with a vengeance.
A CEGB memo noted that:

> A.P.C. Ltd., having initially declined to render for Dungeness 'B', at a late stage decided to make an offer with the result that in February, 1965 when the various offers were received their offer was less comprehensive and detailed than normally is the case. The process of tender assessment and contract negotiation was carried out to programme and in the event A.P.C. were required to mount a considerable effort to overcome a programme of recruitment of additional staff to overcome some losses that had occurred during the run-down of Trawsfynydd.[16]

This does not form a particularly reassuring background, but, in the event, the contract was awarded to APC and so construction duly began. To say that the building of the station met difficulties would be a very considerable understatement. The design itself met objections from the nuclear inspectorate, as this letter dated January 1969 shows:

> After detailed and intensive assessments by the INI and much consultation between the INI and the CEGB, I have concluded that the detailed design of the AGR at Dungeness B is such that I would be unable to recommend to the Minister that he should give his consent to fuel loading . . .[17]

The reasons for this lay in the shutdown mechanism. Unlike the magnox reactors, the AGR design had a second gas baffle pressure vessel within the main pressure vessel. This was a consequence of the complicated gas-flow system. The shutdown mechanism used control rods held out of the reactor by electromagnets, and if the power to these were to fail, the rods could drop back under gravity. Unfortunately, the channels for these rods had to pass through both the main pressure vessel and the baffle pressure vessel. The Inspectorate felt that a major incident involving the reactor would quite likely produce a misalignment between the holes in the main pressure vessel and the baffle pressure vessel. The report went on to say:

> The distortion and partial or complete failure of the pressurised gas baffle will surely prevent a number or all of the 57 control rods from entering the core and the shutting down the reactor when required. No other means are provided for doing this.

As a consequence, a secondary shutdown system was installed which involved injecting nitrogen gas (nitrogen is a neutron absorber) into the core.

When it came to the construction, almost every part of the building seemed to have a defect. A report of 1970 lists some of these:

> Foundations — delays of several weeks occurred as contract proceeded.
>
> Steel work — delays amounting to several weeks on the current programme are occurring.
>
> Internal structures — the membrane, pressure cylinder, core restraint cylinder moderator support grid complex for R1 was completed for stress relief and subsequent skid-in to the pressure vessel bottom some 10 months late on the original programme although only a few weeks behind the current revised programme issued in October 1967.
>
> Boilers — the dates when delivery of boiler material is due at site will not be met and commencement of boiler direction will be some months later than the current programme.
>
> Turbo alternators . . . There are current delays of up to 2 months on certain turbine components being manufactured and several months delay on the alternators being produced at Heaton works.
>
> All these faults led to very considerable delays, and the cost rose not only because of the remedial work, but because a large and expensive power station was standing idle instead of generating electricity.[18]

Unfortunately these were not the only problems. More remedial work was needed after the discovery of corrosion in the magnox reactors, and the equivalent fittings in the AGR had to be taken out and replaced with ones of a different material. This is perhaps one of the few faults which cannot be attributed directly to the builders.

Some interesting background to the tender is revealed in a fairly lengthy report written by a former employee of APC. This has been preserved in a ministry file, but with an attached note carrying a 'health warning' that the source may not be entirely unbiased. The report is deeply critical of the whole affair.

APC had been formed as the fifth consortium, and its tender for Trawsfynydd resulted in the new consortium obtaining the contract to build the station in 1959. After that, it struggled to find further business, and became involved in potential mergers with other consortia and companies, none of which were successful. The report covers the history of APC in considerable detail, then moves on to the saga of the Dungeness B tender:

> It was decided by the management that a small budget should be made available to APC to produce token tenders for CEGB for Dungeness B. The attitude generally being that although there was virtually no possibility of securing order for Dungeness B it was necessary to indicate to CEGB that APC continued to be in existence so that it could rebuild and get back into business. Such money as was available for AGR was to be largely spent in reactor design.
>
> In parallel with these events there was anxiety within UKAEA that AGR would not receive adequate representation at the Dungeness B tender assessments unless APC put in a tender because it was considered that TNPG and EE Co had already turned their major efforts towards light water reactors. UKAEA were prepared to

assist APC in preparing sections of the supporting reactor technical work for an AGR design.

This left APC with a decision to make concerning the status of the offers to be made to CEGB bearing in mind the small amount of work done. The cost information which had been accumulated suggested that the water reactor would be bound to win the order for Dungeness B, but the available detailed experience and knowledge within APC of water reactors was so slight and the expected cost so low that it was dubious whether the cost information available could be believed. On the other hand with a gas cooled system APC felt itself a much stronger ground even though the detailed design and costing had not been carried out rigorously . . . . In the event the tenders were sent off with a firm price for AGR and a budget offer for the PWR.

Nobody was more surprised than the staff of APC when their offer for an AGR secured acceptance.

The situation within APC at that time was that the company was committed to a construction timetable (211 weeks for the first unit) without a detailed design, with considerable novelty in almost all the plant, with an organisation which had shrunk considerably since the days of its Trawsfynydd activity and with some of its resources committed to work on the Tokai Mura reactor in support of GEC.

The contract award was in September 1965 and construction of the first unit due for completion of construction in October 1969.

In this situation, one of two lines of advance was possible, either the construction programme could be the master and design decisions made to suit or the construction programme had been modified to allow detailed design to be formulated. In the event, for obvious reasons, the construction programme became the master.

A further problem arose when the firm which had been due to design and produce the gas circulators closed down.

This led to the necessity for APC to find another supplier for the gas circulators. A contract was placed with AEI (Rugby) to engineer the gas circulators in about the summer of 1966. Thus about a year had passed and the gas circulators design/development programme was in a state of flux. Mergers in the electrical industry subsequently destroyed the AEI circulator team.

It seemed to APC that Richardsons Westgarth['s] [one of the members of the consortium] commercial position was such that there was a substantial risk that they might not be able to complete their other contractual obligations on Dungeness B. These were still substantial, consisting essentially of the steam condensing and feed water heating plant for the station. In order to avoid this risk it was decided to place the contract for these items elsewhere and negotiations were entered into with AEA (Trafford Park) in about the autumn of 1966 for alternative supply. These events led to RWs being in the position of underwriting the risks of the project as a member company of APC without any expectation of work on the project and they withdrew from the group leaving Fairey Engineering and International Combustion as the sole member companies of APC, Crompton Parkinson having disappeared earlier in a rationalisation of the electrical industry . . .

Another aspect of the design which interacted with the ordering of components associated with the boilers concerned the high-pressure steam pipework.

At the beginning of the contract it was necessary to check that the forces and stresses generated by thermal expansion and contraction of the pipework were acceptable. Pipework routes had been drawn for the tender, but no analytical work had been done. Aiton & Co of Derby were engaged to carry out the work and to detail the pipework. The first results from this showed that the pipework routing, plant layout and pipework material was such that the limitations of thrust determined by the turbine were not satisfied. The analytical exercise was extended to find a pipework route which would satisfy the requirements. The conclusions were that the expansion loops required were so large as to project beyond the confines of the proposed buildings and there was no alternative but to change the high-pressure pipework material to stainless steel. Much design office work was used in this exercise and the decision was important for other plant suppliers. For example, if difficult problems were to be avoided, the valves associated with the boilers which would be welded to the steam pipe work had been manufactured in the same material as the pipes.

These illustrations are perhaps sufficient to show that the general state of the station design was unsatisfactory at the time of tender and construction timetables (based on erection of an established design) could not have been realistic. The amount of design work required in a short time was such as to require the undivided attention of staff. There were additional factors which arose to ensure that this would not occur. First, it was necessary to try to secure another order to secure the future of the company. CEGB decided to negotiate a contract with TNPG for Hinkley Point B so that there was a competitor in the field in at least as strong a position as APC. That left as a short-range possibility for another order only Hunterston B. Effort was put into a new tender to the SSEB for that station, but the order was lost to TNPG...

Morale was also being eroded by the rationalisation of the industry that was in progress, with the different consortia being encouraged to merge into larger units:

With the failure of the merger negotiations it was quite clear that APC had no place in the nuclear industry in the UK. This was confirmed by CEGB's evidence to the Select Committee on 22 May 1969.

These events led the final breakup of the APC team since the people involved could see no prospect of employment beyond completion of the Dungeness B contract. At the same time BNDC [one of the new consortia], who had taken over management of the Dungeness B project, were either unwilling or unable to offer satisfactory prospects. It is perhaps worthy of note that BNDC undertook no financial commitment to the project, whether it was successful or not.

SUMMARY

For various reasons largely associated with the reorganisation of the nuclear industry APC went into the Dungeness B tender quoting essentially a priced design study for a system without the backing of detailed station design work. Because of its previous history, the company had missed out in experience of new developments in the industry and was faced with the task of building totally novel plant against an unrealistic construction programme.

Because the financing considerations (which are dominated by the construction programme) dictated it, construction proceeded against the assumption that ad hoc design decisions would permit construction to go ahead as planned and be technically successful.

A severe check to the construction programme was received in 1968 by distortion of the pressure vessel liner.

> However, in the background were a number of other items, not the least of which was the boiler, which had been substantially revised because the initial design assumptions were proved to be wrong by R&D work set in hand to check them.
>
> The initial construction programme might have been regarded as unrealistic, but achievement of any reasonable programme required the undivided attention of the team carrying out the work. In fact, external events conspired to undermine the morale of the team and led to its breakup.
>
> The boiler pressure vessel membrane difficulties have been given a certain amount of publicity, but it would not be surprising if other items of plant were in trouble and that resolutions of the problems might be difficult against the constraints which exist in a partly constructive station even assuming that the staff still working on the project have enough of the background information. It may well be that there is more unpalatable news to be received before the project is completed.[19]

In this context, it is ironic that at the time of the bid the American publication *Nucleonics Week* had described UPC's design as 'fully-worked-up'.

The report had been written in 1970, five years after the award of the contract. And the author was quite correct: there was a good deal of unpalatable news to come.

Even when it seemed that the initial troubles were over, other faults for which the builders could be held responsible emerged. In 1972, it was realised that galvanised wire had been used to attach thermocouples to banks of stainless steel tubes in the super heater and reheat sections of its boilers. When a wire is galvanised, it is dipped into molten zinc so that the covering of zinc metal will protect the wire from corrosion. Unfortunately, the zinc could diffuse into the stainless steel, which would make it more brittle. The end result was that the tubes within the boilers had to be replaced at considerable expense.

Disillusionment with the AGR set in quite rapidly. A memo of November 1970 covering a brief to the minister noted that:

> As a supplement to the brief we have collected and indexed the glorificatory [*sic*] statements published in the middle 1960's by Government, AEA, CEGB and others about the breakthrough in technology anticipated by the placing of the Dungeness 'B' contract . . .[20]

All this extra work and delay meant that the cost of the power station was rising steadily, far above the original estimate. It became clear that APC and the companies backing it lacked the financial resources to complete the work. This presented problems for the CEGB: it could force the firms into liquidation and sue them, or come to some financial agreement which would effectively cover the losses. As a briefing note to the minister put it:

> Some considerations that were important for CEGB were, for example, that insistence on the contractors meeting the extra cost in full would probably have resulted in a lengthy lawsuit followed by the liquidation of both ICL and Faireys. There could have been no certainty that the CEGB would have been able to realise more from a liquidator than through their recent agreement with two Companies.

Moreover, work at Dungeness B would come to a standstill and bearing in mind that the CEGB's objective was to complete Dungeness B as expeditiously and economically as possible, the settlement was the best that could be achieved.[21]

Figure 13.11. Dungeness B after completion.

Responsibility for the completion of the station was passed to another company — the British Nuclear Design Company (BNDC). Even then progress was slow. According to the CEGB in May 1978, the programme was ten years behind schedule, and still a long way from completion. A variety of reasons were given for the delays:

Industrial relations: Labour disputes and low productivity — 23 months.

Technical problems included: Manufacture — 16 months; safety changes — 12 months; data changes — 12 months; other changes — 7 months.

Underestimation of time required (compared with the original contract period) — 45 months.

This added up to a total of 115 months delay.

The CEGB went on to say that major technical problems identified had cost implications totalling over £61 million. These included:

> Nuclear boilers. Comparatively soon after the boiler contract was placed, two designs by the contractor for the boiler support system were rejected on grounds of corrosion and fatigue. Moreover, the original boiler design proved unsatisfactory within the space available and a new design was necessary.
>
> Internal insulation. One of the subcontractors was unable to meet the design criteria, and experienced difficulty in obtaining suitable grades of stainless steel.

> The design of installation has now been agreed, the direction on site is exacting and difficult.
>
> Concrete pressure vessel membrane. The interface of the concrete pressure vessel is lined with a steel membrane which amongst other things ensures gas tightness of the reactor vessel. The original boiler contract attempt to correct the steel membrane but found difficulty because of the severe distortion of the large vessel during welding operations. After much investigation, it was decided to use another contractor to dismantle the existing membrane and use new materials and techniques to increase the size.
>
> Backup cooling system. There is now general acceptance of the need for most reactor systems to have backup cooling. This feature was not originally considered necessary for Dungeness B, but the Nuclear Installations Inspectorate subsequently asked for the provision of alternative secure supplies of water and electrical power in order to effect vessel and boiler cooling and gas reactors circulation in the extreme emergency conditions. The additional requirement at such a late stage necessitated additional plant modification.
>
> The current estimated actual cost is £344 million, as against an original estimate at March 1965 of £89 million.[22]

Reactor one did not generate electricity until April 1983, 13 years after schedule. The final cost was around £685 million, although given the inflation that took place during the 1970s, it is very difficult to make any comparison with the original bid. Dungeness B was, however, not the only AGR station to be ordered, although it was the first. Stations were ordered for Hinkley Point B, Hunterston, Hartlepool and Heysham, but these too were subject to delay. In a 1974 publication about the nuclear power programme, the CEGB noted that:

> However, nine years later no AGR has obtained commercial service, the adverse experience of design and construction has been formidable and none has been sold abroad. Capital costs of the CEGB stations have escalated on average by 50% and the costs of fuel to replace electricity production lost through delays will exceed the original estimated capital cost. De-rating appears unavoidable and there are doubts about the service life. No further orders for AGRs can be contemplated in the near future.[23]

The ordering of the SGHWR design at Stake Ness and the obvious disarray of the AGR programme caused the incoming Conservative government of 1970 to order a complete review of the reactor programme under an official in the Department of Trade and Industry, labelled the Thermal Reactor Working Party. As an early draft of the report put it:

> The broad issue before the Working Party has been whether the advantage of continuing the gas-cooled line, with its postulated longer term prospects for the HTR is outweighed by the suggested short-term advantages available from the change in reactor technology to water-cooled systems, and if so which water-cooled system is to be preferred.[24]

The two water-cooled systems referred to were the American BWR design, and the British SGHWR. The decision eventually fell on the SGHWR, and orders were placed for commercial stations, which were abandoned during the public spending cuts of the late 1970s.

The two charts (Figures 13.12 and 13.13) show some of the reasons given for the delays, and these charts were drawn up long before the stations were actually completed.

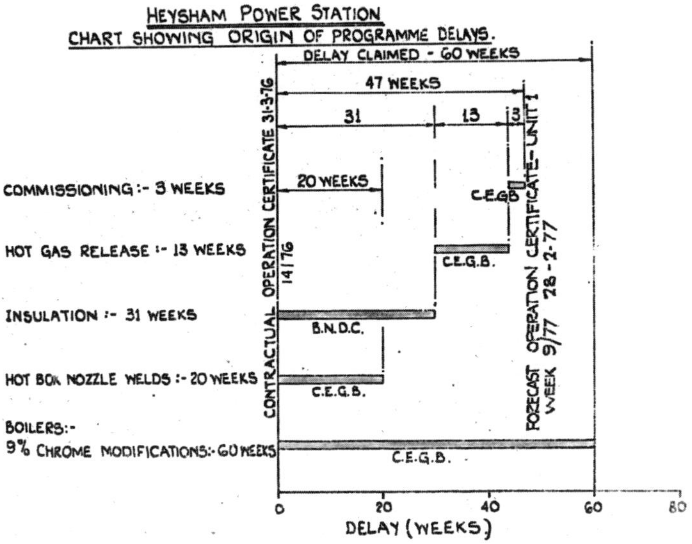

Figure 13.12. Delays at Heysham.

The Hunterston Incident

In April 1977, it was discovered that there was some leakage of CO_2 into the labyrinth cooling water of one of the circulators of the second reactor, R4, which meant that there was a defect in the weld. To repair the crack would have been a simple matter, but it would have required shutting the reactor down, depressurising it and removing the circulator unit, thus interrupting operation for about two weeks. As it already had been planned to shut the plant down in October to carry out some work on the conventional plant, it was decided to repair the circulator at the same time. It was later found that the cooling of the labyrinth was not essential and therefore the inlet and outlet valves were closed, thus completely isolating this part of the cooling system.

In October 1977 the reactor was shut down and the pressure gradually reduced from 38 bars. By 11 October the pressure had dropped below the pressure of the sea water inlet of the heat exchanger and, as a result, sea water began to leak into the

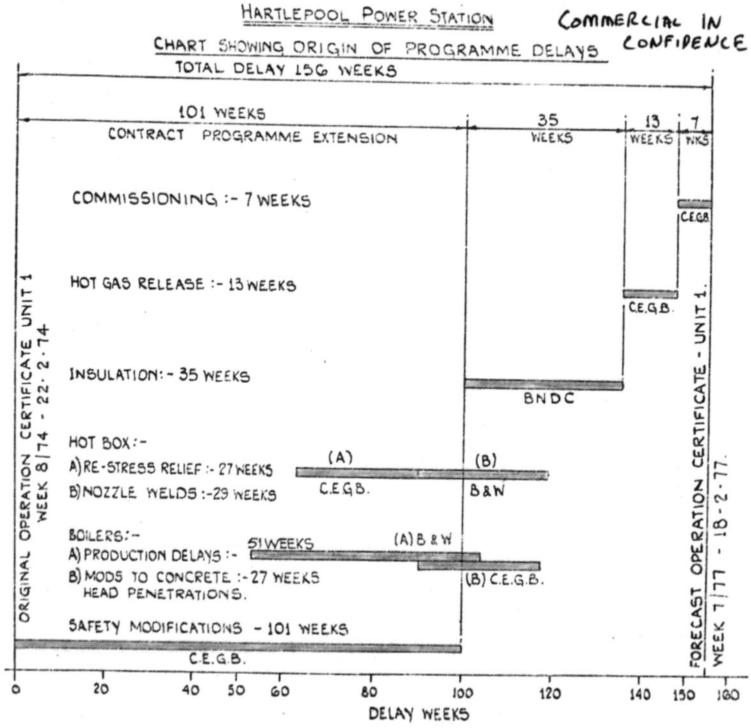

Figure 13.13. Delays at Hartlepool.

depressurised reactor through the defective labyrinth weld. The outlet valve from the circulator labyrinth which had been turned off in July, and logged as such, was in fact found to be partly open. About 8,000 litres of sea water flooded into the space below the boilers. When the sea water evaporated, salt was deposited on the stainless cover plates, the mineral wool insulation and the mild steel liner. About 10% of the insulation was affected and needed to be replaced. A thorough and detailed survey was carried out to ascertain the full extent of the damage before refurbishing started. This phase took five months. The removal and replacement of the affected insulation, cover plates, studs and the cleaning of the liner took a further 20 months. The total cost of the repair was about £15 million.[25]

The Stations

Fourteen commercial stations were built in all, and they were ordered in two waves. The first ten were ordered between 1965 and 1970, but, as can be seen from Table 13.2, there were very considerable problems with the construction. The delays at

Dungeness have already been discussed, but the station at Hartlepool probably rivalled it in the time it took to become operational.

Hartlepool introduced a further advance in design of the AGR with what were described as 'podded boilers'. This meant that the boilers were constructed within the pressure vessel itself, meaning that the whole of the cooling and steam raising circuits were enclosed. This can be seen in Figure 13.14.

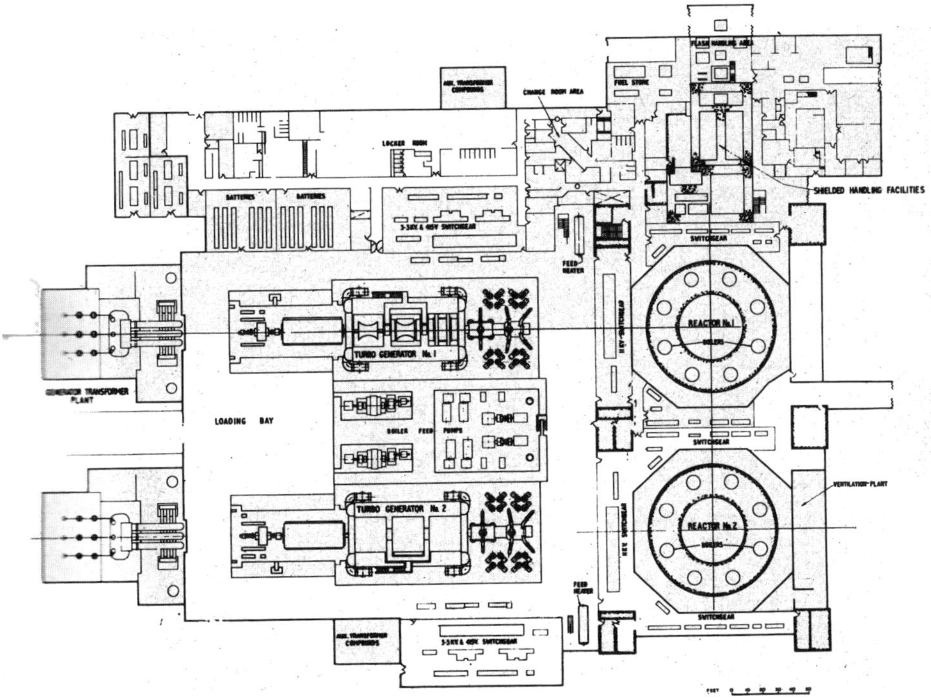

Figure 13.14. The layout of the Hartlepool AGR, showing the podded boilers contained within the pressure vessel.

After the Heysham A order, there was a hiatus. This was partly because the problems thrown up had discredited the AGR as a system. The ten stations amounted to around 10 GW of generating power, and there was simply not the demand for electricity, since the energy crisis of the early 1970s had led to much increased energy saving efficiencies. As the first AGRs fell further behind, it was announced that the next nuclear orders would be for SGHWR stations. These failed to materialise, and in 1980 four more AGRs were ordered. These stations, at Heysham and Torness, were built to a design which had already been used in earlier stations, and which had many of the bugs ironed out. As a consequence, these proved a good deal more straightforward to construct.

After privatisation of the electrical industry, the AGRs became part of the Nuclear Energy company, which was still publicly owned. In 1996, they became part of a private company, British Energy. In 2009, British Energy was acquired by Électricité de France (EDF), and in 2010, changed its name to EDF Energy.

Table 13.2. Station layout.

	Construction Start	First Criticality	First Grid Connection	Commercial Operation	Construction time (years)
Dungeness B1	October 1965	December 1982	April 1983	April 1985	20
Dungeness B2	October 1965	December 1985	December 1985	April 1989	24
Hunterston B1	November 1967	January 1976	February 1976	February 1976	9
Hunterston B2	November 1967	March 1977	March 1977	March 1977	10
Hinkley Point B1	September 1967	September 1976	October 1976	October 1978	11
Hinkley Point B2	September 1967	February 1976	February 1976	September 1976	9
Hartlepool A1	October 1968	June 1983	August 1983	April 1989	21
Hartlepool A2	October 1968	September 1984	October 1984	April 1989	21
Heysham A1	December 1970	April 1983	July 1983	April 1989	19
Heysham A2	December 1970	June 1984	October 1984	April 1989	19
Heysham B1	August 1980	June 1988	July 1988	April 1989	9
Heysham B2	August 1980	November 1988	November 1988	April 1989	9
Torness 1	August 1980	March 1988	May 1988	May 1988	8
Torness 2	August 1980	December 1988	February 1989	February 1989	9

1 TNA: PRO DSIR 23/29890. Beryllium development work at reactor fuel element labs, UKAEA, Springfields. GB Greenough, 1 October 1962.

2 'Beryllium Hits Snag in British Reactor', *American Metal Market*, 15 August 1961.

3 TNA: PRO AB 6/2172. Advanced gas cooled reactor; research and development.

4 TNA: PRO AB 6/2168. Zero energy reactor HERO. 'HERO and NERO II', 25 November 1958.

5 TNA: PRO AB 16/2195. Advanced gas-cooled reactor (AGR). Press release: Windscale's HERO. Another New Reactor to be Built. See also TNA: PRO AB 38/149. HERO: reports and correspondence.

6 TNA: PRO AB 17/84. Heated Experimental Reactor Zero Energy (HERO).

7 TNA: PRO AB 17/86. The Windscale Advanced Gas-cooled Reactor.

8 *Ibid.*

9 TNA: PRO EG1/361. Prototype Advanced Gas Cooled Reactor (AGR) Mark 1 and Mark 2.

10 As quoted in TNA: PRO AB 48/816. Second nuclear power programme: tender assessment for Dungeness B.

11 'Dungeness B. Why the CEGB Did It', *The Economist*, 31 July 1965.

12 TNA: PRO AB 48/830. Dungeness B nuclear power station. J Gaussens, Commissariat a L'Energie Atomique to RN Simeone, UKAEA, 1 September 1965.

13 TNA: PRO AB 48/830. Dungeness B nuclear power station. RN Simeone, UKAEA, to J Gaussens, Commissariat a L'Energie Atomique, 28 September 1965.

14 TNA: PRO AB 48/816. Second nuclear power programme: tender assessment for Dungeness B. 'Authority Tactics over Dungeness B'.

15 TNA: PRO AB 48/816. Second nuclear power programme: tender assessment for Dungeness B. 'Notes on Tender Offer Based on First Reading of the Summary (Unpriced) Volume A of the Tender Submissions', 2 February 1965.

16 TNA: PRO POWE 14/2328. Dungeness 'B' nuclear power station: CEGB contract. CEGB memo on Dungeness 'Project History', undated.

17 TNA: PRO POWE 14/2328. Dungeness 'B' nuclear power station: CEGB contract. T Griffiths, 14 January 1969.

18 *Ibid.*

19 TNA: PRO EG 7/130. Dungeness B: Advanced Gas Cooled Reactor II: delays in construction. 'DUNGENESS B', RW Nichols, 28 September 1970.

20 TNA: PRO POWE 14/2341. Dungeness 'B' nuclear power station: CEGB contract. Dungeness 'B' Defensive Brief, BE Stephenson, 18 November 1970.

21 TNA: PRO POWE 14/2341. Dungeness 'B' nuclear power station: CEGB contract. 'The Troubles at Dungeness 'B'. Defensive Questions and Answers', 1 December 1970.

22 CEGB Dungeness B nuclear power station. Background note (May 1978).

23 TNA: PRO EG 12/137. Reactor choice. 'Nuclear Power — Choice of thermal reactor', CEGB, April 1974.

24 TNA: PRO EG 12/72. Thermal Reactor Working Party: report. 'Thermal Reactor Working Party Final Report (Second Partial Draft)', 16 December 1971.

25 This section is based upon 'Advanced Gas-Cooled Reactors' RM Yeomans, South of Scotland Electricity Board, as part of *International Atomic Energy Agency,*

Vienna (Austria). International Working Group on Gas-Cooled Reactors. Specialists meeting on gas-cooled reactor safety and licensing aspects, Lausanne, Switzerland, 1–3 September 1980. Summary report. January 1981. International Atomic Energy Agency, Vienna (Austria). International Working Group on High-Temperature Reactors. IWGGCR–1, pp. 17–38.

Chapter 14

The SGHWR

One of the principal objections to using heavy water as a moderator was its cost. There were various methods of production: one involved the electrolysis of water requiring large amounts of electricity, and both Canada and Norway had extensive hydroelectric schemes which could be used to produce heavy water. On the other hand, the heavy water would not need to be renewed: it would merely add to the capital cost of a reactor in the same way that obtaining pure graphite added to the cost of the gas-cooled reactors.

Heavy water was no novelty to Harwell: many of the materials testing reactors (the DIDO design) and others used it as a moderator, but these were relatively small, so the cost was not excessive. Designing a power reactor using heavy water would not be difficult, and it could be a useful insurance in case of problems with the gas-cooled reactors.[1] From this grew the proposal that a small scale demonstration reactor should be built at Winfrith Heath. A memo of June 1959 sums up the thinking at the time:

> The S.C.H.W. [Steam Cooled Heavy Water reactor] is regarded as an insurance in the case of trouble with the A.G.R. It is extremely doubtful if the S.C.H.W. has a future if the A.G.R. is successful. For this reason it has a lower priority than either the A.G.R. or the fast reactor insofar as the Industrial Group is concerned ... It is my understanding that we are not likely to be interested in a large B.W.R. for C.E.G.B. use, if the A.G.R. is successful. If the A.G.R. is unsuccessful, then we have the choice of an S.C.H.W. or a B.W.R. based on U.S. development ...[2]

A report was then prepared on possible heavy water designs. It noted that

> The capital cost and fuel inventory cost are low and directly comparable with the AGR.
>
> A low enrichment is probably achievable.
>
> With a separately cooled nuclear moderator, the SCHW from the control and safety point of view is certain to be able to use plutonium rich fuel and therefore in addition to being a feed reactor would also act as a plutonium using reactor.[3]

Early ideas had been for a gas-cooled heavy water-moderated reactor with an indirect steam cycle,[4] but it would have had a high capital cost — and this was always the weak point in the economics of nuclear power. Another possibility was a steam-cooled reactor, but this would have implied stainless steel canning for the fuel, which in turn would have meant using enriched fuel since stainless steel is an absorber of neutrons.

After discussing the steam-cooled reactor, the report came to the conclusion that it was not the best of options, and that a steam-generating reactor might be preferable.

> The possibility of generating steam within the core in a boiling zone was foreseen from the beginning of the SCHW study. It is now apparent that a reactor so designed not only offers prospects of greater simplicity in design and better neutron economy, but offers a large saving and capital cost due to great reduction in D2O [heavy water] inventory. Unfortunately greater simplicity in design is not attended by a similar simplification in physics, and the enrichment, the operating characteristics and the safety characteristics cannot be predicted with present knowledge sufficiently accurately for project purposes. It was therefore decided that in preference to going ahead with a SCHW project, time should be devoted to establishing behaviour and design of an improved model now known as the Steam Generating Heavy Water Reactor.

There were advantages to the new design: one was that it used only about one third of the amount of heavy water moderator as the steam-cooled heavy water reactor, and another was that the fuel elements could be clad in zirconium rather than stainless steel. Zirconium absorbs far fewer neutrons than stainless steel, which gave the reactor a much better neutron economy, meaning that the fuel would not need to be enriched as much — the higher the enrichment, the higher the fuel cost.

The new design meant that the steam to drive the turbo generators was taken directly from the reactor itself, rather than through a heat exchanger as in other designs of reactor.[5] From the outset, the fuel elements were designed so that they could be used directly in subsequent commercial reactor designs.[6] The fuel material was uranium dioxide in the form of sintered pellets, with the uranium enriched to just over 2%. These pellets were contained in Zircaloy tubing to form individual fuel pins, and 36 pins were mounted in a circular array to form an individual fuel assembly, which would then be loaded into the pressure tubes. In the 100 MW Winfrith design, there were 104 fuel channels. In a 600 MW station, the number of fuel channels would be increased to 532, and they would be of the same design. Thus the reactor design was easily scalable.[7]

The reactor core was housed in a large vessel or tank called a calandria, which contained the heavy water moderator. The pressure tubes containing the fuel elements passed vertically through this tank. The heavy water in the calandria was not pressurised and formed a separate circuit from that of the main coolant in the pressure tubes, which was light water. The light water coolant was pumped up through the pressure tubes past the fuel elements in the tubes. The water then boiled in the core, and the steam produced was separated from the recirculating water in an external

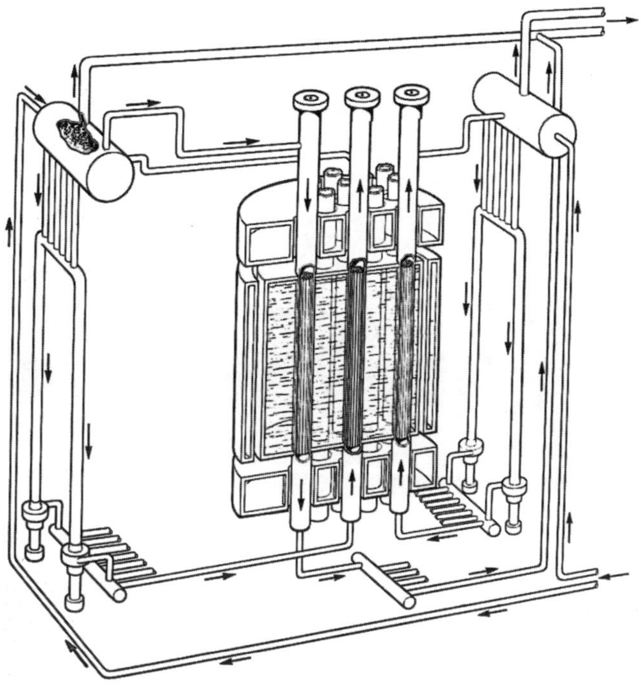

Figure 14.1. This shows the core and pipework of the SGHWR. The calandria containing heavy water is in the middle of the drawing; the pipes passing through it contain water under pressure plus the fuel rods. Steam is taken from the water after it has been heated.

circuit. The heavy water in the calandria would be maintained at a temperature of about 80°C. The system was in part moderated by the coolant, about 30% of the moderation occurring in the light water and the remainder in the heavy water.

Construction of the Winfrith SGHWR was authorised in February 1963, and work began in May. The construction schedule set out in 1962 estimated that it would take 206 weeks from the start of building work to the reactor reaching full power. In the end it took 207 weeks[8] — a very stark contrast to the saga that was just beginning at Dungeness.

One of the advantages of a pressure tube reactor is that access to individual channels and hence to the fuel elements is relatively easy, making refuelling very much more straightforward. It was estimated that a quarter of the core of a 350 MW(E) power station could be replaced in a weekend.[9] The SGHWR was simpler to operate than many designs in that it needed no control rods or other mechanisms to control the chain reaction. Instead, the reactor power level was controlled by small variations of the height of the moderator in the calandria tank. This made it relatively well suited to load-following operation, in which the reactor output may be varied in step with the normal daily cycle of electricity demand. Normally, a nuclear power station

Figure 14.2. The Winfrith SGHWR — built with only one week's delay. The cooling towers in the background are constructed to be as inconspicuous as possible.

is held at a constant power output, and this provides what is called the base load for the national electricity grid. Demand will vary during the day, and this has to be provided by other stations, such as gas-fired stations. The Winfrith station showed that it could be cycled from 70% to 100% on a regular basis.[10]

A further advantage of the SGHWR compared with the AGR was that construction was a good deal easier. The graphite core of the AGR had to be built in the pressure shell on site, and as the saga of Dungeness B was to demonstrate, there was a lot to go wrong. For the Winfrith SGHWR, the calandria and channel tube assemblies were built off site by the various manufacturers, which apart from being simpler, was also cheaper. The same would have applied to commercial SGHWRs.

Communication between the AEA and CEGB was not all that it might have been. The Parliamentary Select Committee on the Electricity Supply Industry noted that the CEGB was not kept informed of the decision to go ahead with the SGHWR. Apparently, the CEGB were informed through discussions but not shown the comparative evaluation. Hinton, who was now the Chairman of the CEGB, remarked, 'It is a mistake in policy for a research organisation to launch out into expensive prototype work without taking their main potential user with them.'[11] A comment such as this reinforces the perception that the AEA often pursued designs that were interesting to them without consideration of any commercial implications.

Commercial development of the SGHWR ran into another problem. The CEGB had ordered AGR stations, and the firms involved were running into considerable difficulties. The last thing the CEGB wanted to do was to become involved in the development of yet another unproven design. The obvious reluctance of the CEGB provoked an extraordinary letter from the SGHWR design office at Risley addressed to 'The Rt. Hon. Anthony Wedgwood Benn, Minister of Technology' and 'The Rt. Hon. Roy Mason, Minister of Power'. The letter was described as coming from 'An Ad-Hoc Committee Representing the Staff of the S.G.H.W.R. Design Office, U.K.A.E.A., Risley'.

The letter began by saying:

> We, the staff of the S.G.H.W.R. Design Office ... are deeply concerned that the reorganisation of the nuclear power industry makes no provision for the immediate commercial exploitation of the S.G.H.W.R. system. We see a very real danger that Britain's only economically-viable reactor system will soon be abandoned. It is in the national interest that the S.G.H.W.R. be introduced into the home nuclear power programme now.
>
> Some of the main reasons for reorganising the nuclear power industry are: —
>
> (a) to give the country cheaper nuclear power;
> (b) to win a share of the export market;
> (c) to enable new reactors developed by the U.K.A.E.A. to be commercially exploited.
>
> These requirements can only be met at the present time by the immediate commercial exploitation of the SGHWR — the only British reactor which can compete in overseas markets.[12]

This was followed up by an appendix giving a host of reasons why the SGHWR should be selected.

For a group of engineers within the AEA to write to ministers in this fashion was quite unprecedented. Unfortunately, the chances of getting much action from a step such as this were remote. Wedgwood Benn (to be known in later years in a more demotic style as Tony Benn) and Mason played a straight bat, acknowledging the letter but without making any promises.

The design office responded by saying 'We, representing the staff of the SGHWR Design Office, Risley, are disappointed with your reply ... '.[13] On the other hand, the chance of ministers overriding any decision taken by the CEGB was remote. Direct interference on a matter like that would have probably caused the resignation of the CEGB Chairman, and the choice of power station was not that important an issue politically.

The design team were also quite correct when they said that the SGHWR was the only British reactor which could compete in overseas markets. The magnox design was by now effectively obsolete, and the only other design which the British could offer would be the AGR, but the first commercial AGR was still a long way from completion. The chances of selling one abroad were effectively non-existent.

There were quite strong export opportunities for the SGHWR, all of which fell through for one reason or another. There had been high hopes of selling one to Finland, but this apparently was blocked by Russian political pressure (at that time,

Finland was ostensibly neutral in the Cold War, but was very much within the Russian orbit). The Australians had decided on the SGHWR for a site at Jervis Bay, but an incoming government opposed to nuclear power was to result in its cancellation — Australia has never built a nuclear power station. Another possibility was a bid for a power station in Greece, with part of the payment being a barter including Greek tobacco, which was apparently not of a sufficiently high standard for the UK market.

But as the AGR programme ran into greater and greater difficulties, the SGHWR became an increasingly favoured choice. Indeed, in 1971 there was a proposal by the NOSHEB to build an SGHWR at Stake Ness,[14] but the government would not underwrite the risk of the NOSHEB going it alone. A detailed design of a 500 MW SGHWR unit had been prepared and this design obtained outline permits from the Nuclear Installations Inspectorate.[15] This would have been the first ever nuclear power station ordered by the NOSHEB, and one of the reasons why the government was not prepared to back it was that it would be a new design operated by an inexperienced electricity board. It was also tied in with the lack of orders elsewhere.

> Unfortunately the NOSHEB approach went wrong at an early stage. With the fashionable desire to copy every document to everyone who may conceivably be concerned, St Andrews House sent to Treasury a copy of a letter to me which quantified the various liabilities which NOSHEB thought they might incur if the SGHWR went sour on them and which they wanted underwritten by the Exchequer. Some of these liabilities amounted to some £14M. From that time on we have never been able to get the Treasury to view the tender proposal objectively, since they feared this was but a step to a later request for underwriting NOSHEB's risks …
>
> If in the event TNPG were not to win the Jervis Bay [in Australia] order and CEGB refused to adopt the system, it is virtually certain that we could not secure Treasury agreement to underwrite NOSHEB's risks. I cannot see that in these circumstances there would be much chance of NOSHEB proceeding alone and the SGHWR would probably have to be abandoned.[16]

The NOSHEB proposal fell through, and there was still a reluctance in many quarters to recommend the SGHWR for the remainder of the UK power programme on the basis that it was still an untried system. The argument was somewhat circular: no one knew whether a large-scale SGWHR would be a success, and the only way to find out was to build one. On the other hand, no one wanted to build one in case it was not a success.

This was summed up in a comment from a paper submitted to the Thermal Reactor Working Party of the early 1970s.

> We have burned our fingers up to the elbow with the AGR. We must be pretty convinced that the SGHWR course would not be a repeat dose. As I see, it, the crucial issue is the confidence that we can place on the potentialities for success with the SGHWR.[17]

But in August 1972, John Davies, who was then the Secretary of State for Trade and Industry, made a statement in the House of Commons where he announced that the government would:

> ... commission a complete and specific design and component development programme for the Steam Generating Heavy Water Reactor. A 100 MW prototype of this reactor has been operating satisfactorily for four years at Winfrith in Dorset and it is accordingly a strong contender for adoption in the UK grid system. This work is likely to take some 18 months.[18]

This decision was endorsed by the incoming Labour government of 1974. At a Cabinet meeting in June 1974 the Secretary of State for Energy, Eric Varley, said:

> ... no orders for nuclear power stations had been placed since 1970. The previous Government had put off a decision, and Labour's Programme for Britain had promised to devote more resources to the building of nuclear power stations. He had chaired two meetings of the Nuclear Power Advisory Board established by the previous Government, but had received no clear advice from them ... No option commanded general agreement, and any choice would entail some commercial risk; but in his view the primary considerations were safety, reliability in operation, and the need to support British technology, and on these grounds he considered that the Steam Generating Heavy Water Reactor (SGHWR) should be adopted for the next nuclear orders ...
>
> The Chief Inspector of Nuclear Installations had advised that there should be no fundamental difficulty in clearing an SGHWR design, initially for remote sites, without delaying the start of construction. The other thermal systems all had substantial disadvantages: Magnox, which now provided 10 per cent of our supply of electricity, was an outdated design and would be prohibitively expensive to reorder; the Advanced Gas-Cooled Reactors had encountered many difficulties and were unlikely to provide satisfactory operating experience for at least another two years; the High-Temperature Reactor would not be adequately proven before the early 1980s; CANDU would require much more heavy water than the SGHWR, and used natural rather than low enriched uranium. The claims of the Light Water Reactor (LWR) were passionately advocated and opposed. Doubts about its safety had yet to be convincingly allayed, however, and the Nuclear Installations Inspectorate might not be able to clear it for nearly two years, or be able to do so without design modifications. Adoption of the SGHWR would need to be accompanied by a deal with the Canadians on heavy water and heavy water technology, on engineering, manufacturing and construction experience and on opportunities for United Kingdom manufacturers to supply nuclear and conventional plant for CANDUs sold in Canada and overseas; and preliminary discussions to this end had already taken place.[19]

Apparently the decision would not be universally welcome:

> ... although the choice of the SGHWR would meet the views expressed by the Select Committee on Science and Technology and would be particularly welcomed by the South of Scotland Electricity Board, there would be strong resistance from the Central Electricity Generating Board (CEGB), the National Nuclear Corporation and the General Electric Company — the Corporation's main shareholder —

> who all supported the LWR. The Chairman of the CEGB might demand a formal instruction to order the SGHWR, and might even resign.

Harold Wilson, the Prime Minister, noted that

> The question of safety weighed heavily in reaching this decision, and account must be taken of the doubts about the safety of the LWR which had been expressed by Sir Alan Cottrell, who was a leading metallurgist, as well as by Lord Hinton, the former Chairman of the CEGB, and the Select Committee on Science and Technology.[20]

As a result, in February 1975, the go-ahead was announced by Varley in a written answer in the House of Commons for two SGHWR plants at Sizewell B (four units totalling 2,600 MW) and Torness (two units) of 660 MWe capacity per reactor.

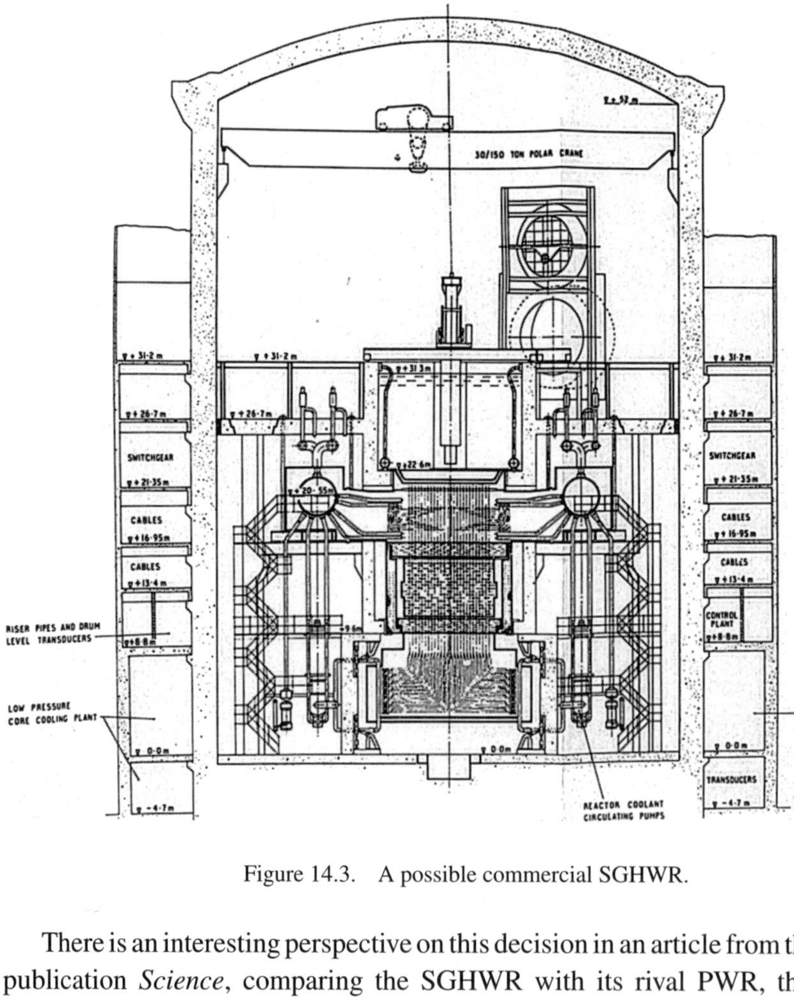

Figure 14.3. A possible commercial SGHWR.

There is an interesting perspective on this decision in an article from the American publication *Science*, comparing the SGHWR with its rival PWR, the American design by Westinghouse. The PWR was thought to have considerable safety issues with its large pressure vessel, and one notable critic of the design was the former government Chief Scientific Adviser, Sir Alan Cottrell. The editorial commented that:

> On examination, misgivings about the safety of the American reactor seemed to have as much to do with the frailties of the British nuclear construction industry as with the inherent hazards of the Westinghouse design. Insiders acknowledge that the British have shown a particular weakness in what the Americans call "project management" on the complicated nuclear power station jobs. Chronic troubles and construction of power stations using the British advance gas reactor (AGR) which was viewed as a promising design for domestic and overseas development in the 1970s, have delayed and virtually discredited the programme.

Then:

> As for the merits of the SGHWR, it is true that no such reactor is now operating on a commercial scale, but the 100 MW pilot reactor at Winfrith in south-east England is said to been built on schedule and within budget and to have been performing well since 1967. SGHWR proponents say the problem of scale up to the size projected for the new plants will be quite manageable. One reason is that steam under high pressure is not contained in a big pressure vessel, as in the PWR, but in a series of much smaller pressure tubes, enhancing safety and making construction easier.[21]

Ultimately, though, the SGHWR failed to be adopted for a variety of reasons. By the mid-1970s, as Varley had noted, the CEGB was disillusioned with the AGR, strongly favoured the American light water reactor as a proven design, and were not happy with the prospect of having to put up with another untried and untested system. They wanted something they knew would work. This comes out very clearly in a report prepared in 1974 by the government's nuclear power advisory board.

Discussing water-cooled systems, the CEGB made its position very clear:

> There is a difference of opinion as to whether we should turn to LWR for our main ordering programme or to SGHWR.
>
> The CEGB want the most tried system in order to secure the timely delivery and operation of nuclear power stations in the 1980s. They have had to conclude that the LWR has no present equal. The capacity ordered in 1973 was about 40,000 MW. The CEGB believe that to avoid repeating past failures the UK needs a radically new approach to design, manufacture and construction for any future reactor system; and that PWR is the most developed in this respect. For no other reactor system is there a comparable demonstration of the ability of manufacturers to build on a commercial basis.[22]

On the other hand, the AEA was not going to endorse an entirely foreign design, since that would be an admission that the indigenous British designs were simply not capable of doing the job. When it came to the SGHWR, the advisory board said:

> There is no direct evidence from commercial construction operation. But that are several important factors relevant to assessing the risk of moving to commercial

> ordering without a commercial-sized demonstration plant. The parameters and much of the central technology of SGHWR are similar to those of the BWR. Experience with Winfrith prototype is of more relevance than the small Windscale experiment AGR was to the decision to embark on a commercial AGR programme. It is larger (100 MW as against 34 MW), has been operating successfully for six years and there is a high degree of commonality with a commercial design because [of] the modular form of construction; it was designed to reproduce the operating conditions of a commercial unit so that the pressure tube assembly and fuel are similar to what will be required a rating of up to 1300 MW. The SGHWR fuel has not yet reached full burn-up but is behaving well. Other things equal, the CEGB would like to build larger reactor units (1150–1300 MW) because they reckon them to be cheaper. But to go to the size with SGHWR direct from the 100 MW prototype would be a large extrapolation. Some members believe it would be more sensible to begin with a 600–660 MW unit, increasing as experience was gained.

This is faint praise, and the feeling that the London office of the AEA was not enthusiastic about the SGHWR is shown by a letter written from Risley by H Cartwright, who was then Director of water reactors for the AEA:

> From the occasional discussions we have had about the SGHWR, I recognise you are prepared to keep an open mind about its future and I recognise that it is up to us to prove that the system has its place.
>
> However, I have been perturbed to receive from time to time the back-wash of comment from quite senior people in the Authority indicating little enthusiasm for the system. This itself is probably of no consequence but, as I believe that the SGHWR may prove to be a key project if we are to do any export business, we should not at this stage be running any risk of giving outside people, particularly people overseas, the impression that we are lukewarm about the SGHWR.[23]

In 1976, the National Nuclear Corporation was asked to undertake a comparative assessment of three reactor types — AGR, PWR, and SGHWR. The SGHWR was turned down on the grounds that:

> There will be no operational experience of commercial sizes for a decade.
>
> It would provide no chance of exports in the foreseeable future.
>
> It was clearly more costly than the PWR or AGR.
>
> It would require expenditure on development in the next seven years considerably larger than both the PWR and AGR together in that period.
>
> The import of heavy water would be a significant load on the balance of payments.[24]

It was laughable to expect that the UK would ever export any AGRs, and nearly as absurd to suggest that the UK might make a success in exporting PWRs. As to the effect of the load on the balance of payments of heavy water, the argument seemed to be getting thinner and thinner. As for the other reasons — why undertake a large prototype in the first place, at a cost of close on £100 million, if you are not going to develop it any further?

But the statement that it was clearly more costly than the AGR is interesting, since a report had been commissioned at the request of the Managing Director of the reactor group to make an estimate of the relative costs of the two types of station. The terms of reference for the panel included:

> to compare estimates of the capital costs of 350 MW (E) AGR and SGHWR nuclear power stations built to similar standards and extent of supply and based on construction in the UK commencing during the period 1967/68, the comparison to include the additional information necessary to make a comparison of operating cost ...[25]

The reason for the choice of size of station is that a design for a 300 MW (E) AGR had been prepared for the Greek Atomic Energy Commission, and a tender for a 350 MW (E) SGHWR had been prepared for a Finnish utility. The report was based upon these two designs. The panel met 27 times, and produced a report of 47 pages, nine appendices and six figures. It can therefore be said to be a fairly thorough investigation.

The costs for a first-off 350 MW(E) station in the UK are shown in Table 14.1.

Table 14.1. Cost of stations in the UK.

	AGR		SGHWR	
	£M	£M/kW	£M	£M/kW
Plant Cost (including heavy water)	19.84	56.7	15.20	41.4
Authority on-cost	7.99		6.67	
Tender Price (Plant + Authority cost)	27.83	79.5	21.88	62.5
Customer's on-costs	5.6		4.49	
Total capital cost including fuel	39.23	112	30.33	86.6
Generating costs	0.562 d/kWh		0.473 d/kWh	

These figures show that in every respect the SGHWR was cheaper than the AGR. The report concluded:

> The estimates arrived at by the Panel indicate that the total capital cost of a first-off 350 MW (E) AGR station on UK coastal site is approximately 29% higher than that of an SGHWR station, and that the generating cost, on CEGB ground rules, is approximately 19% higher.
>
> For a repeat station in the UK, the corresponding figures are 28% and 17%.
>
> There are uncertainties in each system which could result in some increase or decrease in costs. The Panel considers, however, that in the unlikely event that all costings and technical uncertainties were to operate in favour of the AGR and against the SGHWR the resulting changes will not go more than a quarter of the way to closing the gap in cost between the two systems.[26]

A follow-up paper a little later in 1967 tried a similar exercise, but included the tender price for the Hinkley Point AGR bid for comparison. Hinkley B had two reactors each of 625 MW (E). The cost of the 350 MW SGHWR was scaled up to an equivalent size. The Hinkley B tender price was quoted at £75.44 million whereas the equivalent SGHWR was costed at £50.13 million. Hinkley B would cost very much more than its tender price, but with the inflation of the 1970s it would be difficult to compare the final cost with the tender price.

It is true that the report was written ten years before the decision to abandon the SGHWR in favour of the AGR was taken. But this makes the decision even more baffling, since in the intervening ten years, the saga of Dungeness B and Hartlepool had gradually unfolded, and any cost estimates made for an AGR in 1966 would certainly have underestimated the true cost by a very considerable degree.

There are two possible conclusions which can be drawn. One is that most of the cost estimates are fairly meaningless and can be interpreted in ways which will favour almost any system. The other is that the AEA were still showing an institutional bias in favour of gas-cooled reactors, and were prepared to stretch the truth a very long way.

However, despite the decision of 1974, cuts in public spending along with increasing projected costs of the SGHWR meant that the government put on hold financing of the initial SGHWR contracts. By mid-1977, the National Nuclear Corporation (NNC) recommended a programme of new AGRs and PWRs, instead of the SGHWR. Although these recommendations had not been made public, the rumours began to circulate, so much so that the House of Commons Select Committee on Science and Technology decided to investigate.

> During the early summer of 1976 the Committee became aware of persistent rumours in the national Press and elsewhere that the Government were considering the cancellation of the SGHWR programme in which they had placed such faith two years previously. Confirmation of the fact that a further review of nuclear reactor policy was in train was provided in a series of parliamentary answers by the present Secretary of State for Energy and his ministerial colleagues in late June and early July. Finally, towards the end of July, the Chancellor of the Exchequer announced a new round of public expenditure cuts, including a one-year deferment of expenditure of approximately £40 million on the SGHWR.
>
> Although the select committee were at that time fully engaged . . . on an enquiry into alternative energy sources, we felt it incumbent upon us to embark on a separate and urgent investigation of the SGHWR programme. This was due in part to our earlier involvement in the discussions leading to the choice of the SGHWR for the next series of nuclear stations, and in part to our concern — shared by many outside of the Select Committee — about the damage which would be inflicted on the United Kingdom's nuclear industry by further delay and discussion of the programme which had only been adopted after many years of debate and uncertainty. The government having said in July 1974 that "the

> uncertainty is now over", many were alarmed this summer at the prospect of renewed argument.[27]

The committee heard evidence from a variety of sources, including the CEGB and the AEA.

> The principal organisations now in favour of cancelling the Steam Generating Heavy Water Reactor programme are the Central Electricity Generating Board (CEGB) and the United Kingdom Atomic Energy Authority (UKAEA). The opposition of the CEGB comes as no surprise. The present Chairman of the Board, Sir Arthur Hawkins, told the Committee as far back as 1972 that the SGHWR was "out of date as a technology". In December 1973 he described the prototype reactor at Winfrith as "obsolete" and expressed a strong preference of his Board for buying in American light water technology in the form of the Westinghouse pressurised light water reactor (BWR). In 1976 he told us that the Board recommended that the SGHWR "should be abandoned".

This was an extraordinary statement by Hawkins. In what sense can a power reactor be said to be 'obsolete'? As Chairman of the CEGB, he should have been interested in obtaining the cheapest electricity possible, regardless of the nature of the technology involved. He then expressed 'a strong preference' for the PWR, whose technology was even older, and made the SGHWR look sophisticated by comparison.

> The position of the UKAEA is somewhat different. The Authority designed and operate the only existing reactor of this type (the 100 MW prototype at Winfrith Heath). While at no time in the past expressing a positive preference for the SGHWR as opposed to other British reactors, the Authority maintained the view during our two previous enquiries that the SGHWR was "a proven reactor" and "a very successful development", and rejected the CEGB claim that it was obsolete. They believed, however, that if the SGHWR were to be taken up, a decision should be made soon, and in evidence to the Energy Resources Sub-Committee in 1974 the AEA Chairman, Sir John Hill, expressed the view that "it is a technology which should have been exploited commercially five years ago, if it were to have a reasonable chance of being accepted on a worldwide basis". But at the same meeting Sir John Hill emphasised the Authority's view that "in this country we should continue with our own technology". Accordingly, if any change of policy now is to be convincing to those outside the AEA, it is incumbent on the Authority to bring forward the new facts, previously unknown or unforeseen, which justify such change. Without such evidence the credibility of the Authority's advice must, as the Secretary of State has already suggested, be open to question.

For a select committee to describe the AEA's credibility as 'open to question' is quite extraordinary. But more was to come:

> The high estimated cost of SGHWR stations was said by the AEA to be due in part to higher safety standards, including "unnecessarily stringent radioactivity release criteria", and in part to the "much smaller and stretched out programme" of ordering resulting from the downward revision of electricity demand estimates.

> We pressed both the CEGB and the AEA for more information about reactor costs. We were concerned in particular to know on what evidence they base their claim that the SGHWR would be more expensive than other reactor systems, since we are not aware that any reactor other than the SGHWR has been designed or redesigned to be the new more stringent safety criteria issued by the CEGB in early 1975. Witnesses from both the Board and the Authority were singularly unforthcoming in this regard.

There were suspicions, not only in the select committee but elsewhere, that the CEGB were artificially inflating the apparent cost of the SGHWR by applying much more stringent safety standards than was the case with the AGR and PWR. Certainly, the SSEB had said in a letter to the select committee that the SGHWR reference design was 'unnecessarily costly', partly 'as a result of invoking safety and release criteria that are more stringent than PWR's'. (A report had been produced by the consortia in November 1973 specifically addressing the issue of safety.[28]) Indeed, the AEA itself seemed uncertain about the costs:

> The Chairman of the AEA admitted that the Authority has seen no detailed costs although they had some preliminary figures from the Nuclear Power Company. Both he and the Deputy Chairman, Dr Marshall, thought that the choice of reactor systems should not be based "upon calculations about how many pence per unit it is going to produce".

On the other hand, it does not seem clear what criteria Dr Hill was using. Perhaps this statement might have some relevance when applied to the AEA, but it should have been the CEGB's major priority.

This episode showed the select committee system at its best. Instead of policy groups meeting behind closed doors, the main protagonists had to appear in public to justify their actions — or, as in the case above, fail to justify them.

Despite the efforts of the select committee and others, early in 1978, the then Secretary of State for Energy, Tony Benn, made an announcement in the House of Commons that the SGHWR was to be abandoned and that the CEGB and SSEB were to each build a twin-unit AGR station. In addition, Benn said the government supported the industry's intention to order a PWR station.

> The House will recall that on 28th June 1976 I announced that I was taking stock of progress with the steam generating heavy water reactor programme at the suggestion of the United Kingdom Atomic Energy Authority.
>
> Since then we have carried out a thorough review of thermal reactor policy. The National Nuclear Corporation has submitted its comparative assessment of thermal reactor systems, which has been made available to the House. The Nuclear Installations Inspectorate — NII — has given its advice on the generic safety issues of the pressurised water reactor, which has also been made available to the House . . .
>
> It is the unanimous advice of all concerned that in the changed circumstances of today the SGHWR should not be adopted for the next power station orders.

> The Government have accordingly decided that it would be right to discontinue work on the SGHWR.
>
> The Government agree with the electricity supply boards that two early nuclear orders are needed and that these must be advanced gas-cooled reactors. The Government have therefore decided to authorise the Central Electricity Generating Board and South of Scotland Electricity Board to begin work at once with a view to ordering one AGR station each as soon as possible.
>
> This decision will enable our nuclear industry to build on our extensive experience of gas-cooled technology. The generating boards have already begun to accumulate operating experience with the AGRs which have so far been commissioned. The completion of the remaining stations in the existing AGR programme and the successful construction of the next AGR orders will be the first priority in our thermal nuclear programme.
>
> The Government also consider, having regard to the importance of nuclear power and present knowledge of the different systems, that the United Kingdom's thermal reactor strategy should not at this stage be dependent upon an exclusive commitment to any one reactor system, and that in addition to the AGR we must develop the option of adopting the PWR system in the early 1980s ...
>
> The electricity supply industry has indicated that, to establish the PWR as a valid option, it wishes to declare an intention that, provided design work is satisfactorily completed and all necessary Government and other consents and safety clearances have been obtained, it will order a PWR station. It does not consider that a start on site could be made before 1982. This intention, which does not call for an immediate order or a letter of intent at the present time, is endorsed by the Government.[29]

The SGHWR at Winfrith continued to run for 23 years until being closed down in 1990. It is now being decommissioned and dismantled.

---

1 TNA: PRO AB 15/4588. Studies of heavy water boiling reactors. BL Goodlet, H Chilton, RJ Haslam, J Howieson and JJ Syrett, 20 September 1955.

2 TNA: PRO AB 64/433. Typical design of 2 × 300 MW AGR. JV Dunworth to HW Bowker, 9 June 1959.

3 TNA: PRO AB 15/6235. Progress with S.C.H.W. reactor systems. RV Moore and S Fawcett.

4 TNA: PRO AB 15/5999. Reactor Technology Conference with Industry held at Atomic Energy Research Establishment, Harwell on 11th June, 1958: paper I the advanced gas cooled (AGR) reactor and the gas cooled heavy water (GCHW) reactor. S Fawcett. See also TNA: PRO AB 15/6000. Reactor Technology Conference with Industry held at Atomic Energy Research Establishment, Harwell on 11th June, 1958: paper 2 the high temperature gas cooled (HTGC) reactor. LR Shepherd and GE Lockett.

[5] TNA: PRO AB 17/105. The Winfrith SGHWR. This AEA publication gives a full description of the Winfrith station. See also TNA: PRO AB 17/93. Steam Generating Heavy Water Reactor. TNA: PRO AB 17/220. Britain's SGHWR.

[6] TNA: PRO EG 7/38. Steam Generating Heavy Water Reactor (SGHWR) programme.

[7] TNA: PRO EG 7/39. Steam Generating Heavy Water Reactor (SGHWR) programme. 'The SGHW Prototype Reactor.' A Firth, N Bradley and JER Holmes, 1963.

[8] H Cartwright (1968) 'The Commercial SGHWR' in: *Proceedings of the Conference Held at the Institution of Civil Engineers*, held on 14–16 May 1968 at the British Nuclear Energy Society.

[9] 'The Design of the Steam Generating Heavy Water Reactor.' H Cartwright, Director of Water Reactors, UKAEA. Presented to the IAEA Symposium on Heavy Water Reactors, Vienna, 11–15 September 1967.

[10] Simon Rippon (1974). 'Not such a bad reactor', *New Scientist* 63(910), 398–401.

[11] Editorial (1963). 'Critical of UK AEA-CEGB Relationship', *Nuclear Engineering* 8(8), 263.

[12] TNA: PRO EG 7/38. Steam Generating Heavy Water Reactor (SGHWR) programme. 17 January 1969.

[13] TNA: PRO EG 7/38. Steam Generating Heavy Water Reactor (SGHWR) programme. 21 March 1969.

[14] TNA: PRO EG 1/363. Prototype Steam Generating Heavy Water Reactor (SGHWR). 'SGHWR for North of Scotland Hydro-Electricity Board.' St. Clair C Hood, UKAEA, to G Hubbard, Ministry of Technology, 11 August 1967.

[15] TNA: PRO AB 65/869. Stake Ness tender assessment.

[16] TNA: PRO EG 7/93. Steam Generating Heavy Water Reactors (SGHWR): sale to Scotland. MI Michaels (Ministry of Technology) to Sir Charles Cunningham (UKAEA), 8 October 1970.

[17] TNA: PRO EG 12/72. Thermal Reactor Working Party: report. DC Clark to Mr Bullock, 23 December 1971.

[18] Nuclear Reactor Policy, House of Commons Debate (Fifth series), 8 August 1972, Vol. 842, cc. 1491–1492.

[19] TNA: PRO CAB 128/54. Meetings: 1–25.

[20] *Ibid.*

[21] J Walsh (1974). 'British Choose Own Reactor for Nuclear Power Program', *Science* 185(4150), 511.

[22] Department of Energy (1974). *Choice of Thermal Reactor Systems*, [White Paper]. London: HMSO.

[23] TNA: PRO AB 38/349. Advanced Gas-cooled Reactor (AGR). Letter from H Cartwright to JCC Stewart, UK AEA, London 14 September 1965.

[24] Nuclear Power (1981). *The Government's Response to the Select Committee on Energy's Report on the Nuclear Power Programme*, [White Paper]. London: HMSO (Cmnd 8317).

[25] TNA: PRO AB 38/350. Steam Generating Heavy Water.

[26] *Ibid.*

[27] House of Commons (1976). *First Report from the Select Committee on Science and Technology. The SGHWR Programme.* London: HMSO.

[28] TNA: PRO EG 12/134. Specific proposals for Steam Generating Heavy Water Reactor (SGHWR) and High Temperature Reactor (HTR) development. 'Status of SGHWR with Particular Reference to Safety.' The Nuclear Power Group Limited, British Nuclear Design and Construction Limited, November 1973.

[29] Thermal Reactor Policy, House of Commons Debate (Fifth series), 25 January 1978, Vol. 942, cc. 1391–1392.

Chapter 15

DRAGON and the HTR

Harwell was already thinking of designs for advanced gas-cooled reactors in the late 1940s, and in particular, there was a proposal for a high-temperature helium-cooled graphite-moderated reactor for submarine propulsion (described elsewhere), but when its main organiser, Jack Diamond, left to become professor of mechanical engineering at the University of Manchester, the concept became neglected in favour of the carbon dioxide-cooled PIPPA design. In any event, such a design would have been totally impracticable given the state of the art at the time.

The idea of a high-temperature reactor was taken up again at Harwell in the mid-1950s, and its progress shows up much of the rivalry and difference of approach between Risley and Harwell. The AEA did not have unlimited resources, and Hinton at Risley preferred going forward in relatively modest steps. This was not true for Harwell, where a number of teams were working on a variety of systems often apparently chosen for their scientific interest rather than their practical application in a power reactor, with systems such as the liquid metal cooled reactor or the homogenous aqueous reactor being promoted. More practical systems such as the light water-cooled reactors, exemplified by LEO, were dropped, possibly because they did not have the attraction of the more challenging systems. Ironically, light water reactors have gone on to dominate the nuclear power market, whereas the vast majority of the systems which were being investigated at Harwell proved impractical for one reason or another. In Harwell's defence, the only way to find out whether a system was viable was to study it to find out.

As interest in the high-temperature reactor revived at the end of 1955, a working party was set up at Harwell.[1] The new design was also intended to exploit what was described as the thorium cycle, whereby thorium 232 is converted to uranium 233, which is a fissile isotope. Thorium is both cheap and abundant, and this was seen as another way of stretching out the amount of uranium used, since uranium was then thought to be in short supply.

Work began on a study of a fuel testing reactor of 30 MW which would be about 4 m in diameter and 2.5 m high, contained within a steel pressure vessel. The coolant inlet temperature would be 350°C and the outlet temperature 850°C. The ideas for the fuel elements were still very uncertain. A further possibility was generating power by passing the hot gas from the reactor through a gas turbine, eliminating the steam cycle and, with it, the heat exchangers and boilers. It also became clear that some form of high-temperature zero-energy experiment would be needed, which would eventually materialise as the ZENITH reactor, based at Winfrith.

As a result, a report was produced which gave the details for a preliminary design. This was for a 10 MW helium-cooled reactor experiment in which the fuel elements would be beads of uranium dioxide encased in graphite. Most of the fission products would be solid, and stay in the beads, but the more volatile ones might well escape into the gas flow. This meant having some kind of system to purge the gas of the escaping fission products. (The report containing these proposals was to be circulated some 18 months later to the OEEC (Organisation for European Economic Cooperation) members under a new cover.) This design would be very similar to the final result.

On the other hand, the range of unknowns was still very large, and in terms of a power reactor, the system as it stood was not at all practicable. It was perfectly reasonable to design a small experimental reactor in which fission products are allowed to escape into the main coolant stream, but this could not be permitted in a large power reactor. Adding the purge system would also increase the cost and complexity of the design.

Encasing the fuel in graphite in some form meant that many of the difficulties with the fuel elements would be side-stepped, but no one knew how impermeable graphite could be made or how well it would stand up to irradiation at high-temperature. Similarly, while it was not too difficult to design a steel pressure vessel for a small reactor experiment working at high temperatures, when the vessel was scaled up to a commercial size the problem was altogether different.

Nevertheless progress had been sufficiently encouraging for the AEA to form a High-Temperature Gas-Cooled Reactor Research Committee to study the experiment, briefly called HUGO, with Sir John Cockcroft in the chair. Sir Leonard Owen, Director of Engineering and deputy to Hinton, led the northern team from Risley, which was distinctly sceptical about such design points as gas turbine driven circulators. Owen also wanted a more practical gas than helium, which was only available in quantity in the USA. This hostility to helium persisted at Risley right until the day when it became known that there were large quantities in North Sea gas.

Cockcroft persevered with the design committee. He had been successful in putting through the new site at Winfrith as an out station of Harwell, and it was agreed that if the fast reactor went north, the HTR would stay south. When money became available, it was intended that ZENITH and the HTR would be built at Winfrith as one of a set of new reactor experiments that Harwell would control.

To the disappointment of the Harwell team, construction and the detailed design of the HTR would be in the hands of Risley.

Risley and Harwell were still at loggerheads with regards to the coolant. Risley remained opposed to the use of helium, whereas Harwell were adamant that carbon dioxide could not be considered. Harwell insisted on a design which would permit outlet temperatures of 1,000°C and which had power densities as high as those to be expected in a commercial HTR, which meant that the experimental reactor of 20 MW would need to use pressures as high as 20 atmospheres for the coolant gas. Treasury approval was sought for a zero-energy assembly, estimated to cost £4.6 million.[2]

A 37-month programme for the experimental reactor was drawn up, starting in August 1957, with construction beginning in January 1958, completion in September 1960 and criticality being achieved in March 1961. It was planned to seek Treasury approval for the reactor, which had been estimated to cost £4.6 million, in mid-November. The firms of Ruston & Hornsby and Rolls-Royce, experts in the gas turbine field, were invited to attach staff to the project. No conflict was seen between the HTR and the AGR, on which work had begun, since the time scales were very different, and also because it was intended that the HTR would exploit the thorium fuel cycle. Planning of the Windscale AGR had already started, and the HTR was regarded as the step beyond.

The project was thrown into disarray by the fire at Windscale in October 1957. Within the AEA the repercussions of the fire were far-reaching. It was recognised that the complete reorganisation of safety procedures would be necessary and much effort would have to be devoted first to the enquiry and then to clearing up the mess. One of the first victims was the HTR, and at a meeting of the design committee in November, Risley announced that no design effort was available and the project would have to be put off for several months. The working parties studying fuel elements, coolant processing, physics and safety, would continue but members were told that Cockcroft and Owen had agreed that as a result of the postponement of the construction of the HTGCR, the design committee should be reconstituted as a research committee, with Cockcroft in the chair.

It was clear that Harwell and Risley would not have the resources to tackle the project for some considerable time, but there were other options. A paper on the HTR was prepared for a meeting of the European Atomic Energy Society to be held in Rome in November 1957, when the subject would be gas-cooled reactors, including a session at the end on 'other types of inactive gas reactors and gas reactors where fission products are released'.[3]

The next step came at a meeting in Paris in March 1958 when Cockcroft proposed that the high-temperature, gas-cooled reactor project be established at Winfrith but as a joint European project. The project would be under the control of a Chief Executive who, although appointed by an international board of management, would be a national of the host country. This was considered necessary in view of the legal and safety responsibilities that country would have to assume. International supervision would be ensured by the type of management structure instituted at CERN. It was anticipated that research contracts relevant to fuel development and other items would be placed in laboratories of the participating countries.

As usual with joint international projects, a good deal of negotiation was required but finally an agreement was signed at the headquarters of the OEEC on 23 March 1959 by the UKAEA, Austria, the Danish Atomic Energy Commission, the Euratom Commission, the Norwegian Institutt for Atomenergi, the Swedish AB Atomenergi, and Switzerland. Under the agreement estimated expenditure on the project was £13.6 million over five years. It was agreed that £10 million would be shared between the signatories with any additional expenditure, up to £3.6 million, being borne by the UK, to whom any reactor experiment and installations or equipment built or acquired under the joint programme will belong at the end of the five-year period.[4]

Before the design for DRAGON was finalised, experimental studies had to be carried out on the design of the reactor core. This was done using a zero-energy reactor named ZENITH,[5] which was built to operate in temperature conditions similar to those expected in a high-temperature power reactor. ZENITH's core contained uranium, thorium and graphite. Pellets of the materials were assembled in graphite sleeves and arranged in an almost cylindrical stack. Four radium-beryllium neutron sources were used to generate a neutron flux in the fuel. The flux fell off exponentially with height, and measurements of the rate of change of neutron flux with height could be made for a number of different thorium/uranium/graphite mixtures to give a comparison with theory.

Nitrogen gas was circulated through the core from an external circuit mounted in a pit beneath the reactor vessel, and was heated by a 250 kW heater as it entered the core to raise the core temperature to 800°C. At these temperatures it was important to maintain the purity of the gas so a purification system was used to remove traces of carbon monoxide and carbon dioxide. The reactor itself was operated at a maximum nuclear power of 100 W, which was negligible in comparison with the energy used to heat the core. The use of ZENITH meant that much of the preliminary design work needed for DRAGON could then be checked experimentally.

One of the features of DRAGON was that no metal cladding was to be used for the fuel, which would considerably improve the neutron economy of the reactor. In the initial concept of the reactor experiment, the fuel rods contained compacts of uranium oxide pellets in a graphite matrix. It was thought that this fuel would release the fission products xenon, krypton and iodine as they formed, and these would be swept away by the helium coolant and filtered out. Early fuel tests in the

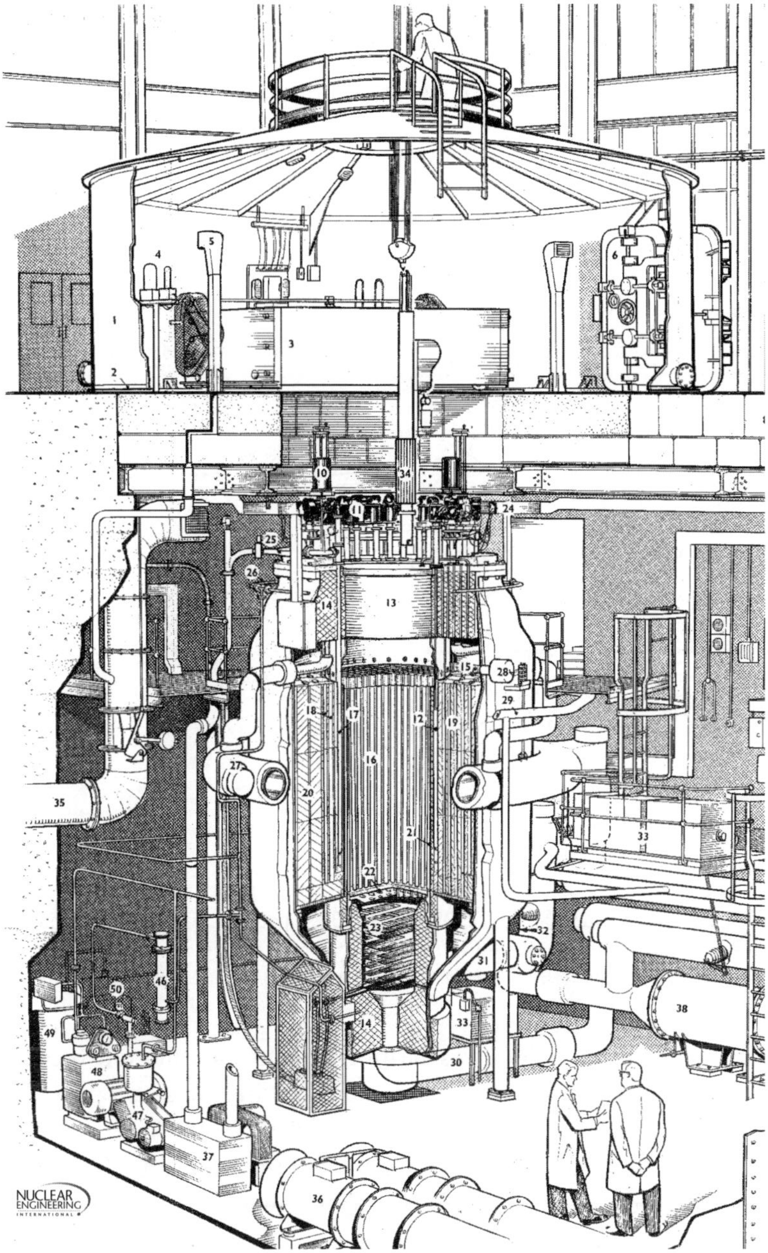

Figure 15.1. The ZENITH reactor, built at Winfrith to test out various configurations of the core for a high-temperature reactor.

Pluto reactor at Harwell showed that even at 1,000°C most of these were retained in the fuel matrix. This encouraged the development of a revolutionary coated particle fuel that released less than one part in ten million of the fission products.

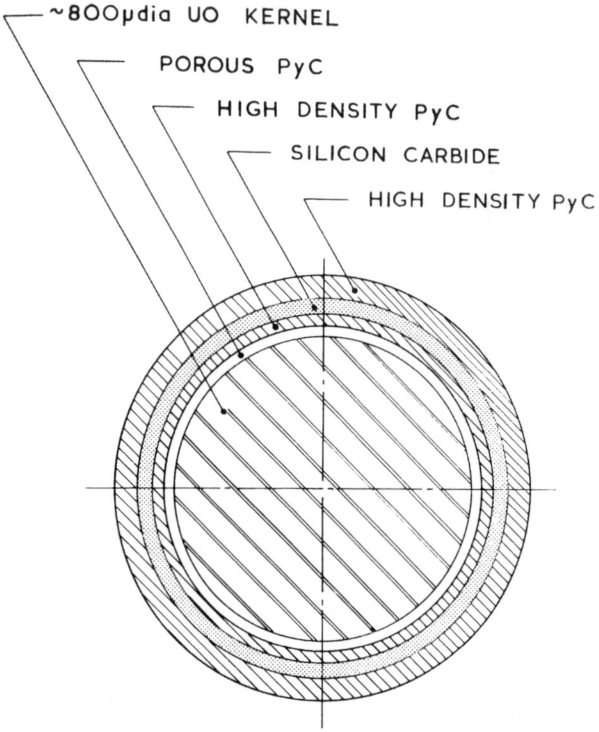

Figure 15.2. Fuel particle developed for DRAGON. These particles were around 1 mm in diameter, and several million would be needed for a full load. PyC refers to pyrolised carbon; i.e., an organic liquid is sprayed on to the particle then heated until it decomposes.

Another feature of DRAGON was the investigation of the thorium breeding cycle. This uses natural thorium, which contains almost entirely one isotope — ^{232}Th. The thorium captures a neutron to become ^{233}Th, which then beta decays (half-life 21.83 minutes) first to ^{233}Pa (half-life 5 ms) then to ^{233}U (half-life 160,000 years). ^{233}U is fissile, and so can be used as fuel, either by extracting it chemically from the thorium during reprocessing, or more simply by just leaving it in place.

^{233}U has several advantages as a fuel. One is that no actinides such as americium or californium are produced. Breeding from ^{238}U to produce ^{239}Pu means that ^{240}P and higher isotopes are formed. Even when ^{233}U does absorb neutrons, it would become successively ^{234}U then ^{235}U, which again is fissile. The absence of actinides reduces the nuclear waste problem considerably. A second advantage is that when ^{233}U undergoes fissions, it can produce two or more neutrons, to such an extent that

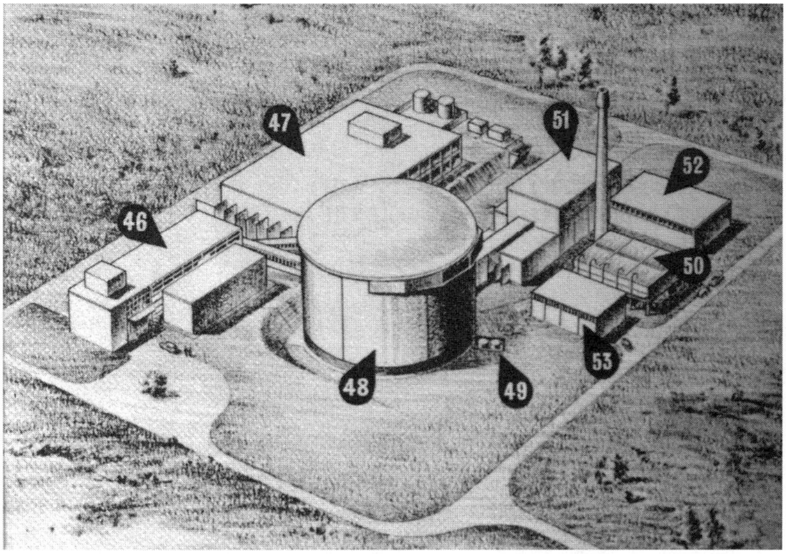

Figure 15.3. Layout of the DRAGON site at Winfrith.

more ^{233}U can be produced from the thorium than is destroyed, providing the reactor design has good neutron economy. This makes it a very efficient fuel.

The core consisted of 37 fuel elements in a hexagonal array with an effective diameter of 1.08 m. This array was surrounded by 30 prismatic graphite columns of the inner reflector, machined on one side to match the profile of the adjacent fuel element and on the other to form a circle of 1.5 m diameter. The 24 control rods operated in holes in the inner reflector. The relatively small size of the DRAGON core meant that its neutron efficiency was not very high: the hot core, just critical, with control rods withdrawn, lost 32% of the neutrons by leakage, whereas it was calculated that in large power reactors of about 1,000 MW (Th), the leakage would be around 2%.[6]

The overall length of a fuel element was 2.54 m, of which 1.6 m in the middle contained fuel. The helium coolant entered the core from below and passed upward through channels between the fuel rods. The maximum thermal power was 21.5 MW with an inlet gas temperature of 350°C, an outlet temperature of 750°C, and a helium mass flow of nearly 10 kg/ s at 20 atmospheres pressure.

The helium inventory of the DRAGON primary coolant system was about 355 kg, of which, during operation, 175 kg were kept in the reserve stores and the dump tanks. Of the other half, 68 kg were flowing in the main heat removal circuit, and the rest was slowly circulating through the fission product removal plant (36 kg), the helium purification plant (19 kg) and the transfer chamber (45.5 kg). The heatsink

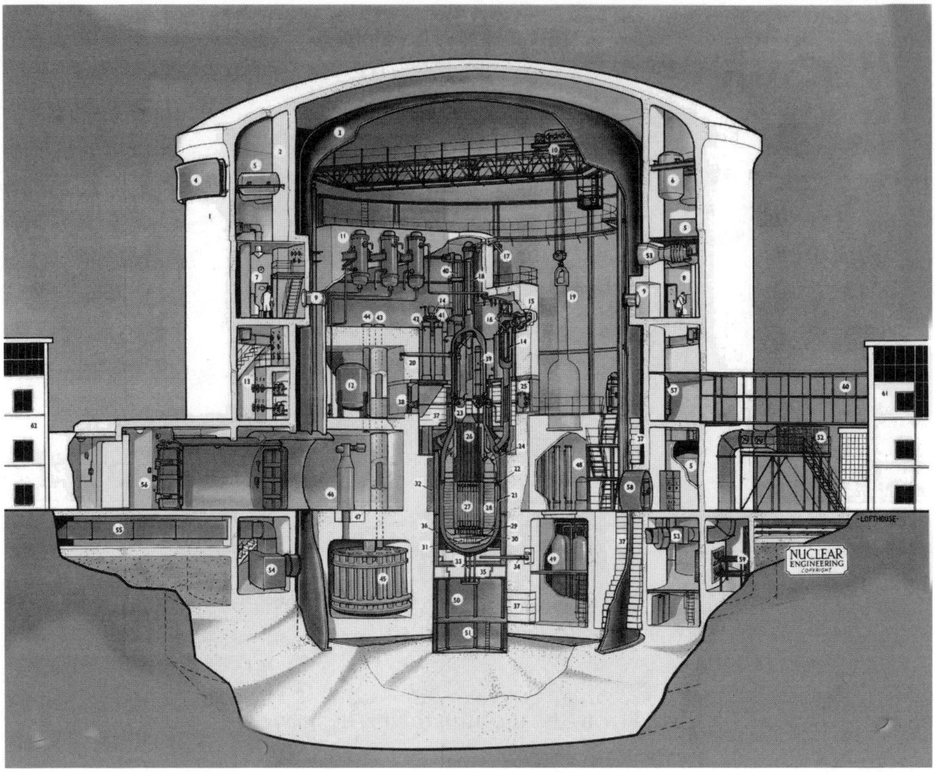

Figure 15.4. Cutaway view of DRAGON.

contained the remaining 10 kg. Losses due to refuelling shutdowns (20–30 kg per shutdown) were mainly caused by changing the vessel contents from helium to air.

During routine operation, the average helium leak was less than 0.2 kg/day or 0.12% of the circulating inventory. In the beginning of 1974, losses during operation reached 2.0 kg/day and after months of searching, a number of leaks were found in the stainless steel pipework leading to the helium purification plant. The leaks, almost invisible pores and crevices in the otherwise healthy levels of pipe, were produced by chloride corrosion. All leaks occurred in narrow sections of the pipes that had been wrapped with PVC insulating tape during commissioning for the purpose of marking the various flow paths and components of the circuit. When the circuit operated at temperatures roughly between 80 and 120°C, the innermost layer of PVC tape decomposed, leaving gaseous HCl trapped under the still intact outer layers of tape. (On pipe sections under 80°C the PVC tape remained stable and above around 120°C the complete wrapping cracked and fell off.) After the discovery of the leaks caused by chloride corrosion all accessible stainless steel pipework was searched and more than 200 tape markings were removed. All sections of stainless steel pipework that had carried tape markings were cleaned and sections that had operated above 80°C were replaced. The result was a drastic reduction of unaccounted helium losses to 0.2 kg/day.

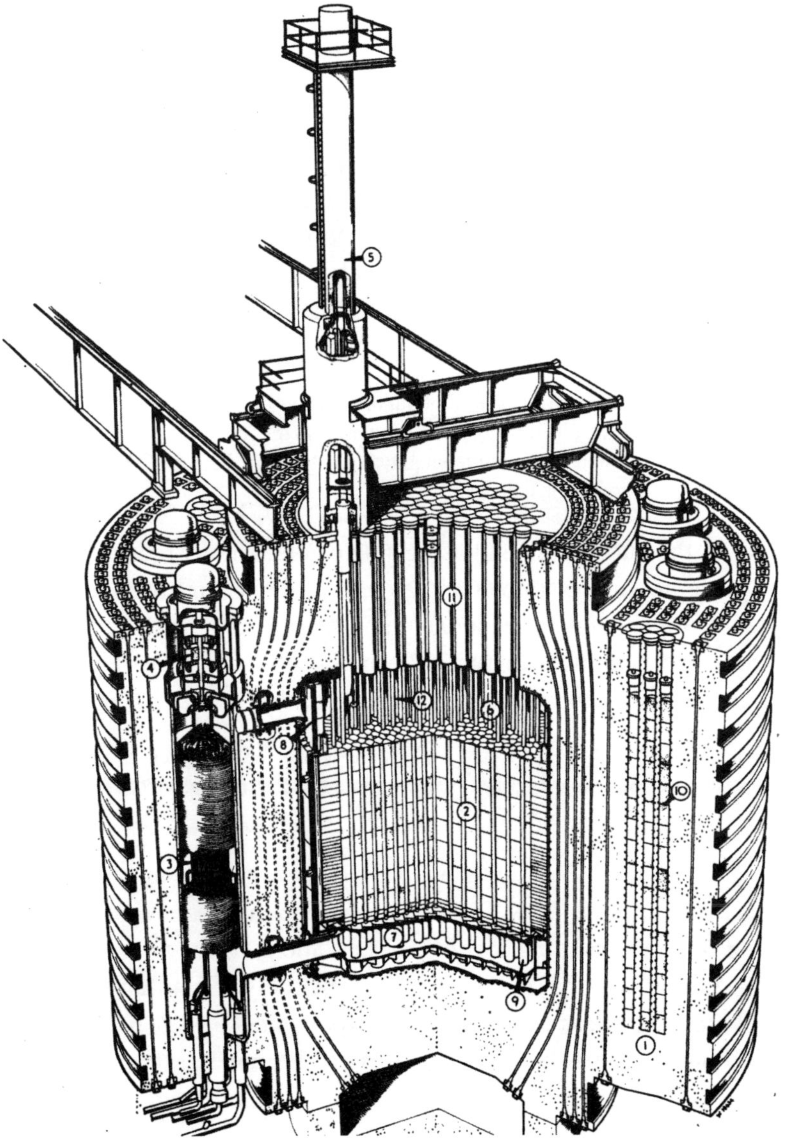

Figure 15.5. Proposed 630 MW(E) HTR. This would have the boilers housed in the pressure vessel itself.

DRAGON ran for over ten years, but finally closed in 1976 mainly due to a reluctance of the participating countries to fund it any further. Whilst it had been a success, there seemed little point continuing with a technology that was unlikely to be exploited further.

A Commercial HTR?

Studies were certainly made for various uses of HTRs, including commercial power stations, and rather more unusually, marine propulsion.[7] Designs were drawn up based on the DRAGON experiment.[8] A report was produced in 1962 by the HTR design office at Risley entitled 'The Civil HTR Reference Design Study.'[9] Even before this design was finalised, some cost estimates had already been made. This was for a 1,000 MW (H) power station which was based as closely as possible on the DRAGON reactor and was costed against the civil AGR. The conclusions were that:

> The final tender price for H.T.R. is about the same as the A.G.R. figure. It appears that what has been gained in higher efficiencies and higher power density has been lost in the provision of the purge chemical plant and in the heavy civil costs for the double containment scheme.[10]

Removing the purge plant and using single containment reduced the price considerably such that 'much simpler and more robust elements become possible with anticipated major savings in component and fabrication costs'. Even so, the HTR was not regarded as a threat to the AGR on cost grounds. Indeed, the summary of the Reference Design Study included a comment that:

> The capital cost to be expected for a large power reactor based as closely as possible on the Dragon design is not sufficiently low for the system to offer a great attraction.

Despite this initial lack of interest, the CEGB began taking a second look at a possible HTR. The Ministry of Technology was not impressed by the news that an HTR might be in the running for the power stations to follow the AGR. 'I found Mr Gore's comment — that C.E.G.B. are prematurely committing themselves to a decision of great significance to British industry without any clear economic case — most disturbing'.[11] The policy of the CEGB had been that it

> ...had considered the introduction of the S.G.H.W.R. into the U.K. generating system. They concluded that, in view of their commitment to Mark II A.G.R., the cost differential in favour of the S.G.H.W.R. was not enough to justify a radical change in technology. Instead, the C.E.G.B. has indicated a strong interest in the Mark III G.C.R [i.e., an HTR]. This reactor will not, however, be available and accepted as a proven system for some considerable time. Continuing to develop the S.G.H.W.R. in 1970/71 would keep it available as an alternative to the Mark III G.C.R. for home use.[12]

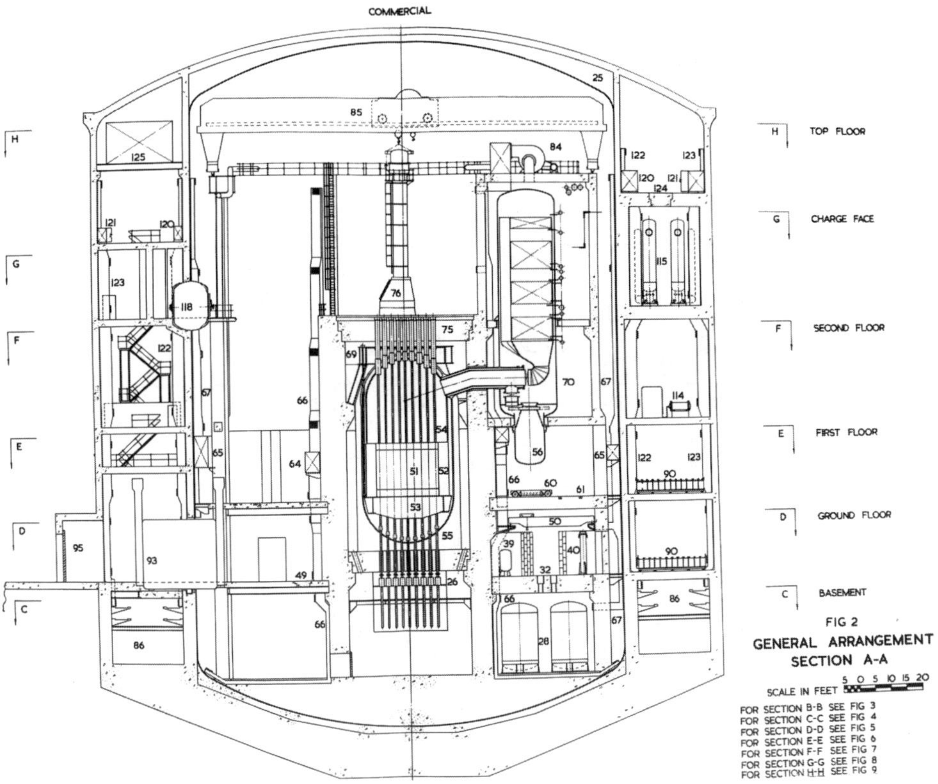

Figure 15.6. The reference design for an HTR. This was found to have little advantage over the AGR.

The two remaining consortia, BNDC and TNPG, both drew up detailed HTR designs for the CEGB as a tender for a proposed power station at Oldbury B,[13] which were submitted to the AEA for evaluation. The new variation on the HTR included a replaceable moderator, low enrichment, steam raising units as opposed to direct gas turbine cycle, fuel based on coated particles as developed in DRAGON, and helium cooling.[14]

There were several problems with building a commercial station. Firstly, although DRAGON had been a success, it was really too small to base a full-sized commercial design on it. This meant that a considerable amount of money — some tens of millions — would be needed for further research and development, which would take time. Secondly, the CEGB and AEA were struggling with the AGR. To suggest going one step further with a technology which was still producing problem after problem was distinctly optimistic. As a result, the proposals were dropped when the government announced its decision to build the SGHWR. When the SGHWR was dropped, the government ordered more AGRs and a PWR, and these would be the last power stations built in the UK.

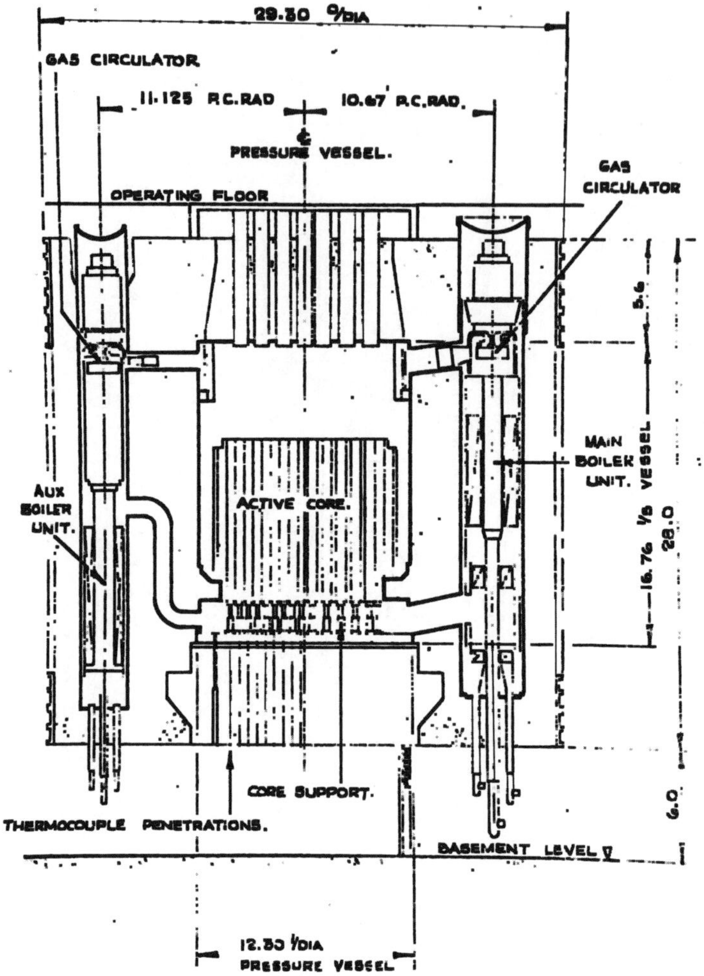

Figure 15.7. The TNPG tender for a commercial HTR station.

HTR stations were built in America and Germany but were not a long-term success.

---

[1] TNA: PRO AB 38/1206. Dragon Project history. EN Shaw. Much of this section is based on this account.

[2] TNA: PRO AB 6/1658. High temperature gas-cooled reactors (solid, homogeneous): technical aspects. 'High Temperature Zero Energy Reactor Assemblies.' Sir J Cockcroft, 21 June 1957.

[3] TNA: PRO AB 38/1206. Dragon Project history. EN Shaw. Much of this section is based on this account.

[4] TNA: PRO AB 32/1147. Official history of Dragon.

[5] TNA: PRO AB 17/293. The Atomic Energy Research Programme. AEA publication (1960), pp. 30–31.

[6] TNA: PRO AB 32/563. High Temperature Reactors and the Dragon Project: papers presented at a British Nuclear Energy Society (BNES) symposium, London, 23–24 May 1966; session 2. 'Reactor Physics of the Dragon Reactor Experiment.' KO Hintermann, E Schröder and H Guttmann.

[7] TNA: PRO AB 7/10755. Marine HTR design study: an assessment of the De Havilland Y113 feasibility study. R Anscomb.

[8] TNA: PRO AB 32/704. Preliminary study for a 630 MW(e) low enriched homogeneous high temperature gas cooled reactor. June 1968.

[9] TNA: PRO AB 7/14486. The civil HTR reference design study. JD Thorn.

[10] TNA: PRO AB 7/12966. First cost estimate for the HTR reference design. RS Challender.

[11] TNA: PRO EG 7/95. Advanced Gas Cooled Reactors Mark III: departmental papers.

[12] *Ibid.*

[13] TNA: PRO EG 12/134. Specific proposals for Steam Generating Heavy Water Reactor (SGHWR) and High Temperature Reactor (HTR) development. See also TNA: PRO EG 7/101. Thermal Reactor Working Party: papers and minutes. TNA: PRO EG 12/67. Thermal Reactor Working Party Study Task 3: economics of High Temperature Reactors (HTRs) and Steam Generating Heavy Water Reactors (SGHWRs).

[14] TNA: PRO EG 12/134. Specific proposals for Steam Generating Heavy Water Reactor (SGHWR) and High Temperature Reactor (HTR) development.

Chapter 16

Atomic Energy at Sea

The Royal Navy's first nuclear submarine was HMS Dreadnought, launched on Trafalgar Day (21 October) 1960, and commissioned in April 1963. The choice of name in itself was distinctly symbolic — the previous Dreadnought, launched in 1905, had rendered all previous battleships obsolete. Thus with nuclear submarines — they too rendered their predecessors obsolete. Dreadnought was all British, with one exception: she was powered by a reactor of American design. Admiral Rickover, in charge of the US Navy nuclear submarine programme, had initially been opposed to the transfer of any nuclear technology to Britain, but Lord Mountbatten, then First Sea Lord, using both diplomacy and charm, persuaded Rickover to change his mind. According to the *Proceedings of the US Naval Institute* in 1981, 'The introvert iconoclast from the Ukraine . . . fell under the spell and aura of Queen Victoria's grandson'.[1]

Under the terms of the agreement, the design of the latest submarine reactor, the S5W, was made available for the British to copy, although with some unusual conditions. Rickover decreed that the transfer would not be government to government, but company to company, and he specified that the British company in question should be Rolls-Royce.

Rolls-Royce already had considerable experience in the nuclear submarine propulsion field as part of the on-going British effort to develop an indigenous system. Indeed, the Royal Navy had been interested in nuclear propulsion from the very early days of nuclear power, but had been hampered by lack of both money and resources, and in particular, the supply of highly enriched uranium. As early as June 1944, the Admiralty approached Sir John Anderson (one of the few government ministers aware of the atomic programme at the time, and the minister responsible for the British wartime atomic effort) about the applications of atomic energy, and as a result of this, J Diamond[2] was seconded to the project and sent to join the British team in Canada. In January 1945, more men were sent from the Admiralty to add to the naval presence and gain experience in nuclear technology.[3]

Not a great deal more could be done until Harwell was up and running, but as a result of the collaboration between the Admiralty and the nuclear scientists, a paper on the design of an enriched uranium reactor for a submarine was presented at the Harwell Power Conference of 1951.[4] At this stage, Britain's first power reactor was still five years in the future, but the naval reactor was drawn up along similar lines — a gas-cooled graphite moderated design. Some of the work that was done on this reactor design would later be applied to the high-temperature gas-cooled power reactor project.

Using natural uranium was quite impracticable — such a reactor would be impossibly large and heavy for use in a submarine. Thus enriched uranium would be needed, and it was likely that fuel enriched in ^{235}U to twice the natural amount would become available in a few years from the time of the report. Given this assumption, it was possible to make sufficiently reliable estimates of size, heat output and nuclear characteristics of a gas-cooled reactor using slightly enriched fuel to allow design studies to get under way.

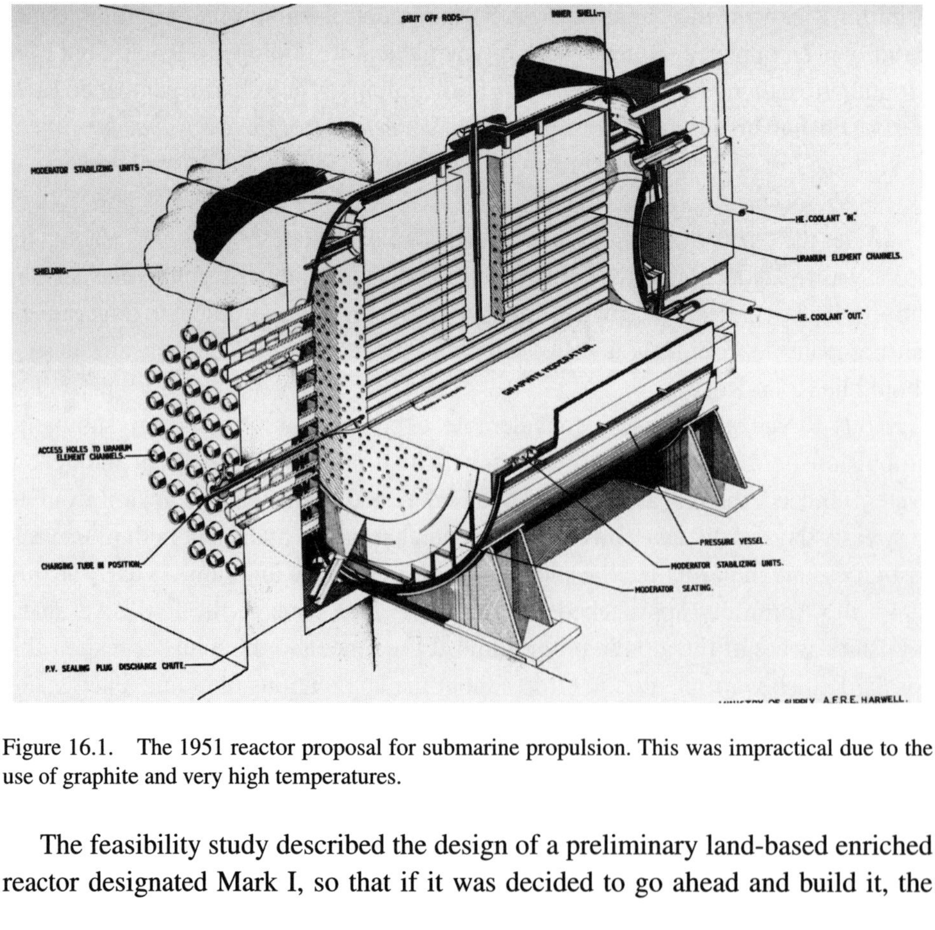

Figure 16.1. The 1951 reactor proposal for submarine propulsion. This was impractical due to the use of graphite and very high temperatures.

The feasibility study described the design of a preliminary land-based enriched reactor designated Mark I, so that if it was decided to go ahead and build it, the

Admiralty could sponsor a further reactor intended specifically for a submarine, the Mark II. The Mark I study was taken further, with Admiralty advice on the general aspects of dimensions, heat output, and so on.

Graphite was chosen as the moderator since, at that time, almost no work had been done on water-cooled reactors in the UK. Heavy water was another possible choice as moderator, but although several research reactors were built at Harwell in the early 1950s which used heavy water as a moderator, there is no evidence that it was ever considered for submarine propulsion. There were other drawbacks to a graphite-moderated reactor: the Navy thought that the main engines of a submarine should be capable of being brought up to full power from low power in not much more than about five minutes. The large mass of graphite, with a correspondingly large heat capacity, would make this impossible without far exceeding the designated uranium temperature. There were also doubts about the suitability of graphite as a structural material — in particular, how well it would stand up to shock, as it was both brittle and weak. This was not a problem in a land-based reactor, but in a submarine being depth charged it might have been a different matter.

Helium was chosen as the coolant, with the only other worthwhile alternative being carbon dioxide. Using carbon dioxide would have made for a larger and thus heavier reactor, since helium had better heat transfer properties. The use of carbon dioxide as a coolant would have meant a fuel element temperature of around 800°C as opposed to around 650°C with helium. Even so, the paper commented that with 'a reactor of this type, a submarine is certain to be very large, probably about 5000 tons overall form displacement'. HMS Dreadnought, Britain's first nuclear submarine, was actually 4,000 tons displacement when dived, and the contemporary 'A' class submarines were 1,600 tons displacement.

One aspect of the design that did not appear to be studied in any detail was the fuel elements. It is almost axiomatic that the design of any reactor is dependent on the nature of its fuel elements. The only experience in the UK at that time had been with uranium metal contained within aluminium. Given that aluminium melts at 660°C, it would have been unsuitable at these temperatures. For comparison, the outlet temperature of the gas in the magnox stations was 400°C, and in the later AGR reactors (first commissioned 1962) the temperature was around 650°C. The DRAGON experimental reactor, first commissioned in 1962, used helium at 750°C. Hence the design figures for the naval reactor with its fuel element temperature of 650°C look distinctly optimistic for 1951 unless a good deal of money and resources was spent on further development of the fuel elements.

Whilst the design would have made a very respectable power reactor, it was certainly ill-suited for submarine propulsion. On the other hand, given the state of the art in Britain in the late 1940s, there were not many other options available.

The Mark II reactor would need 8 tonnes of enriched uranium, although the designers were still working with an enrichment of only 3%. The graphite would contribute another 20 tonnes weight. The pressure vessel enclosing the reactor would have a wall 3.5 inches thick and a diameter of 16 feet. Engineers from Harwell had been taken to HMS Dolphin at Fort Blockhouse in Gosport, a submarine base, and given a tour of the current 'A' class submarines. These used batteries for underwater propulsion, each carrying 224 half ton cells, which would be recharged once the submarine had surfaced, using the ship's diesel engines. It seems that the 16 feet diameter of the reactor was probably based around existing submarine designs such as the 'A' class submarines. Submarine hull design was to change very drastically after trials of the USS Albacore, which had a hull fully optimised for high speeds underwater — the design being helped by studying the wind tunnel experiments on airships carried out by the Royal Aircraft Establishment at Farnborough. The new hull shape could accommodate the volume needed for reactors much more easily.

A draft schedule given in the paper had the design work on the Mark I being completed by the end of 1951, construction taking up 1952 and 1953, with the reactor running by the start of 1954. The design for the Mark II, intended for use at sea, was to be completed by the end of 1954.

The reactor would, of course, be only part of the system — a heat exchanger, boiler and turbine would be needed, and according to the planned schedule, the specification and drawings of these would be completed by mid-1955, as would the design of the submarine. It was hoped that the submarine would then be ready for trials by mid-1958.[5] Certainly, contracts were issued to commercial firms for design work on the boilers[6] and on the propulsion side under the code name of 'Devonport Power Station'.[7]

As work progressed, the design team were beginning to have doubts about the use of a graphite-moderated reactor. In January 1952, the controller of the Navy sent a report to the senior members of the Admiralty, describing alternatives. One was for some form of water-cooled reactor, but

> The need for a nuclear submarine is not so great... as to justify a recommendation to the Ministry of Supply to take extraordinary steps to develop what is considered to be an interim solution to the submarine propulsion problem.[8]

Quite why the Admiralty thought nuclear power to be an 'interim' solution is not clear, but the comment is also a reference to the rival system of underwater propulsion, using hydrogen peroxide as a source of oxygen for diesel motors. This derived from German wartime work, which used hydrogen peroxide in a form known as HTP (high test peroxide), which was 85% hydrogen peroxide and 15% water. The German U-boat U1407 have been scuttled at the end of the war, but was salvaged and eventually re-commissioned into the Navy as HMS Meteorite. This led to the design and construction of two further submarines, the Explorer class. These were HMS Excalibur and HMS Explorer, which were commissioned in 1958. Although they were very fast underwater, the use of HTP was distinctly hazardous, HMS Explorer being known by its crew as HMS Exploder. HTP was also considered for use in torpedoes, but an explosion in Portland Harbour in 1955 when HMS Sidon was loading an HTP torpedo resulted in the sinking of the submarine and the death of 13 men (an explosion of an HTP torpedo is also thought to be the cause of the loss of the Russian submarine Kursk in 200). The Explorer class was soon abandoned as nuclear propulsion became more feasible.

It was becoming obvious that a gas-cooled graphite-moderated reactor would not be a very feasible option for a submarine. There was a further problem in that Diamond, who had been leading the work on behalf of the Admiralty, left Harwell in 1952 to become professor of engineering at Manchester University. This effectively brought the current work to an end, and it was clear that a fresh approach would be needed.

By 1952, Harwell and Risley had started to look at other types of reactor systems, and more possibilities were beginning to emerge. Apart from the gas-cooled reactor, there were effectively two other systems which might be suitable for submarine use — either a liquid metal-cooled reactor or some form of pressurised water reactor (PWR).

The liquid metal-cooled option would require a very great deal of development and would probably have been an over-ambitious choice for a British submarine reactor (the Dounreay fast reactor, which was liquid metal cooled, first went critical in November 1959). The United States Navy's second nuclear submarine, USS Seawolf, which was launched in July 1955 and commissioned in March 1957, used a liquid sodium cooled reactor. It was not regarded as a success, and was only operational for a short period before being replaced by a PWR, which would then become standard in the United States Navy. Harwell was also taking some interest in a PWR at this time, with plans to build a prototype to be named LEO. It thus made sense for the Admiralty to work in parallel with Harwell on a water-cooled reactor.

The First Lord of the Admiralty was a political post, whose occupant would then have been a member of the Cabinet before the three services were united in the Ministry of Defence. In 1953, the First Lord was James Thomas, Member of Parliament for Hereford, and a note written by the Deputy Chief of the Naval Staff begins, 'You wished to be kept informed of the position as regards Nuclear Propulsion for the Navy',[9] and attached a copy of a report written for a meeting of the Defence Research Policy Committee (chaired, at that time, by Cockcroft). The report gave an estimated date for the launch of a nuclear powered submarine as being no earlier than 1960, eight years later, although it did note that 'Nearly all ancillary investigation and development can proceed independently of which of the two reactors is ultimately chosen'. The two types of reactor considered were the PWR and the liquid metal reactor; the cost of developing the PWR was put at around £15 million and the liquid metal reactor at £11 million.

A follow-up report suggested that both types of reactor should be studied further, although there seemed to be a preference for the liquid metal reactor as providing better performance and being more compact, so allowing for a smaller submarine. The report was obviously a little too technical for the First Lord, who wrote a slightly plaintive note at the top of his copy: 'Can someone explain this to me in simple language?! JPLT'.

Whichever system was chosen, there was little more that could be done until highly enriched uranium was available, and even then the Navy would be competing with the military requirement for highly enriched uranium for weapons. Knowledge that the United States Navy had settled on a PWR persuaded the Admiralty to follow suit, and work on the new system eventually began in 1955. The initial target was to have a prototype plant which would achieve criticality by the middle of 1961. Several industrial firms became involved, and a new company called Vickers Nuclear Engineering Ltd was set up with Vickers-Armstrong, Rolls-Royce, and Foster Wheeler as partners.

Considerable theoretical work had been carried out at Harwell on LEO, a possible land-based PWR, but the project died out soon after the submarine work had begun. This left a great deal of development work to be carried out on PWRs, as there had been no prior experience of them in the UK. There were also many problems associated with fitting a reactor into a submarine which had no land-based counterpart. One of the major problems was that of shielding — in a land-based reactor, weight is no problem and a biological shield of several feet of concrete can be used. This is not an option in a submarine.

In 1954 Harwell suggested to the Navy that a 'swimming pool' reactor be built to test out different materials for shielding. (This is a type of reactor that has a core immersed in an open pool of water, with the water acting as neutron moderator, cooling agent and radiation shield all in one.) The reactor would need a few kilograms of enriched ^{235}U, but by 1955 that was no longer a problem.

The new reactor was built at Harwell for a cost of £180,000, of which the Admiralty would pay £80,000, with an annual fee of £16,000 for the use of the facilities.[10] It was eventually named LIDO,[11] and can be seen in Figure 16.2. The name is obviously a pun, since a lido in the UK is an outdoor public swimming pool.

The shielding was one of the more difficult parts of the design. Depending on the positioning of the reactor and the shielding used, radiation dose levels could be calculated at different parts of the submarine. These calculations were extremely tedious and time-consuming, and used an early form of computing, whereby some

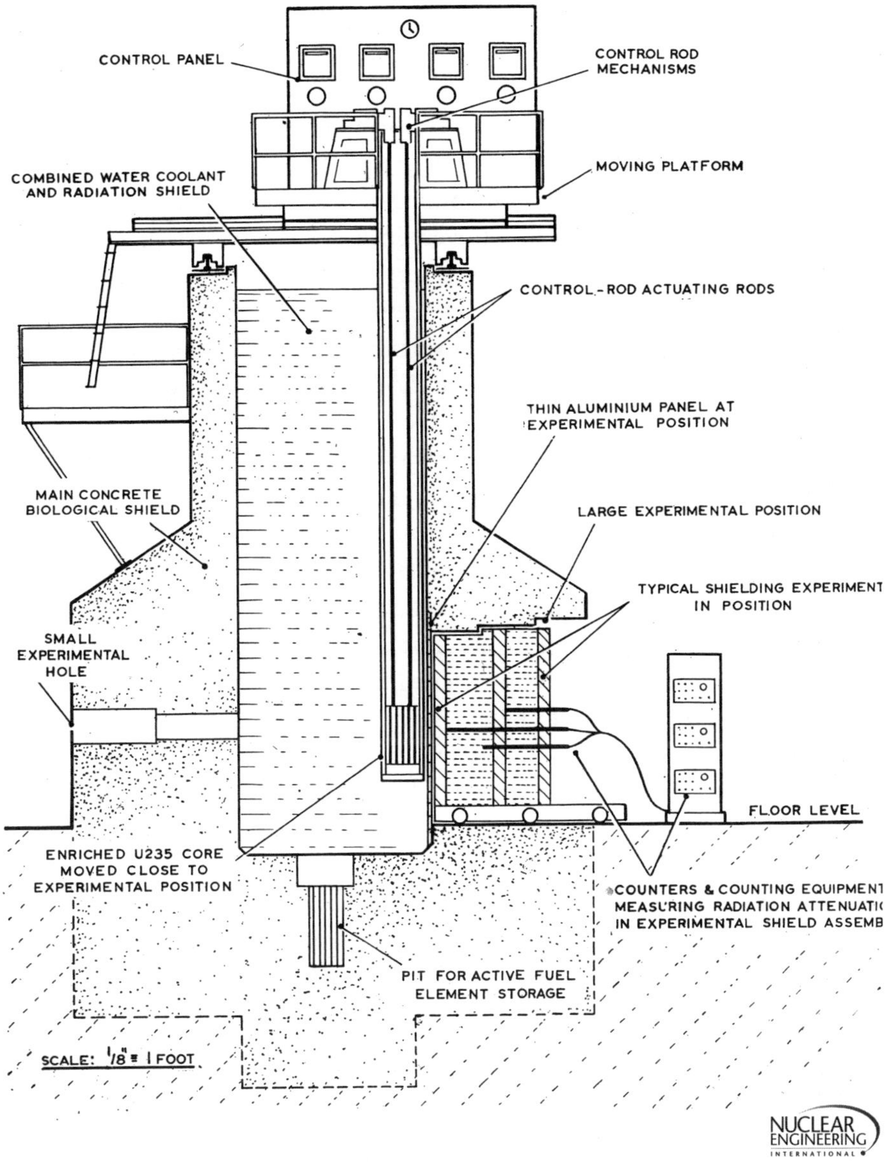

Figure 16.2. LIDO, designed to study materials for shielding from radiation in a submarine.

hundreds of thousands of calculations could be evaluated 'in about seven minutes of computer time'.[12] The time pressures were such that the experimental teams employed on the shielding experiments used a shift system of working, meaning that the facilities were in use 24 hours a day.

A naval section was then set up at Harwell with Captain Harrison-Smith as senior naval representative. This section was gradually expanded, so that by the autumn of 1955, there were 12 staff working on the project, but by 1957, there were 16 members of the Royal Naval Scientific Service, 14 employees from Rolls-Royce, 22 from Vickers, five from Foster-Wheeler, six naval officers, one constructor officer, and three draughtsman attached to the naval section, with 40 AERE scientific and experimental grades and around 23 similar grades working in the Industrial Group at Risley. Including members of staff working in the Admiralty design department, a total of around 160 professional staff were involved.

The core environment in a PWR was very different from that in a gas-cooled reactor, and as far as fuel elements were concerned, the designers were starting from scratch. Hence a major research project began in order to develop fuel rods which could cope with the problems of corrosion in very hot water (the water temperature may well be in excess of 300°C in a PWR; the high pressures prevent the water from boiling). Two lines of investigation were begun, and pursued in parallel so that one would act as an insurance in case the other failed.

One system would use pellets of uranium dioxide in stainless steel cans, whereas the other system would use uranium metal and zirconium as the cladding material. Zirconium was the preferred choice as stainless steel absorbed too many neutrons. Testing fuel elements was a lengthy process: They had to be designed, fabricated, set up within a channel of a reactor, irradiated for a considerable period of time and then removed. More time had to be given for the fission products to decay, after which the fuel rods could be examined. Depending on availability of reactor space and other factors, this whole sequence could take up to 15 months. Furthermore, the fuel elements for a submarine reactor would have to be extremely reliable — far more reliable than for a land-based reactor since it would be impossible to remove defective fuel elements whilst at sea.

Following a visit to the United States by an Admiralty technical mission in June 1957, it was decided to change direction from the stainless steel fuel elements which had become the main line of development back to the zirconium type elements, since it had become apparent that the United States Navy were also using zirconium for their fuel elements.

There were other limitations imposed on the reactor design. One early design decision was that the core should not exceed five feet in diameter. Another constraint was the supply of ^{235}U — 80 kg were made available for the project, and further supplies would be hard to come by. (The Orange Herald device which was tested in the Pacific in 1957 used 120 kg of ^{235}U, which went up in smoke.)

As part of the development programme, it was decided that a zero-energy reactor should be built by Rolls-Royce. This reactor was named Neptune. The fuel elements used highly enriched uranium (93%) alloyed with aluminium, since it was necessary to be able to recover the uranium when the experiments were finished so that it could be made ready for the reactor of the first submarine — being a zero-energy reactor meant that theoretically none of the uranium should have been used up. The core was assembled from fuel plates 0.020 inches thick by 3 inches wide by 12 inches long, arranged as packs in stainless steel boxes. Several hundred of these were needed to build the core.

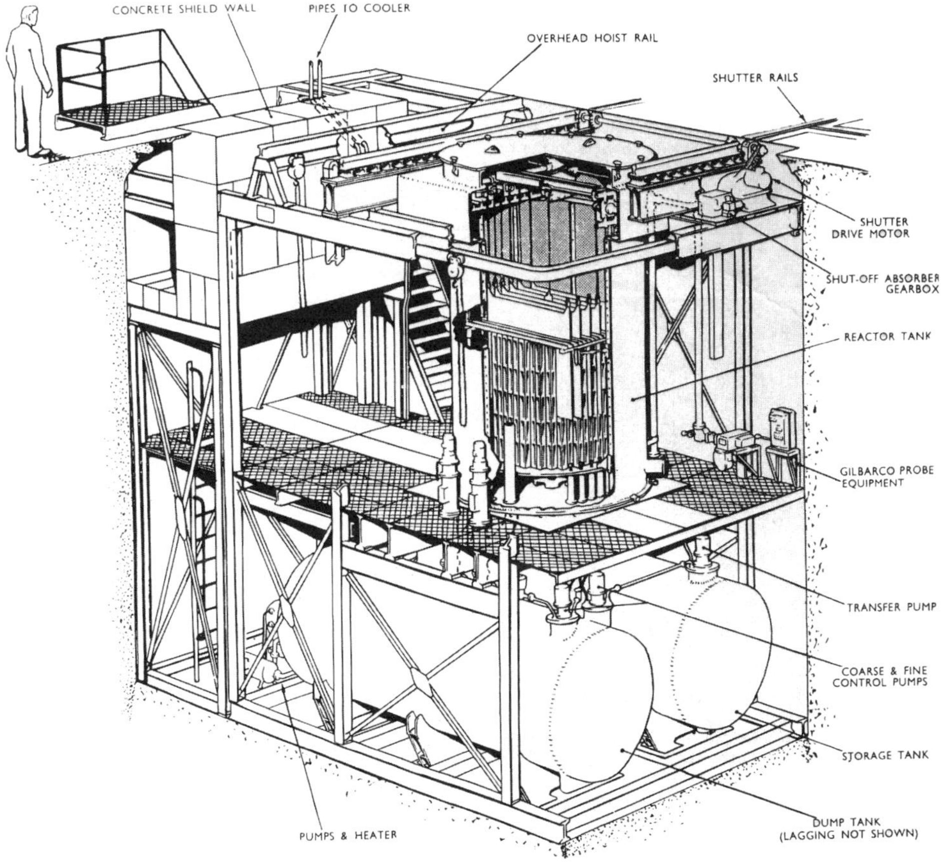

Fig. 2.— Arrangement of reactor in pit showing main vessel and storage and dump tanks.

Figure 16.3. The Neptune naval reactor built at Harwell.

The Admiralty were charged £1,400,000 for the 46 kg of uranium used in the Neptune reactor — which works out as roughly £30,000 per kilogram (the 120 kg of ^{235}U in Orange Herald was noted in one air staff memo as having a value of £2.5 million — only £20,000 per kilogram!).

There was also the question of a prototype reactor, which would have been land-based, and where it should be situated. There was no room at Harwell nor at Windscale, Winfrith had not yet become available, and so Dounreay was chosen as the site.

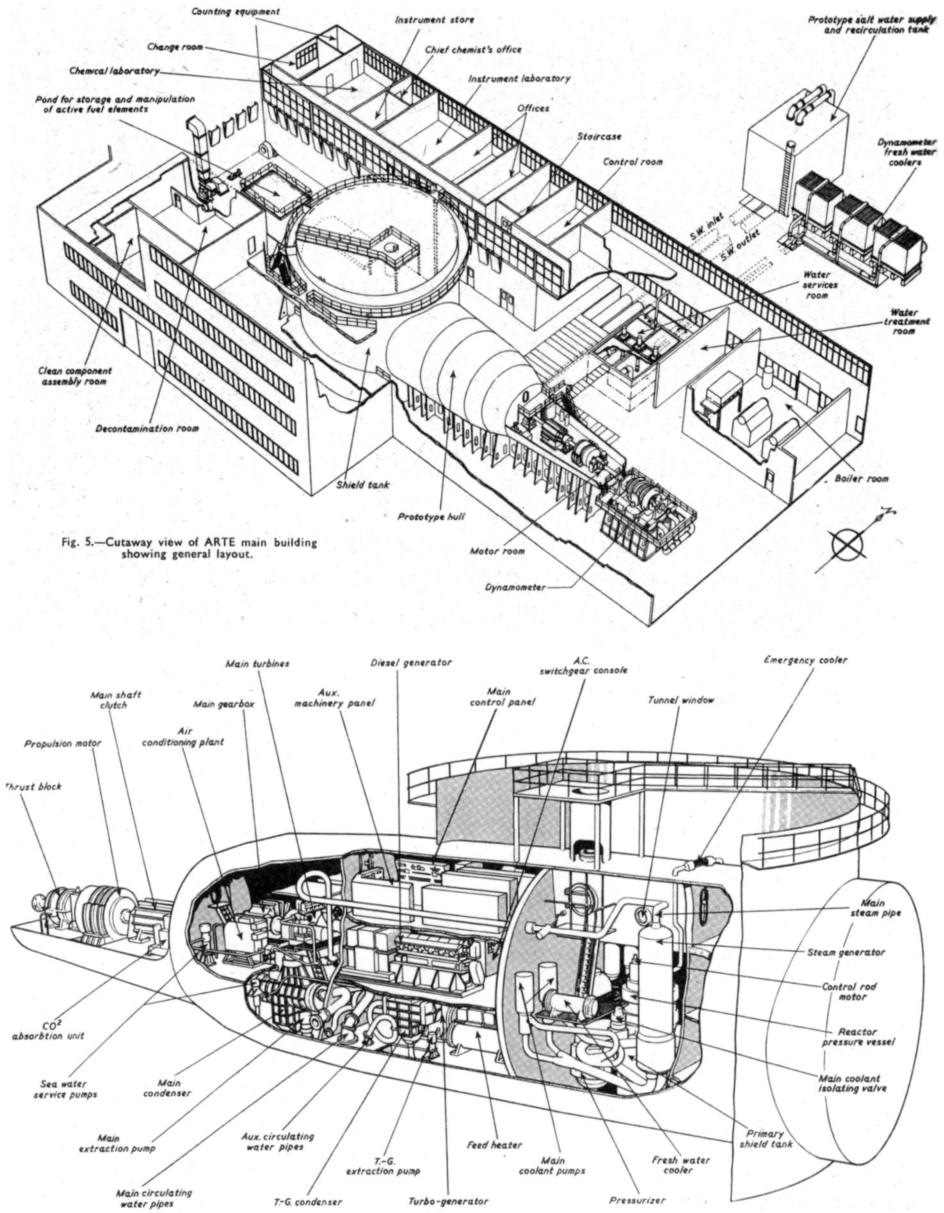

Figure 16.4. The Admiralty installation at Dounreay.

Approval was given for the project in 1956, and construction began in May 1957. During 1958, after the decision to purchase the complete plant for Dreadnought from the US, the future of the project was uncertain, but eventually it was given the go-ahead once more. The establishment was known as the ARTE (Admiralty Reactor

Test Establishment). The purpose of the design was to train submarine crews as well as to give facilities for design and testing of machinery, and that every effort was made to make the equipment as realistic as possible. Since the mock-up had been built on land, the sides of the submarine were not shielded for radiation — submerged, the sea water would act as a shield — and so a shield tank had to be built around the reactor section.

The reactor work was making good progress despite the occasional setback, when agreement was reached in July 1958 between the British and American governments on cooperation in the use of atomic energy. As a consequence of the personal and professional friendship between Admiral Mountbatten and Admiral Rickover, another agreement was reached between the two countries whereby the United States authorised sale of one complete submarine propulsion plant, the S5G.

Although the nuclear work at Harwell was closed down in 1959, much of the other work on propulsion which had been part of the project proved to be very useful in later nuclear powered submarines — in particular, British submarines would prove to be extremely quiet. The later developments in reactors for the Royal Navy are beyond the scope of this book.

Marine Reactors

It is surprising again how soon the shipbuilding industry became interested in atomic propulsion. The British Shipbuilding Research Association wrote to John Wilmot, then Minister of Supply, in May 1946:

> This Association was formed in 1944 with the active backing of the Department of Scientific and Industrial Research, and, as you are probably aware, exists to promote and facilitate in every way possible research and other scientific work in connection with shipbuilding, ship repairing and marine engineering industry and other allied trades and industries. It enjoys the backing of the large majority of firms in the industry.
>
> At a recent meeting of the Council of the Association, its governing body, consideration was given to a statement made by you in the House of Commons on the 28th March about the possible industrial application of atomic energy. You referred to the problem of effectively screening atomic energy plant and equipment, but stated that it is considered that it is not impossible that a way may be found to utilise nuclear energy to propel large ships.
>
> It was agreed by the Council that, as this is a matter of considerable importance to the shipbuilding and marine engineering industry, the letter should be sent to enquire whether there is any further information may be able to supply about the plans for the application of nuclear energy to ship propulsion. I am to state that the council is anxious and willing that the Association should collaborate in this aspect of the work at an early stage. Should you desire a small deputation to wait upon you to discuss the matter further, then we should be only too pleased to meet your request.[13]

The issue was left in abeyance for the next ten years, as Harwell and Risley were too busy with other matters. The only British power reactor designs were gas-cooled, and as late as 1957 Hinton was still thinking in terms of a 'miniature PIPPA' for ship propulsion.[14]

Figure 16.5. Look, no funnel! Illustration of an atomic powered liner, from ATOM 1963.

By the end of the 1950s, nuclear-powered ships were under design or consideration in America, Germany and Japan. Not surprisingly, Britain was also interested in this new technology, and in true British style, a committee (the Committee on Nuclear Propulsion for Merchant Ships) was set up. This was chaired by Thomas Galbraith, the Conservative MP for Glasgow Hillhead, who held the post of Civil Lord to the Admiralty. The Civil Lord was the minister responsible for the Royal Navy's civilian staff and properties. It was not a Cabinet post. In March 1958, he announced in parliament that 'The Admiralty regards the development of nuclear propulsion for ships as of the greatest importance both for the Royal Navy and for the Merchant Navy' and that 'we intend to go ahead with nuclear propulsion for merchant ships'.[15] He added that:

> The Committee of which I am chairman was formed less than a year ago, and in that time it has examined a great many nuclear propulsion systems to see whether any of them could be put straight into a ship without first building a prototype on shore. Unfortunately, this has turned out to be impossible, and it will first be necessary to build a shore prototype.
>
> The Atomic Energy Authority, in collaboration with the various shipping and shipbuilding interests, is now engaged on preliminary work for this project. What we want to do is to build an economic, or near-economic, ship to start with. The atomic-powered ships which one hears so much about and which are supposed to be building in other countries now do not even profess to be paying propositions, and we believe that it is much better to go for what is economic rather than to seek to make a splash with a machine which can have no commercial application.

Various engineering firms and shipbuilders had been invited to put in tenders for a nuclear-powered cargo ship, and in May 1959, eight proposals for nuclear ships were submitted to the Admiralty, seven of which had been prepared by industry and one by the AEA. The Admiralty, the Ministry of Transport and Civil Aviation, other government departments and the Marine Nuclear Propulsion Committee were given a two day presentation of the various designs. These are outlined below.

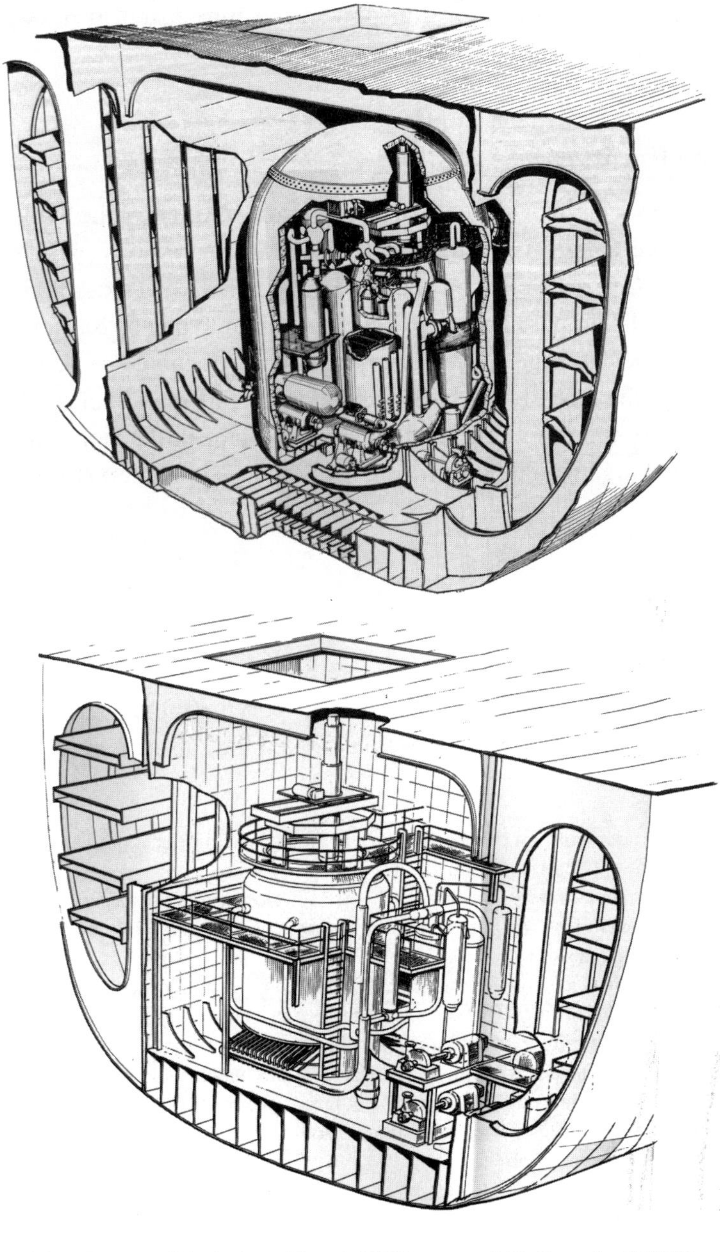

Figure 16.6. Two possible designs. Top: A BWR proposal. Bottom: An SCHW proposal.

AEI-John Thompson nuclear energy company limited

This design was for a BWR, a result of the company's collaboration with General Electric of America who had played a leading part in the development of the BWR in the USA. It was estimated that a complete unit could be delivered in 30 months for which certain core components would be purchased from GE. The reactor would need refuelling after 380 days at full power; the time taken to refuel would be approximately 100 hours.

Babcock and Wilcox, Ltd

Through their association with Babcock and Wilcox of America, the British Babcock and Wilcox were able to gain direct experience of the various pressurised water projects that the American company had undertaken including the American nuclear ship Savannah. The proposed reactor would be similar to that on Savannah, but with an output 2.5 times as large while occupying only 20% more space. The company pointed out that the PWR is the basic system adopted for all nuclear ships to date and was probably the most developed compact reactor in the world at the present time. The fuel charge would be sufficient for 500 days operation at full power.

De Havilland

De Havilland proposed a high-temperature gas-cooled reactor similar to DRAGON, which was distinctly ambitious. Even more ambitious was the idea of using gas turbines rather than a steam circuit, and an all-beryllia moderated core. The proposal was submitted to the AEA for evaluation and the subsequent report[16] was not particularly favourable:

> The two reactor concept proposed by de Havilland would be economically unacceptable for a 22,000 shp installation;
>
> a fundamental safety question is whether a fission product purge system (that is, the removal of fission gases from the helium coolant) can safely be installed and operated in a ship;
>
> the design of the core of a marine HTR which is capable of withstanding the shock acceleration currently being specified is extremely difficult;
>
> adapting the primary shielding to serve as a containment vessel would create serious maintenance and testing problems. It would become so highly irradiated as to be virtually inaccessible, and for this reason the proposal is not acceptable;
>
> a spherical reactor vessel is unsuitable for a small reactor system based on solid moderator materials.

Among the other proposals was a gas-cooled reactor, using carbon dioxide, and uranium dioxide as the fuel from the General Electric Atomic Energy Group; an organic moderated reactor, which had been developed largely by Atomics International of America from the Hawker Siddeley Nuclear Power Company; a BWR from Mitchell Engineering Consortium; and a steam-cooled heavy water-moderated reactor from Vickers.

Harwell had devoted considerable effort to the design of a PWR (LEO) and also to a similar system for submarines, before the Navy accepted an American design. It may be symptomatic of the compartmentalisation of institutions such as Harwell that as far as can be seen from the records, no use was made of this work in considering propulsion systems for marine purposes.

The presentations had aroused considerable publicity in the technical press[17] and parliament. The Minister for Transport (Harold Watkinson until October 1959, when he was succeeded by Ernest Marples) was repeatedly pressed as to the progress of the evaluations, although one wonders slightly as to the expertise of some MPs. In February 1960, Mr Hector Hughes (MP for Aberdeen North) asked: 'Can the Minister say how long it will be before this power could be available for fishing trawlers?'[18]

In a covering note for a paper to Cabinet in 1959, the First Lord of the Admiralty, the Earl of Selkirk, noted that 'The history of the past two years . . . is one of hope deferred, not once but several times'.[19] That could be said to the story of the entire saga.

One curious feature of the report is that it covers progress in other countries and notes which type of reactor has been selected. America had launched a nuclear-powered ship in the form of the Savannah. Russia had produced a nuclear-powered icebreaker, the Lenin. Britain and America were using nuclear power for their submarines, and America would soon be using it for its surface fleet. All these ships were powered by the same type of reactor — the PWR.

Galbraith's had taken advice from a technical sub-committee — effectively from the AEA. The report says of the PWR that it is 'a system which does not offer sufficient development potential to promise eventual economy'. Unfortunately, no justification is given for the remark, nor why, if it was not economic, it was adopted by America, Russia and Japan.

Instead, the report recommended either a form of BWR or an organic-moderated reactor (OMR). Considering that little or no development work had been done in the UK on the OMR, this does seem a somewhat bizarre choice. The sub-committee 'almost unanimously confirmed its belief that the nuclear propulsion of our high-powered large merchant ships will become economic in time'. Unfortunately, the sub-committee was wrong in both its choice of reactor and in the economics of nuclear power at sea.

In the meantime, five companies were asked to send in tenders and designs for a 56,000 ton tanker based on one of these two reactor systems. Quite some time

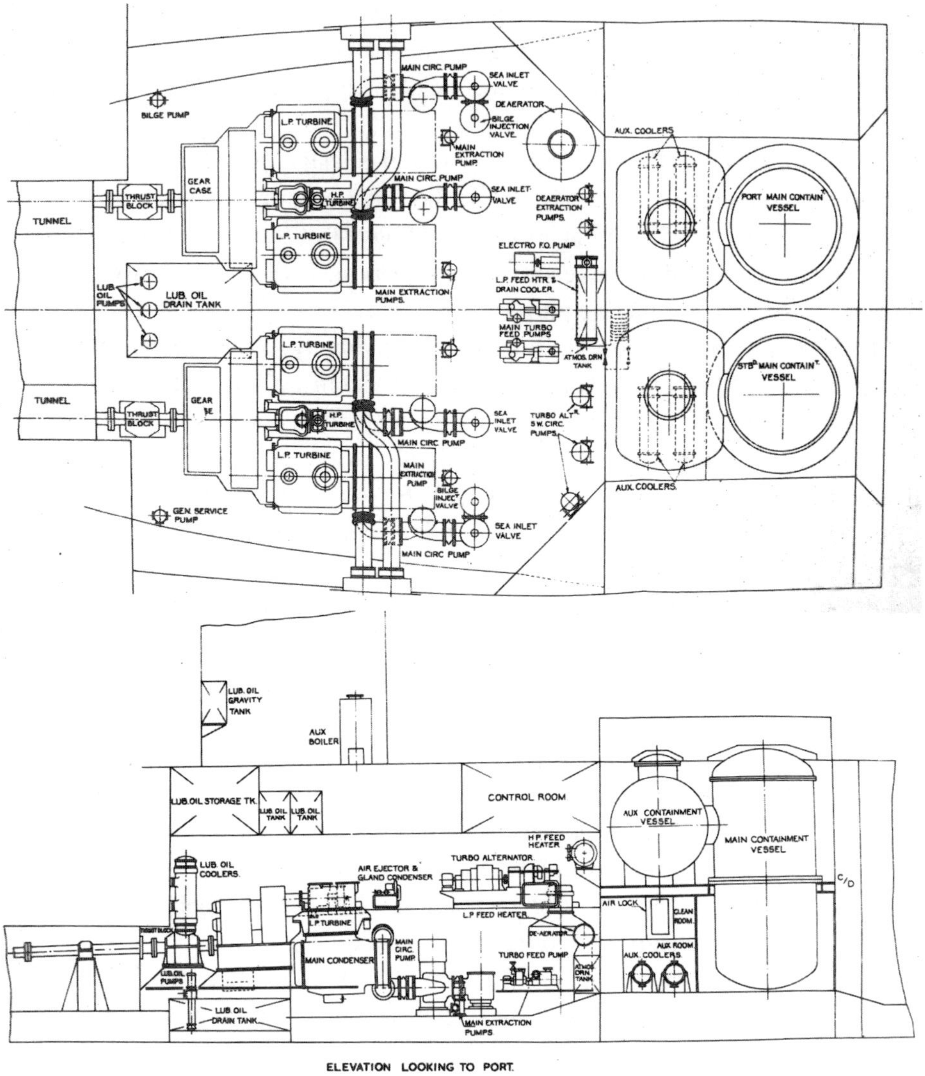

Figure 16.7. A Vickers proposal for a nuclear powered tanker.

elapsed before eventually, in November 1961, Marples announced in the House of Commons that

> ... while it would certainly be technically feasible to build a nuclear-powered ship now, nuclear propulsion for marine purposes does not offer sufficient economic promise to justify building a merchant ship at the present time. The Government have, therefore, decided that the right course in present circumstances is to authorise a vigorous programme of research, aimed at a reactor system which is economically attractive to a wide range of shipping. The programme will be carried out by the Atomic Energy Authority in conjunction with industry.[20]

The companies involved were not happy with the decision: they had built up design teams and kept them together for 18 months while the committee deliberated. They pressed for compensation, and in 1963, five firms were offered £50,000 each as recompense.

New proposals came forward, this time using what might be described as a modular system. One was based on the Belgian Vulcaine reactor, which was being developed by the AEA and a consortium of Belgian companies, the other was described as an Integral Boiling Reactor (IBR). The point of the IBR was that it was entirely self-contained, could be built ashore, then dropped into the ship as it was being fitted out and all the necessary pipe work connected up. The hope was that series production would bring the costs down, and the modular nature would reduce fitting out costs.

Despite this, all the designs still ran up against the same major problem. Whichever system was considered, the costs invariably worked out far higher than for conventional propulsion. None of the nuclear-powered ships which have been built — Russian icebreakers and prototype nuclear-powered commercial ships (such as the American Savannah, the German Otto Hahn, and the Japanese Mutsu) — have been a success.

---

1 As quoted in Sir Robert Hill (1995). 'Forty years on: the origins and successes of the UK naval nuclear propulsion programme', *Transactions of the Institute of Marine Engineers* 108(1), pp. 1–14.

2 J Diamond (1912–1990) was professor of engineering at the University of Manchester from 1953–1977, when he retired. Originally appointed as professor of mechanical engineering in 1953, he was later promoted to the Beyer chair of engineering, effectively the head of department. He was University Pro-Vice Chancellor from 1970–1977. Diamond was one of the four members of the Board of Enquiry into the Windscale fire.

3 TNA: PRO AB 1/313B. Use of atomic energy for power by the Admiralty. WA Akers, 1 January 1945.

4 TNA: PRO AB 15/2043. An enriched uranium reactor for submarine propulsion. J Diamond and J Smith. AERE Harwell, September 1951.

5 TNA: PRO AB 6/790. Information on US reactors.

6 TNA: PRO AB 6/747. Boiler design for marine application: collaboration with the Admiralty.

7 TNA: PRO ADM 116/5968. Nuclear propulsion: exchange of information with USA.

8 TNA: PRO ADM 1/26860. Nuclear fuel submarines.

9 *Ibid.*

10 TNA: PRO AB 16/1642. Collaboration with the Admiralty.

[11] TNA: PRO AB 17/202. LIDO. Shielding Reactor.

[12] TNA: PRO AB 8/966/2. Part 2 of 2 (Initial problems of the submarine PWR design and related experimental programme — Royal Naval College, Greenwich. J Edwards, September 1961. Much of what follows in this chapter is based on this account.

[13] TNA: PRO AB 16/90. Use of atomic energy for power: ship propulsion.

[14] TNA: PRO AB 16/1822. Nuclear propulsion of ships: policy. 'Nuclear Propulsion of Ships by Means of a Graphite Moderated Gas Cooled Reactor.' Note by Sir Christopher Hinton, undated.

[15] Vote A. Numbers, House of Commons Debate (Fifth series), 4 March 1958, Vol. 583, c. 1117.

[16] TNA: PRO AB 7/10755. Marine HTR design study: an assessment of the De Havilland Y113 feasibility study. R Anscomb.

[17] (1959). 'Ship Proposals', *Nuclear Engineering International*, 4(39), 243.

[18] Nuclear Propulsion, House of Commons Debate (Fifth series), 3 February 1960, Vol. 616, c. 995.

[19] TNA: PRO AB 16/4784. Ministerial Committee on Nuclear Propulsion for Merchant Ships. 'Nuclear Propulsion For Ships Revised Draft By First Lord', undated.

[20] Nuclear Propulsion, House of Commons Debate (Fifth series), 8 November 1961, Vol. 648, c. 980.

Chapter 17

Finale

The last four AGR stations had been ordered by Tony Benn, Secretary of State for Energy in the Callaghan government of 1976–1979. A Conservative government led by Margaret Thatcher was elected in the 1979 general election, and the change of administration would have a very considerable impact on the nuclear programme.

The CEGB had been pressing the case for a PWR power station for some considerable time, and the new Secretary of State, David Howell, gave his support to their case when he announced in parliament on 18 December 1979 'our wish that, subject to the necessary consents and safety clearances, the PWR should be the next nuclear power station order, with the aim of starting construction in 1982'.

As an example of how hope can triumph over expectation, he went on to say

> Looking ahead, the electricity supply industry has advised that even on cautious assumptions it would need to order at least one new nuclear power station a year in the decade from 1982, or a programme of the order of 15,000 megawatts over 10 years.[1]

In the event, Sizewell B would be the last nuclear power station to be built in Britain. Before consent for construction was given, there was to be a public enquiry, which was chaired by Sir Frank Layfield. This would last for three years, with 16 million words being given in evidence. The National Archives has a section devoted entirely to the enquiry with a total of 2,808 files of statements and evidence presented. This public enquiry, together with an almost equally long drawn out enquiry into the proposed Windscale reprocessing plant (THORP) showed the degree of hostility to nuclear power that had grown up in Britain, led by such groups as Greenpeace and Friends of the Earth. There would be a later proposal to build another PWR, Hinkley Point C, with the prospect of yet another public enquiry, but this, and all future stations, would be stopped not by pressure from environmentalists, but from another policy of the Thatcher government: privatisation.

When the CEGB was privatised at the start of the 1990s, the nuclear power stations remained in public ownership since it was felt that private investors would not take on potential liabilities of decommissioning. No private electricity company has ever considered building nuclear power stations. Ironically, the AGR stations and Sizewell B have ended up in the hands of a nationalised industry, not British, but French.

Now that the PWR had become the reactor of choice of the CEGB, the purpose and function of the AEA was shrinking rapidly. BNFL would be kept in business for years to come, supplying fuel to the existing power stations, but these fuel elements were tried and tested. There was little or no more research and development left to be done. The gas-cooled reactors which for so long had been the mainstay of the development effort of Harwell and Risley had been abandoned. Any design for a commercial HTR based on DRAGON had also long since been abandoned. The Commercial Fast Reactor would soon be seen as no longer viable. Funding, other than a trickle for research, was stopped by Cecil Parkinson in 1988.

Within not much more than a decade, all the reactors at Harwell and at Winfrith had been closed down. Fusion research would continue at Culham, and the Chapelcross reactors will still be used to produce tritium for the military, but the UKAEA had no real function left to perform.

There was one very important and expensive job left to carry out; one that had not even been considered in the 1950s. This was what was to be done with redundant reactors, or what today is described as 'decommissioning'.

The idea of what might be involved in decommissioning began to surface in the early 1980s, particularly with the closure of the Windscale AGR. For some years previously, in anticipation of its closure, the prospect of decommissioning and demolishing it had been studied. The plan had evolved successfully to the point where the AEA could take the decision in the second half of 1981 that they should like to see it demolished.

There were several reasons for wishing to do this. As a prototype of the commercial AGRs, and with its graphite moderator and gas-cooling similar to that of the UK's magnox stations, it afforded a much better immediate prospect than any other UK reactor for doing pioneering work which would provide knowledge that would be of value to the electricity boards if they wished to consider demolition of the commercial stations when they came to the end of their working life. In general, there was a growing realisation in the UK that decommissioning of obsolete nuclear installations must be studied and a variety of techniques examined in order to gain expertise. In addition there was the wish to take down a facility that had reached the end of its life rather than leave it disused.

The paper describing how the Windscale AGR might be dealt with went on to make the point that

> three quarters of the activity resides in the stainless steel which comprises only 5% of the total mass and that 97% of the activity is in the steel components which comprise no more than 45% of the total mass.

This will gradually decay; the activity 'drops by a factor of about 10 in the first 10 years, by another factor of four in the following 20 years, but only by a factor 10 in the next 300 years'.[2]

As to the isotopes responsible:

> The early radioactive decay can be largely ascribed to the iron 55 and cobalt 60 isotopes with half-lives of 2.7 years and 5.2 years respectively. The long-term activity largely rests with the nickel 63 isotope which has a 100 year half-life and it is that isotope which makes the stainless steel the dominant material for so long. Ultimately, after several hundred years, the graphite will remain the most radioactive because of the carbon-14 content, the half-life [of] which is 5700 years. The decay in the graphite over the first 50 years is largely associated with impurities.

In 1999, it was decided that the dismantling of the reactor core and pressure vessel should begin, and decommissioning was finally completed in the middle of 2011.

The research reactors had not been run at anything like the power levels of the commercial reactors, and the radiation levels had been much lower. This made it easier to dismantle them. GLEEP and LIDO, to give two examples, have now been completely demolished. At Winfrith, NESTOR and DIMPLE were the last reactors to be shut down, ceasing operations in 1995. Following decommissioning and removal of the reactors, in 2006 the reactor hall which housed both facilities was demolished. The area is now grassed over. ZEBRA was demolished in 2006 and decommissioning completed in 2010, with the clearance of its office block.

Figure 17.1. The final days of the GLEEP reactor at Harwell. It has now been finally demolished. (Image courtesy of NDA and copyright NDA.)

During 1994–1995 both reactors were taken to stage two decommissioning, and it is now intended that they should remain in the state of care and maintenance until 2040, by which time most of the radioactive material within the reactors will have decayed sufficiently to be disposed of as low-level waste. The ancillary buildings have been demolished and the area landscaped. Other reactors, where radiation levels were higher, have been defueled and left in care and maintenance. Radioactivity decreases with time, and isotopes such as tritium, with its half-life of just over 12 years, will gradually decay away.

Although Sizewell B was the last nuclear power station to be built in Britain, there are plans at the moment to build new stations at sites such as Hinkley. These will not be British designs built by British companies, since those skills have now been lost. There was very considerable opposition to the building of Sizewell; opposition to the new stations is at present muted, but may intensify as and when construction begins.

Public attitudes to nuclear power have varied very considerably over the past 60 years. There was very great opposition to nuclear weapons in Britain in the 1950s, notably with the CND marches to Aldermaston, but at the time this did not feed over into opposition to nuclear power. The building of Calder Hall was seen as a British achievement in which the country could take pride. Even the Windscale fire of 1957 failed to arouse much opposition to nuclear power.

Today, there is a considerable degree of local opposition to any new development, in particular to nuclear power, in what has been described as NIMBYism (Not In My Back Yard). This was not always the case. A letter written by the town clerk of Wick, the nearest town to Dounreay, in 1963, concerning the proposed prototype fast reactor is not a letter which could be written today.

> May I say at the outset that Wick Town Council regard it as an honour to have been associated, however indirectly, with the work at Dounreay, and are gratified to know that the experiment has obtained such a measure of success that a further development of this nature is being contemplated.
>
> There are many areas in our country which would profit immeasurably at the present time from being chosen as the location for the new reactor but there must surely be few which can establish a more honest claim than Caithness. Not only is new industry of this type badly needed to improve our employment situation but there is also the unique factor that the county is already at the home of the first project in this field. Even if the power generated has to be carried many miles south to feed more rapidly developing areas the expenditure entailed must be substantially offset by the advantages and savings involved in siting in close proximity to the present plant and having access to existing services.
>
> I wish on behalf of my Authority to support most vigorously the views expressed in Mr Russell's letter and I would most obliged if you would bring this further representation to the notice of your principals. An additional copy of the letter is enclosed for this purpose.[3]

Figure 17.2. *Sic transit gloria mundi*. The SGHWR at Winfrith is pulled down.

Nuclear installations were often built in remote locations, and were able to give employment in areas where there was little industry, and the PFR was built at Dounreay for that very reason. Nevertheless, it is difficult to imagine such enthusiasm being expressed to day. There remains one question: was it all worthwhile?

The first part of the programme was military in nature, and the power programme followed from that. Initially, it seemed a great success, and the opening of Calder Hall was probably the high point of the whole programme. Hubris was followed by nemesis in the form of the Windscale fire. The AEA was in many ways very lucky — the fire could have been a good deal more catastrophic than it was.

The Commercial Programme

There is an interesting question as to how commercial the programme was. A great deal of money was spent on research and development. The SGHWR cost over £150 million, and the money spent on the fast reactors came to some hundreds of millions of pounds. Both generated electricity, but in comparison to their cost, this was insignificant. There was also the cost of all the research reactors, and all these were subsumed into the general AEA budget. Should these costs be included in estimating the cost of the electricity generated by the nuclear programme?

There is a precedent to say that it should not. Development of the jet engine was funded by the military budget, and civilian use of the jet engine was funded from that work. On the other hand, much of the work done by the AEA was not done for the military, but done with the commercial programme in mind. With the collapse of the commercial programme, all that money has been written off. Literally billions of pounds were spent by the AEA, and when the last nuclear power station is closed down, that money will have been spent to no avail.

There were other factors which did not help the power programme. The three-way arrangement between the design and construction companies, the AEA and the CEGB was cumbersome and bureaucratic. The role of the AEA was to give advice on matters concerned with the nuclear part of the station, and yet commercial companies have their own nuclear design divisions. In addition, the CEGB set up its own nuclear research laboratories at Berkeley in Gloucestershire.

The economic policies of the Conservative governments of the 1950s have been characterised as 'stop–go'. The same might be said of the nuclear power programme. First there was the programme of 1955, which was slowed down as the fuel crisis receded. Then came the issue of what was to replace the magnox stations. This inevitably lead to a hiatus in the ordering of new power stations. The failure of Dungeness B led to another hiatus. As far as the construction industry was concerned, glut was followed by famine.

There was also the continued failure of the government and the CEGB to forecast electricity demand for the future. The 1960s was a period when it was thought that detailed economic planning was possible. Not everyone was convinced of this, as a memorandum in 1966 from an official in the Ministry of Technology demonstrates:

> The meeting at the Treasury on the future electrical supply programme was long but rewarding. The first part was very general, and mainly remarkable for the outspoken way in which Ministry of Power and CEGB voiced their complete

> lack of confidence in the government's economic policies and economic advisers. There was nothing political or personal about this; they were just explaining that they had been around too long to take the slightest notice of the alleged "economic situation" when it came to serious matters like planning electricity supply.[4]

As well as the industrial weaknesses, the AEA did itself no favours by fighting for the AGR as tenaciously as it did. Perhaps it had a point up to the saga of Dungeness and Hartlepool, but it must have been clear after these fiascos that the AGR was not the way forward. The CEGB is also culpable for not ordering the most economical system. Whether it gave in to political pressure is not clear. Indeed, one of the striking features about the whole power programme is how little politicians had to do with it.

There was also a fault, not unique to Britain, but which was very noticeable in the later stages of the programme and as it slowly lost its momentum, which was to write long analyses of situations as a substitute for action. Making a wrong decision might have been expensive, but sometimes it is better than continued procrastination.

But perhaps the saddest part of the whole saga is the story of the men and women who gave their working careers to research and development, into building the power stations that ran for decades. Despite what happened subsequently, Calder Hall was an outstanding success, and part of the renaissance of science, engineering and technology that took place in Britain in the 1950s. Sadly, that renaissance ran into the sands during the 1960s and 1970s. Britain has not built a power station since Sizewell B, which came on line in 1995, and has lost a generation of scientists and engineers. If nuclear power stations are built again in Britain, they will, by necessity, be built by engineers from other countries.

---

1 Nuclear Power, House of Commons Debate (Fifth series), 18 December 1979, Vol. 976, cc. 287–289.

2 TNA: PRO EG 2/391. H Lawton: Decocommissioning [*sic*] of The Windscale AGR, undated.

3 TNA: PRO AB 16/4541. Prototype Fast Reactor. WG Hogg (Town Clerk) to Dr R Hurst, Director, Dounreay Experimental Reactor Establishment, 16 January 1963.

4 TNA: PRO EG 7/40. Hinkley Point "B" Advanced Gas Cooled Reactor II. G Hubbard to Mr Michaels, 3 October 1966.

Appendix

Chronology

1942

December	World's first nuclear reactor goes critical in Chicago.

1943

December	First British scientists arrive in America to join the Manhattan project.

1945

July	Atomic bombs dropped on Hiroshima and Nagasaki.
August	Atomic bombs dropped on Hiroshima and Nagasaki.
December	Ministers approve atomic pile in Britain for plutonium production.

1946

January	Lord Portal becomes Controller of Production (Atomic Energy). William Penney appointed Chief Superintendent, Armament Research.
February	Atomic Energy Production Division set up at Risley, Lancashire.
April	Work begins on AERE at Harwell.
June	Construction of BEPO begins at Harwell.

1947

January	Decision taken to build British atomic bomb
August	First experimental pile at Harwell (GLEEP) goes critical.
September	Work begins at Windscale site.

1948

January	First uranium cast at Springfields.
July	Second experimental reactor at Harwell (BEPO) goes critical.

1949

August	First Russian atomic weapon test

1950

April	Aldermaston site taken over for atomic weapons work.
October	Windscale Pile 1 goes critical.

1951

June	Windscale Pile 2 goes critical.

1952

March	First billet of metallic plutonium made at Windscale.
October	First British atomic weapon test at Monte Bello, Australia

1953

April	Low separation gaseous diffusion plant in full operation at Capenhurst.
August	Construction of power station at Calder Hall begins.
October	Further British atomic weapons tests in Australia.

1954

January	Atomic energy transferred from Ministry of Supply to the Department of Atomic Energy.
August	UK AEA comes into existence with its first Chairman, Sir Edwin Plowden.

1955

February	The White Paper "A Programme of Nuclear Power" is presented to parliament.
March	Construction of fast reader reactor commences at Dounreay.
August	Construction of power stations at Chapelcross begins.

1956

August	Calder Hall number 1 reactor begins to generate electricity.
October	Official opening of Calder Hall by Her Majesty the Queen.

1957

May	First British H bomb tested at Christmas Island.
July	Work begins on building Atomic Energy Establishment at Winfrith.
October	Windscale Pile 1 catches fire in Britain's first nuclear accident.

1958

July	Final Windscale report presented to parliament. UK AEA decides to close and seal both piles.
August	Further British atomic weapons tests in the Pacific.
October	Preliminary work on prototype AGR begins at Windscale.

1959

February	First reactor at Chapelcross comes into use for electricity generation.
November	Ministerial responsibility for atomic energy transferred to the Minister for Science.
	Dounreay experimental fast reactor (DFR) begins operation on low power.

December	Lord Plowden is replaced by Sir Roger Makins as Chairman of UKAEA.
1960	
October	First British nuclear submarine (HMS Dreadnought) launched.
1961	
August	The first CEGB magnox reactors at Bradwell and Berkeley achieve criticality.
1962	
August	Windscale AGR begins operating at low power.
October	Dounreay Fast Reactor begins generating electricity.
1963	
January	Windscale AGR reaches full power.
May	Construction of SGHWR begins at Winfrith.
July	Dounreay fast reactor (DFR) operates at full design output of 60 MW (H).
1964	
January	Sir William Penney succeeds Sir Roger Makins as Chairman of UKAEA.
October	DRAGON reactor commissioned at Winfrith
1965	
May	Minister of Power accepts CEGB decision to build an AGR power station at Dungeness.
1966	
February	Minister of Technology announces government approval for a prototype fast reactor at Dounreay.
1967	
September	SGHWR becomes critical
October	Dr JM Hill succeeds Lord Penney as Chairman of UKAEA.
1968	
January	SGHWR operates at full power.
December	Harwell reactor BEPO is closed down.
1969	
May	Materials testing Reactor at Dounreay (DMTR) is closed down.
1976	
February	First AGR commissioned at Hunterston B.
1977	
March	PFR achieves full thermal power. DFR is shut down.

1989

March First magnox station (Berkeley) closes down.

1990

September SGHWR at Winfrith closes down.

1994

March Dounreay PFR closes down.

1995

February Sizewell, the first PWR and last nuclear station to be built in the UK, is connected to the grid.

2003

March Calder Hall closes.

Bibliography

Arnold, Lorna:

Windscale 1957. Anatomy of a Nuclear Accident (London: Macmillan Press Ltd, 1992).

Lorna Arnold was an assistant to Margaret Gowing and later was the UK AEA historian. A straightforward account of the accident, although Arnold is careful to ensure that the actions of the AEA and its members are favourably presented.

Jay, Kenneth:

Calder Hall. The Story of Britain's First Atomic Power Station (London: Methuen and Co., 1956).

This was written as a semi-official account from the UK AEA of the design and construction of Calder Hall. For a 'popular' account, it is quite technical in places and contains considerable detail on the engineering side.

Gowing, Margaret:

Independence and Deterrence: Britain and Atomic Energy, 1945–52. Volume 1: Policy Making. (London: Palgrave MacMillan, 1974).

Independence and Deterrence: Britain and Atomic Energy, 1945–52. Volume 2: Policy Execution (London: Palgrave MacMillan, 1974).

Williams, Roger:

The Nuclear Power Decisions (London: Croome Helm Ltd, 1980).

This is an account of the policy decisions concerning nuclear power. It is extremely through and lucid as it follows the vacillations of the power programme of the 1960s and 1970s. It is a relatively early account, so does not cover the 1980s, and written before the relevant papers would have reached The National Archives.

A variety of books and other publications were produced by the AEA in the 1950s and 1960s. Many of these have been preserved in The National Archives at

Kew. They include:

- Four publications on Calder Hall (TNA: AB 17/52, 53, 54 and 56).
- Two on Culham (TNA: AB 17/58 and 59).
- Three on Dounreay (TNA: AB 17/64, 68 and 170).
- The SGHWR (TNA: AB 17/105 and 220).
- 'Britain's Atomic Factories: The Story of Atomic Energy Production in Britain', by Kenneth Jay on Windscale and Capenhurst and published in 1954 (TNA: AB 17/291).
- 'The Nuclear Energy Industry of the United Kingdom', (TNA: AB 17/298) which covers the power and research reactors and gives details of the companies which were responsible for building them.

In the same section of The National Archives there are also copies of various brochures illustrating particular research reactors or programmes.

HG (Gethin) Davey was the Works General Manager at Windscale, and was part of the project from the outset. He wrote a long account of the building and commissioning of the facilities, including Calder Hall, now preserved in The National Archives at Kew. There is a heading printed on the label on the front of the folder 'REMINISCENCES OF AN ATOMIC PIONEER', which someone has drawn a line through and replaced with the more prosaic title 'HG DAVEY's history of Windscale'.[1]

His account combines the technical and the reminiscent. There was some official interest in his account, and he was in correspondence with Margaret Gowing over aspects of the work. It was also illustrated with diagrams and plate photographs, the original prints being available in a separate Public Record Office (PRO) file. Unfortunately, he died before the work was fully complete; nevertheless the book is an invaluable source on the building of the Windscale facilities. There are other files in the PRO containing notes for unfinished chapters. The section in the present book on the British Production Plants and Calder Hall draws heavily on his account.

Sir John Cockcroft also began a biographical account of his work on atomic energy, starting in the immediate post war period. Again this was left incomplete, but it contains some useful accounts of the setting up of Harwell. In other areas it is a rather bland narration of events.[2]

---

[1] TNA: PRO AB 16/2700. HG Davey: History of Windscale.

[2] TNA: PRO AB 27/64. JD Cockcroft: chapters, written in 1968, for book on atomic energy (autobiographical).

Index